The Voyage of the Herman

The Voyage of the Herman

by THEON WRIGHT

in collaboration with Ione Ulrich Sutton

Hawthorn Books, Inc. *Publishers* New York

 This book was manufactured in the United States of America and published simultaneously in Canada by Prentice-Hall of Canada, Ltd., 1870 Birchmount Road, Scarborough, Ontario. Library of Congress Catalogue Card Number: 66-15230.

First Edition: May, 1966

9381

To
George W. Sutton, Jr.

A dedicated optimist who gave far more to his fellow man than he ever expected to receive in return,

an enthusiastic adventurer who, along with his father—Captain George W. Sutton of the *Herman*—was a founding charter member of the Adventurers Club of New York, and

to whom we are indebted for the care and preservation of the material which provides the basis of this book.

Contents

Foreword

Stories of "lost treasures"—and this is one—that have been circulated among *aficionados* of the treasure hunting business for the past hundred years or so, if they concern the Pacific Ocean, almost always are connected with Cocos Island. This point is noted at the outset of the story because the *Voyage of the Herman* has very little to do with Cocos Island.

Most of these yarns are of dubious origin, somewhat apocryphal as to detail, and show a careless regard for known historical facts. But in the case of the voyage of the ninety-foot schooner *Herman* into the Low Archipelago more than sixty years ago, the account is based completely on notes and diaries of the voyagers, letters and journals, and the log of the *Herman*. The purpose of the expedition was to find a fabulous treasure known as the "ecclesiastical treasure of Lima," said to be worth upwards of a hundred million dollars. The only connection between this treasure and Cocos Island is that it was once buried there.

According to Captain James Brown, a grizzled and weather-beaten old mariner who came into San Francisco at the turn of the century with a tale of piracy and murder in the South Seas, he helped dig up this enormous wealth and carry it to a remote island in the Low Archipelago, where, for all anyone knows, it still lies to this day.

Captain Brown's story was not fully understood at the time—even by himself. He possessed certain "proofs," as he called them, including some old coins minted between 1750 and 1800; and his tale gave rise to many misconceptions and confusing reports. There was a lack of factual data, and the accounts in the newspapers were vague and conflicting. But now, more than sixty years later, some of these facts have come to light through disclosure of the diaries and journals of the voyagers on the *Herman,* including the ship's log.

It is on the basis of these documents and data, *not* upon vague stories and legends, that the story of the voyage is set forth in these pages.

Since Captain Brown's story gave impetus to new searches for "lost treasures" of Cocos Islad, which have obsessed treasure hunters for many years, and still obsess them to this day, it seems advisable to say something by way of explanation about Cocos Island itself, in order to make sense out of the old man's tale.

Cocos Island is a jagged upthrust of rock, lonely and sullen under a perpetual cloud of mists, some 480 miles southwest of Panama. It is owned by Costa Rica, and has no commercial importance. Its cliffs, rising sheer from the Pacific Ocean on three sides, present an uninviting approach to mariners. Deep gorges feed down to two coves on the north side, known as Wafer Bay and Chatham Bay, which offer fair anchorages, and are supposed to be the burial ground of vast treasures. There are narrow, rocky beaches on both bays, where small boats can make landings; and these beaches provide the only items of importance to seafaring men. For two centuries after Cocos was first discovered, early in the seventeenth century, it afforded temporary refuge for pirates who infested the trade routes from California to Cape Horn.

The actual record of these piratical activities and the burial of their loot on Cocos has become a confused and amorphous mass of conflicting and often unrelated legends. In order to understand the significance of the so-called "ecclesiastical treasure of Lima" among these legends, it is necessary to review some of these stories, at least three of which were authenticated by the governments of Peru and Great Britain.

The history of piracy on Cocos actually goes back to Sir Edward Davis, the British buccaneer, who operated his famous pirate ship, the *Batchelor's Delight,* out of Cocos *circa* 1684. The annals of piracy are indebted to one William Dampier for much of the basic research on Sir Edward Davis' exploits. Dampier accompanied Davis on the *Batchelor's Delight* when he left the West Indies for the West Coast, and later wrote accounts of pirate raids which were used by Daniel Defoe in *Robinson Crusoe.* However, Dampier probably did not accompany him to Cocos.

Among the records of Davis' raids is a description of his loot on Cocos, consisting of "300,000 pounds of gold and silver bullion, 733 bars of pure gold, each four by three inches measure and two inches thick; as well as bejewelled swords, precious stones and three kettles filled with gold."

This rather precise description is interesting because exactly the same inventory appears in accounts of at least two other treasures—the somewhat legendary treasures of "Bloody Bonita," a renegade Spaniard who operated on the West Coast in the early 1820s, and the more authentic church treasure of Peru, which was looted from Lima in 1821!

During the latter eighteenth and early nineteenth centuries shipments of treasures from the New World to Spain were accelerated by the growing desperation of the Bourbon rulers, Charles IV and Ferdinand VII, and also by the growing threat of rebellion among the Spanish colonies. The activities of buccaneers along the Spanish Main from Cartagena across the Caribbean caused many of these shipments to be made down the West Coast and around Cape Horn. The freebooters of the Caribbean quickly shifted their attention to the West Coast, and Cocos Island became especially favored as an out-of-the-way place for temporarily disposing of their loot.

One of the more active pirates was "Bloody Bonito," whose ravages of West Coast towns and churches formed the basis of many of the Cocos Island legends. However, there were two treasures buried on Cocos that were quite authentic—the so-called "Devonshire treasure," named for the British warship H.M.S. *Devonshire;* and the "Mary Deer treasure," named for a Nova Scotia bark, the *Mary Deer*. The latter has been frequently confused with another ship of a similar name—the *Mary Deere,* and also has sometimes been misspelled the *"Mary Dear."*

The Devonshire treasure was known to have been buried on Cocos. Following a number of raids on Spanish ships, the crew of the British gunboat mutinied, demanding a division of the spoils. The crew took over the ship and sailed to Cocos, where the treasure, estimated to have been worth 3,400,000 English pounds, was buried, presumably on Wafer Bay. The ship was later captured by British warships sent out to find it, and the mutinous crew was executed or sent to penal colonies in Australia.

The second authentic treasure consisted of the official treasury of Peru, worth about eighteen million dollars, which was literally stolen from the revolutionary Government of Peru in the year 1835. At the time there was a war between Peru and Chile, following the insurrection against Spanish colonial rule; and the Chilean army was marching on Lima. The Peruvian Government loaded its official treasury aboard the bark *Mary Deer,* lying in Callao harbor, under the mistaken assumption that it would be safe under the British flag. The master of the bark, Captain Jack Thompson—who had once sailed with "Bloody Bonita"—promptly cut his cables and headed for Cocos Island.

The ship and its crew were later captured by Peruvian gunboats, and all were shot except Captain Thompson and two sailors who agreed to point out the location of the treasure. Captain Thompson managed to escape on a whaling ship, returned to Nova Scotia and died in Cape Breton, in 1842, after confessing his part in the *Mary Deer* affair. Through a man who had taken care of Thompson during his latter days, a Captain John Keating, the treasure came to be identified as the "Keating treasure."

A third equally authentic report concerns the church treasure that disappeared from Lima in the year 1821. Because of the similarity of circumstances with the *Mary Deer* piracy fourteen years later, it has been confused with the latter treasure in some legends of "lost treasures" of Cocos Island.

In July, 1821, when the rebel forces of José de San Martín were moving down upon Lima, the viceroy, José de la Cerna, decided to strip the churches of Lima of their priceless relics, gold and silver statuary, and precious stones. There were about sixty churches in Lima, and the value of the treasure—which reportedly included a life-size solid gold statue of the Virgin—was estimated at the time at more than sixty million dollars.

There was an American schooner, the *Black Witch,* out of Salem, Massachusetts, lying in Callao harbor at the time, under command of a "Captain Henry Smith." He had been waiting to join a rebel fleet under command of "Admiral Corcoran," or Cochrane—a former British naval officer who was actually Lord Cochrane, the Earl of Dundonald. The latter's diary contains an entry, dated August 18, 1821, which says: "The Spaniards today relieved the fortress of Callao and removed plate and money, being the whole wealth of Lima, to the amount of millions of pounds, which had been deposited there for safekeeping."

By some colossal error in judgment, the viceroy ordered the church treasures of Lima loaded on the *Black Witch.* Captain Smith was told to sail around off Callao for several days and return as soon as the rebellion was put down; but the *Black Witch* disappeared and nothing was heard of it officially for eighty years—until Captain Brown arrived in San Francisco, in the year 1901.

The implications of the old Captain's story were not clearly recognized at the time, partly because of the lack of specific knowledge of the lost church treasures of Peru, and partly because Captain Brown himself—as has been noted—did not fully understand the significance of his own story.

Nevertheless, his account was so convincing and well supported by certain collateral information that a small group of adventurous men from San Francisco and New York set forth in July of 1902 in the schooner *Herman* under the leadership of Captain Brown to search for an immense cache of buried treasure on a remote island in the South Seas.

The story of the voyage of the *Herman* has been culled from the records of Captain George W. Sutton, of New Rochelle, New York, who took over command of the expedition when it seemed that Captain Brown was about to shoot or poison all those aboard the ship.

Captain Sutton kept these records with almost fanatical detail, not only during the voyage but for many years after the voyage ended in a series of events, or rather a hurricane of events, that swept over the weary adventurers, leaving them like so much flotsam and jetsam, floating crazily in the wake of a storm.

During those years after the disastrous end of the voyage, Captain Sutton studied the assorted bits of information—the log and charts of the voyage; notes, letters and diaries that he kept; even the ship's documents and newspaper clippings that he had assembled in a massive scrap book. Slowly they began to take shape, as the emerging story of an ancient people takes shape from fragments of pottery and old artifacts dug out of the ground.

Captain Sutton died in 1934, unable to complete his work; but he left the logs, journals and notes to his son, George W. Sutton, Jr. They lay for years, buried among old papers and journals, and then the younger George Sutton began to assemble them; but he died in 1958, without finishing the work. Since then, his widow, Ione Ulrich Sutton, and the writer have collaborated in putting together the records and memories of the fantastic story.

It is now almost seventy years since the *Herman* set sail from San Francisco. Captain Brown and Sutton are dead; and so are Dr. George Luce, John Chetwood and the others who were partners in this strange adventure. All that is left are the records on old and yellowed sheets of papers, accumulated from many places—from the New England coast and San Francisco, down to Australia and the underbelly of the world, that "gray South Pacific" which, as Conrad wrote, "has its secrets, too, but more in the manner of a grave."

Within these fragments of information, George Sutton believed, lay the secret of the lost church treasure of Peru, a mystery that has defied dedicated treasure seekers for almost a century, and may defy them forever.

Mysteries do not require extended introductions, particularly when they concern a hundred million dollars' worth of buried treasure. The thing to do is get on with the story. Nevertheless, in order to place all the events of the tale in proper perspective, a more extensive review of the record of "lost treasures" of Cocos Island is appended to this story so that those readers who are interested in these matters may dig into them.

T.W.

Providence:
The Captain's Story

[1]

In the fall of the year 1901 a strange, bearded old man with pale, bitter eyes appeared in San Francisco, giving the name of Captain James Brown. He talked to only a few people—men of wealth and leisure, with adventurous instincts—seeking to interest them in a venture for which he professed to know the secret of a fabulous treasure. The old man admitted having been a pirate, and there was some indication that he was also a murderer. Some of those to whom he told bits of his story listened at first with curiosity and some interest; but the intractable manners of the old man and his sudden explosions of violent temper, usually brought on by an ingrained suspicion of everyone, soon exhausted this interest, and he ended by sitting alone in the lobby of a small hotel, where he finally fell ill of recurrent malaria —"the fevers," as he called it—and became desperately sick.

A certain Dr. George Luce was living in the hotel, and he often saw the old man sitting in the lobby and from time to time spoke to him; but it was not until he learned that Captain Brown had become ill and was staying in his room that Dr. Luce became interested enough to look in on him.

He made his way up to the old Captain's quarters and found him spread out upon the bed, with a collection of old papers tossed helter-skelter about the place. Brown's weathered face, encircled entirely by white hair, showed the ravages of fever. His pale blue eyes were almost glazed, yet the hard bitterness showed through.

"What the hell do you want?" he demanded, in a voice that was little more than a rumble from the depths of his chest, as he lay on his bed naked and glistening with sweat. "Let an old man died alone—" He sat bolt upright at one point, staring at Dr. Luce as if he had been an apparition, and then sank back, muttering, "The damned blood is all over the place, Cap'n . . . it's making the oysters red in the lagoon."

Dr. Luce was a man past sixty, living in semiretirement. He was not unduly affected by apparent hallucinations, but the need of medical help for the old sailor was too obvious to be ignored. He found himself seeing Captain Brown each day, bringing him medicines and soup, until the Captain began to recover from the attack of fever.

Some time later—perhaps a week or two after Dr. Luce found him sick in bed—Captain Brown began, in a vague, half-coherent way, to tell Dr. Luce a strange story. It was told with reticence, and sometimes with hostility—since the Captain's inborn suspicion of everyone was seldom laid aside; but finally, under the bond of a Masonic oath (both the doctor and Captain were Masons) he divulged secrets which had been only vaguely revealed during his illness.

Once, he looked directly at Dr. Luce, his pale eyes blazing so that the pupils were completely rimmed with white, pointed a finger at the doctor, and roared out: "Did you hear the position? Damn it, man, if you did I'll kill you!" He half rose from the bed, then sank back in weariness from the sickness. "I'm sorry, Doc . . . it's the fevers gets me. But if I told you the position, I got nothing left . . ."

All this was at first quite confusing to Dr. Luce; but little by little, as Brown's health improved, it began to form a pattern of events that had taken place many years ago in the old captain's life. At one point Captain Brown pointed to a weather-beaten portfolio bag, and asked Dr. Luce to bring it over to his bedside. He reached in and dragged out a small leather pouch, in which there were a number of coins—English and Spanish, all minted, as Dr. Luce observed, between the years 1750 and 1790.

"There's millions where that come from," he said. "All of it buried again—after we dug it up from Cocos. And I'm the only man alive knows where it is." He fell back again, as if the mere notion of so much wealth was too much to endure.

It was not long before the elements of this story began to impinge upon Dr. Luce's mind with increasing coherence. One night he decided to disclose part of the old Captain's tale to some friends with whom he was dining.

The friends—Frank Green, an insurance man; Donzel Stoney, a

lawyer, and a small puckish-faced man with a constant twinkle of good humor in his eyes, John Chetwood—all had heard the fragments of the story from the doctor before; but on this night Dr. Luce put all the pieces together as best he could.

It was a story of buried treasure on Cocos Island—a small rocky island in the Pacific Ocean lying several hundred miles off the coast of Panama; and at this time San Francisco was rife with such legends. Expeditions to Cocos Island had been fitted out, from San Francisco and from Vancouver, in British Columbia; and thus far, after perhaps a dozen years of intermittent searchings, the little island had not given up more than a handful of old coins, in spite of the fairly authentic nature of the reports of treasures having been buried there.

"It may be simply an old sailor's yarn," Dr. Luce told his friends, "but on the other hand, Captain Brown gives the only reasonable explanation why no one has found any of the treasures. If he dug it up and carried it away to this other island, as he says he did, this would explain why it isn't there any more."

Donzel Stoney, a short man possessed of an authoritative air, nodded and grunted at the same time. His feelings were divided.

"Most of the Cocos Island stories are like any other stories of buried treasure," he said, slowly. "In only one of the earliest stories—the accounts of William Dampier, who sailed with Sir Edward Davis, the English buccaneer, and wrote about it—was there an actually confirmed record that anyone could go on. In two later cases the British Government and the Government of Peru reported some actual deposits of gold and silver stolen from them. This was less than a hundred years ago, and the records are still quite available and authentic."

It was decided that perhaps they should all meet with Captain Brown, and ask a few questions. Dr. Luce, stroking his gray mustache, grinned at this, and shook his head.

"You won't get much that way. The old fellow is not very talkative. He made me swear as a Mason that I would never reveal what he told me—and that wasn't very much. However"—he looked at the others—"he wants help in setting up an expedition to look for his gold, so I guess I haven't violated much."

Dr. Luce's dilemma, if there was one, was relieved a day or so later when he went to see Captain Brown. The old man was no longer there.

He had left a note for the doctor.

"Dear doctor," the note read, "I am going back to my home in

Auburn, which is near Providence. If you are interested in the matter I discussed with you, please contact me by letter. I will agree to show your people where the island lies, if I am to get one quarter of the treasures which amount to millions. I will not pay any expenses. Yrs. truly, James Brown (Capt.)."

This news was conveyed to Stoney, Chetwood and Green. The latter had a suggestion.

"I have an old friend in New York—a lawyer. He is Arthur Walradt, and I'll ask him to investigate this fellow Brown. If there is nothing to it, we have lost nothing. If it turns out there is something, we may be able to interest enough people to organize an expedition. What do you say?"

As Green had pointed out, nothing would be lost; and thus it was by this somewhat circuitous route that the matter of Captain James Brown came to the attention of George W. Sutton, of New Rochelle, New York.

[2]

Captain George Sutton was a quiet man in his late forties. His brown hair was parted respectably in the middle, and he wore a neatly trimmed handlebar mustache. He had been a seafaring man in his youth, and was now Commodore of the New Rochelle Yacht Club. His had been a genteel kind of sea life.

When Arthur Walradt called him from New York, Sutton was in his office in New Rochelle where he held the quasi-political title of "Chairman of the Board of Sewer Commissioners." Walradt asked him if he could come into New York to see him on a "peculiar matter."

"What's peculiar about it?" Sutton asked.

"You wouldn't believe it if I told you over the telephone, George. It has something to do with a large amount of treasure. Pirates' treasure." Sutton must have evinced, by a grunt or some subliminal transference of thought, his immediate reaction, which was necessarily skeptical; because Walradt, as if to hold Sutton's continued attention, said quickly: "It's about a hundred million dollars' worth, George!"

It was not an amount that could be lightly shrugged off, even assuming it to be something of an exaggeration. One might laugh at a hundred thousand or so—but a hundred million!

"I've received a letter from a friend in San Francisco about a fellow named Brown—Captain James Brown," Walradt went on rapidly. "And I've seen Captain Brown. I'd like to talk with you and see what you make of it."

If Sutton had not known Walradt as a steady, reliable sort of man, not given to practical jokes, he would have dismissed it as a poor attempt at humor. But Walradt was a lawyer, and he seemed quite serious.

"All right, Arthur," he said. "I don't really know what the hell you are talking about, but if you say so, I'll be in on the afternoon train."

It is thus—as Sutton was able to realize sometime afterward—that fools and empires are born. He reached Walradt's offices, in lower Manhattan, late in the afternoon; and since it was late, they arranged to have dinner to talk over the "peculiar matter."

Walradt was a rather small, uninspiring man. Sutton—who was much bigger as to both height and breadth—always liked him. They had become acquainted by reason of their common membership in the New Rochelle Yacht Club.

"It may be a blind alley," Walradt said, with a trace of embarrassment. "Or it may be a stroke of good fortune. It's about a treasure, as I told you, and there's an odd chance there may be something in it. The 'odd chance,' you know, that happens to people like me once in a lifetime. But you'll be in a position to judge the man, George. You've been around and you know ships and sailing men."

He paused and coughed slightly.

"Besides, there is the matter of backing. We'll need some money."

Sutton had no desire to plunge into some costly adventure in search of anything as ephemeral as pirate treasure. He said cautiously: "I don't have a great deal to gamble with, Arthur."

Walradt nodded.

"Obviously, I wouldn't suggest anything foolish. But here—I have a letter I want you to read. It explains this better than I can. We'll go over to Fraunces and you can read it there."

They left the office and walked to Fraunces Tavern, which was nearby. Walradt handed Sutton the letter. It was from E. F. Green, on stationery of the Bohemian Club of San Francisco, dated March 25, 1902.

"Dear Walradt," the letter began, "I don't want you to think I am crazy by springing on you the proposition that follows, but you will have a chance to use your own judgment in this matter. There may come to you, at my request, a man named Capt. James Brown, of Auburn, near Providence, R.I."

The letter then set forth certain "facts," which included a statement that "in the early part of the nineteenth century a very large amount of Spanish and English gold was sent from South America in a sailing vessel to escape revolutionists. The gold was never delivered, but it has always been claimed it was buried on Cocos Island off the Mexican Coast."

Green's letter then got down to details:

"Up to this point we have been dealing with established facts. Now comes this man Brown. He comes to me (or his story) through a Masonic friend, Brown himself being a Mason . . ."

The letter first recounted the way Brown's story had come to Green.

"Captain Brown claims he is the only surviving member of a party led by the son of the Captain who originally buried the treasure on Cocos Island," Green's letter went on. "This party dug up the treasure and buried it again on some island in the South Pacific."

Green's letter continued, reading like a legal brief: ". . . that fights broke out and sickness, possibly aided by Brown's efforts, wiped out all but himself; that he arrived in Australia with some 200,000 or 300,000 English sovereigns, being all he could take away; that he lived well in Australia, and later in England, until, having lost what he had by reverses, he wants to go back for what is left."

Captain Brown had come to San Francisco to try to interest a group in fitting out an expedition, but "the party broke up because of internal dissension caused by Brown's inordinate suspicion and intractableness." Green's own opinion of Brown was anything but flattering. "I have never seen the man," he said, "but he appears to be peculiar, suspicious, cranky and on his own showing pretty near a pirate, and I wouldn't trust him across the street."

In spite of these adverse impressions, and Green's additional comment that he "considered the whole thing a fairy tale," he wound up by remarking: "I can't just see, however, what he can gain by leading a party to the South Pacific on a wild goose chase. Capt. Brown is now in Auburn, near Providence, R.I., and I would not bring him here but he will come to New York. If a conservative judge will say his tale appears plausible and has apparent merit, parties here will fit out an expedition. If he comes to you, will you examine him and let me know your opinion? I believe he had papers which he calls evidence.

I believe your judgment is good. Sift him and if you believe him, let me know. I trust I am not imposing on you."

Sutton, after reading the letter, looked thoughtfully at Walradt, and finally said: "You know, your friend Green seems to have hit on the nub of the whole thing. Why should a man of Brown's age [he had been described as "over seventy"] want to go to the South Seas just for the trip?"

Walradt nodded. He then showed Sutton a letter he had received from Captain Brown, shortly after the arrival of Green's letter. It was brief, merely asking for an appointment, and concluding with the pithy remark: "The subject we are in communication about is a treasure island, which I know all about."

"He came to my office a couple of days ago," Walradt said. "He gave a straightforward story. The man seems to be quite sincere and probably honest, although a bit queer." He pulled out a copy of his own reply to Green and handed this to Sutton. In this letter Walradt had written:

"He [Brown] told me a straightforward story, startling in many of its aspects, but nevertheless consistent throughout. . . . He has a good face, looks in comfortable circumstances, has a clear mind and an open eye, and is just the kind of man who would make a good impression on a Court or jury, and whose story would unquestionably be believed if he were giving testimony in an ordinary matter. In fact, there is nothing about the man's appearance which causes me to distrust anything he says, outside the character of the story itself."

Sutton studied this somewhat damaging dialectic, and shook his head.

"How can anyone be sure he is telling the truth? Does he have any supporting evidence?"

"He claims he has some canceled checks, and other items, which show quite a bit of affluence when he was in England. Checks up to two thousand pounds sterling. His story is that he came to England with quite a supply of money, from the treasure he helped bury. Then he put it into a freebooting venture—running guns into Cuba, I think. Lost his ships and most of his fortune, and now he wants to go back to the island and get the rest. He seems to have a clear recollection of everything."

Walradt explained what he meant by "clear recollection." Several years before, a man's body had been washed up on the coast of Long Island Sound. A Psi Upsilon fraternity pin was found on his clothes, and it was determined that it had once belonged to Arthur Walradt. The dead man had been a fraternity brother, and the pin was a gift from Walradt. Through this pin, the man was identified.

"Brown remembered the incident quite clearly," Walradt said. The subject apparently was brought up during Walradt's talk with Brown, as a kind of seagoing experience, to establish common interests. When Walradt mentioned the matter, the Captain had said: "Yes, of course. I remember reading about it a good many years ago." He had paused, as if to refresh his recollection, and then added, "The man fell off a steamboat, didn't he? The *Rosedale*."

Walradt told Sutton it was the *Rosedale*.

"It was a coastal steamer, running between New York and Bridgeport. This happened sixteen years ago—and yet he remembered it quite clearly."

It occurred to Sutton that sixteen years ago Captain Brown was either in England or running guns into Cuba. He forbore to mention this, however; but he decided he would put Captain Brown's remarkable recollections to some tests when he saw him, to see if they came from "clearness of mind" or were the results of boning up at the public library or newspaper offices, prior to his visit with Walradt, to see what he could find out about Walradt.

In Walradt's letter to Green, he had outlined a tentative proposal: "As it looks to me now, I feel that while it is a long shot, it is worth the risk," he wrote. His suggestion was that a group be formed and a boat purchased, or chartered, in New York, and that Captain Brown be placed in charge of the expedition "to consist of you [Green] and the doctor and one or two others, of whom I can furnish one." They would start ostensibly on a pleasure trip to avoid publicity, and after rounding Cape Horn would proceed to the area where the island was believed to be.

"If you think well of this, a friend of mine would probably put up the money for himself and me, jointly, and go on the trip."

Sutton recognized that he was cast in the role of the "friend" who would be "furnished" and who would "probably put up the money." In spite of some instinctive restraints, the possibilities were too alluring to be dropped. Sutton agreed to go to Auburn in the next few days to "test" the Captain's story.

A day or two later, before taking the night boat to Providence, Sutton spent several hours in the public library digging up information on Cocos Island and its treasures. Part of this effort was to assure himself of his own ability to judge the Captain's story; and part was in anticipation of possible bold falsifications on the part of the Captain. He wanted to test the "clear recollection" to which Walradt had referred. When he arrived in Auburn the next day, taking a carriage down from Providence, he was well fortified with facts.

He found Captain Brown stretched out in a rocking chair, staring out at the slatted islands of Narragansett Bay. The Captain did not take the trouble of getting out of his chair, but merely waved at a straight-backed chair, the only other seating arrangement on the veranda, indicating with his hand that Sutton might sit down if he wished to.

Sutton said, "I'm George Sutton."

The Captain nodded. "Mr. Walradt wrote that you'd be here, Cap'n. Set down."

Sutton was confronted with conflicting impressions. He had expected to find in Captain Brown a certain standard type of ancient mariner, given to spinning yarns perhaps for the plain enjoyment of telling them, or possibly as the result of growing senility and inability to disentangle reality from the reminiscent imaginings of an old man, to whom a tale he has heard and things that have happened may seem to be the same thing. He was prepared, in short, to meet a loquacious old man, unquestionably a romantic and probably a liar.

Captain Brown at first glance did not appear to have any of these characteristics. He was dressed in white duck, and Sutton's first impression was of the old man's size. He was big-boned and broad-framed, stretched out comfortably in the rocking chair. His eyes were a light blue color, faintly opaque like hard chips of ice. His face, rimmed with white hair, had the appearance of an enormous thistle, and the expression of the few muscles and features within the framework of hair and whiskers might have been regarded as simply that of a rather weather-beaten old man. But his eyes were remarkable. There was an odd mixture of malevolence and cunning, pale and rock-hard. They left no element of softness in his face.

There are some men to whom life is never a puzzle or a source of uncertainty. They face it as a hard, uncompromising and often brutal reality, which is to be overcome but never avoided. Captain Brown seemed to Sutton to be such a man. For fifty years, according to the story he told Dr. Luce, he had lived on the sea or near it. Whether this kind of single-minded certainty—self-sufficient, usually stubborn and at times arrogant—is acquired from the unyielding character of the sea, or the sea merely attracts those who possess this quality, is a matter for conjecture, and probably not important.

What was important to Sutton was the sudden realization of the hard character of the man he had to deal with. By his own admission, Captain Brown had been a pirate and a murderer. He was rough, bitter and old; and there was nothing about him that would inspire trust or confidence.

Sutton's initial reflections were interrupted by the opening of a door leading to the veranda. A fairly tall, striking woman came out. Her hair was gray, as were her clear eyes. Her smile was warm and friendly, in contrast to Captain Brown's words and manner. Yet Sutton thought he detected something akin to fear, or at least a kind of pleading expression in her eyes.

Captain Brown still did not rise from his chair. "Mrs. Brown," he said, noncommitally.

Sutton smiled as the woman stepped forward and took his hand. She asked in a clipped English accent if she might bring some tea. Sutton shook his head.

"Later, perhaps—thank you," he said. "I had a bite at the pier."

Captain Brown shook himself, as if wishing to cast aside any extraneous social matters and get down to business. His wife went back into the house.

"You want to know about my island, eh?" the Captain said in a deep rumbling voice. Sutton nodded, feeling that it might be wise to play his own cards close to his vest, and say nothing until Captain Brown had divulged whatever he wished to divulge.

He felt it necessary, however, in the interest of candor and sincerity, to explain that his purpose was to go over the Captain's story and if it seemed probable that there was a chance of locating the island on which Captain Brown said the treasure had been buried, they would then set about organizing an expedition.

Captain Brown nodded again, without seeming to pay much attention, and then he began in a slow, rumbling voice to tell his own story. Much of it was an amplification of what Sutton had already heard; but he was quite interested in checking over in his own mind the things he knew about Cocos Island treasures, to see how these facts compared with the Captain's tale.

It was only after the Captain had gotten a good way through his story that Sutton was suddenly struck with an astonishing point: almost *nothing* Captain Brown said conformed with the traditional Cocos

A revealing photographic portrait of Captain James Brown.

George W. Sutton, sea captain and Chairman of the Board of Sewer Commissioners, New Rochelle, New York.

A photo of George W. Sutton taken near the wharves of San Francisco in 1902.

legends over which Sutton had pored in his researches at the library. As he later told Walradt: "This was puzzling at first. I began to doubt what he was saying. But then it occurred to me that this was the solid grain of truth. The story had not been picked up from the usual sources. It was the story I began to trust. Not the man, mind you . . . his story. There was a solid grain of truth in what he said that I could not find reason to doubt."

The "solid grain of truth" actually occurred about midway in the Captain's account. He told Sutton of his early days at sea, and of meeting a young man in Kingston harbor, in Jamaica, as a result of interceding in a waterfront fight. The young fellow had been attacked by a group of roughs, and was being badly beaten when young Brown—then about twenty-one—stepped in and "they all ran like rats." Brown and the young man became quite close friends after that, and he learned that his new friend, Henry Schmid, was from New Bedford, near Providence.

It developed that young Schmid was owner and master of a vessel—a brigantine, or "hermaphrodite brig," as they were known, which was being fitted out for a trip around Cape Horn to the West Coast. The vessel was the *Sea Foam,* with a crew of fifty-two; and young Schmid asked Brown to sign on as a junior officer. The size of the crew aroused Brown's curiosity; normally a complement of a dozen men could handle a brigantine.

"He didn't tell me right away that his father had been a pirate," Captain Brown noted. "I knew there was something odd about the ship because it carried almost no cargo. A ship of that tonnage doesn't make a run to the West Coast without cargo."

Schmid apparently wanted someone of his own age, in whom he could confide; and soon after the *Sea Foam* sailed out of Kingston harbor, he told young Brown the real purpose of the voyage. He had several charts and maps given him by his father, who had also been captain of a ship, disclosing the location of buried treasure on an "island off the coast of South America."

At this point, Captain Brown drew in a deep breath, and seemed to hold it while he considered things. Then, exhaling with a gusty sigh, he said: "It don't make any difference how much I tell you about this, Cap'n Sutton, because the gold ain't there any more and you can't find it without me."

Apparently satisfied that he was not on the verge of indiscreet disclosures, he went on with the story. There had been a lot of gold and silver treasures buried on Cocos "back about a hundred years ago," and part of it was buried by the crew of an American ship. "The ship was the *Black Witch,*" he said. "Cap'n Schmid's father was master. They got a lot of church treasures out of the Spanish colonies, and buried it on Cocos."

The reference to the "church treasures" and the *Black Witch* struck a bell in Sutton's memory. A vast treasure known as "the ecclesiastical treasure of Lima"—an immense store of church relics, gold and silver ornaments and Spanish money—had disappeared from Callao during the early 1820s, when the Spanish rebels were marching on the city. He remembered reading that it had been loaded aboard an American schooner, the *Black Witch,* under Captain Henry *Smith.* Sutton's eyes must have gleamed with interest, because Captain Brown raised his bushy brows and asked: "You know about that ship?"

"Only the name," Sutton said. "It was reported to be an American privateer, wasn't it?"

The Captain grunted and then continued, as if Sutton's knowledge or lack of it was a matter of no importance. He seemed to be concentrating single-mindedly on the subject at hand. According to young Schmid's story, his father had sailed from Callao and was supposed to have cruised around out of reach of the rebel fleet until the insurrection was put down, and then return with the cargo of riches. Instead, he sailed to Cocos Island, where the treasure was buried.

At this point Captain Brown climbed out of his chair and went into the house. He returned a few minutes later with a worn portfolio, from which he extracted some soiled papers. He glanced over these, and finally selected one—a yellow sheet of paper on which a map had been drawn.

"Don't mind showing ye this now," he said. "It won't do ye any good, Cap'n. The gold ain't there any more."

The map showed the kidney-shaped contours of Cocos Island, with the two coves—Wafer Bay and Chatham Bay—on the north coast. Two islands, one marked "Breakfast," guarded the latter cove. An irregular line was traced up from the beach along what seemed to be a small creek. It then veered off toward a line marked "cliffs." Underneath was written: "Follow coastline of bay to creek. At high water mark step seventy paces upstream west by south. Against skyline there will be gap in hills. From no other point is gap visible. Face rock rising sheer from ground. At height of shoulder is a hole large enough for a fist. Thrust iron bar into hole and pry loose rocks. This will expose cave where treasure is buried."

Sutton's quickened interest must have been apparent to the Captain; but if it was, he paid little attention to it. He continued in a slow voice: "I made this map from memory after Schmid and I burned the original. The map isn't important, because we never went back. We took off most of the gold, and what was left wasn't worth going back for."

Sutton had observed Captain Brown's intense concentration in telling his story. He seemed to be reaching deeply into his mind for danger signals—points on which he needed to cover the narrative with great care, telling only that which needed to be told.

He continued to rock back and forth in his chair as he described the fate ot the *Black Witch* and her master, as it had been told to him by young Schmid. The realization that this must be the story of the "church treasure" of Lima was becoming more and more firmly fixed in Sutton's mind; yet this did not seem to have any importance to the old Captain. Sutton observed that he glanced at him now and then, as if to gauge the effect of his words, and at times he seemed quite puzzled at Sutton's quickened interest.

It occurred to Sutton that Captain Brown might well be "testing" him, perhaps seeking to determine in his own way how much Sutton knew and how far he ought to trust his potential new partner. It was increasingly apparent that the old man literally lived on suspicion.

According to Captain Brown's story, trouble developed among the crew of the *Black Witch,* either before or after the ship made Cocos and the treasure was buried. Members of the crew had gotten wind of the character of the cargo taken aboard at Callao, and insisted on a "division of spoils" in accordance with the code of privateers and armed merchantmen. Captain Schmid (or Smith) apparently refused —whether in deference to the rights of the owners back in Salem or for other reasons was not made clear—and mutiny broke out. It was put down, quite vigorously, judging from Captain Brown's account. "Half of 'em were shot, and the others seized up and flogged."

In any event, after disposing of the gold and silver treasures of the Peruvian churches, the *Black Witch* sailed off, and ran into foul weather off the coast of South America. Without an adequate complement of sailors, half of them having died as a result of the mutiny, it was driven ashore and most of those aboard were lost.

Captain Schmid survived, however, and made his way back to New

Bedford, where he died, after confiding the story of the buried treasure to his son.

Sutton realized that there were some gaps in the story that probably would need checking out; but on the whole it conformed with reports he had read—particularly with respect to the mystery of the "ecclesiastical treasure of Lima."

Captain Brown continued with his story, glancing now and then at Sutton, with a baleful appraisal. It seemed to Sutton that Walradt's comment in his letter to Green—"there is nothing about [the man's appearance] which causes me to distrust anything he says, outside the character of the story itself"—was something of an understatement. In fact, Sutton's impression was almost precisely the reverse: almost everything about Captain Brown caused him to distrust the old pirate, but what was becoming more and more convincing was the character of the story itself!

The Captain, in his unhurried way, narrated the story of the voyage of the *Sea Foam* up from Cape Horn up the West Coast. The ship had put in at Juan Fernández Island and later in Chincha, apparently to avoid any of the major ports—although Sutton's colleagues in San Francisco later found that a vessel named the *Sea Foam* had been off Callao for several days in 1851, presumably on a pearl fishing expedition to the Bay of Dulce.

"We raised Cocos about the middle of November," the Captain went on. "There is a big island outside the bay, and we stood off the island in about six fathom of water. We could see combers on the beach, and had to go in with the longboat."

Captain Schmid took one of the boats, leaving Brown in command aboard ship. Brown watched him through the glasses, walking the shoreline. As he talked about this, Sutton observed that Brown's eyes kindled with that curious barometer of his feelings—in this case, suspicion. Even at the age of twenty-one, Brown seemed to have been infected with a general distrust of his fellow man.

He watched young Schmid turn in toward a line of craggy cliffs, some five hundred yards behind the beach. Then he walked up the creek, which Captain Brown had drawn on the map. After pacing off the distance—presumably seventy yards—he turned to face north, looking directly at the cliffs. After that he walked toward the cliff, and disappeared from Brown's view. The young man must have suffered a torment of uncertainty until Schmid returned to the beach.

That night they studied the map, which Schmid had received from his father; and after the most careful scrutiny, Schmid burned the map. He was fearful that suspicious crew members might attack him that night.

"We burned it so nobody but me and Schmid would know where the cave was," Captain Brown noted. "If we'd been shot, nobody on that ship would know where that treasure was buried."

Sutton asked the Captain: "Did you have any knowledge of this 'church treasure' before you met Henry Schmid, Captain?"

The Captain looked at Sutton, as if to determine the reason for such a question. Then he shook his head.

"No, of course not. How would I have known about it? It was buried there before I was born."

"How could you be sure there *was* such a treasure?" Sutton persisted.

The old man contemplated him with something between surprise and contempt.

"We dug it up," he said.

Sutton nodded. It seemed to be a good answer.

Captain Brown went on to explain in detail how they dug up the treasure, blasting out the face of the cliff and carrying casks and chests of riches down to the shore, where it was put aboard longboats and lightered out to the *Sea Foam*. It required two days and perhaps thirty trips of the longboats. Members of the boat crews, carefully selected by young Schmid, toiled under the tropical sun, working industriously in the blazing heat—aware, no doubt, of the unwritten code of piracy, which requires a proper distribution of a portion of the spoils to all members of the crew. Finally the *Sea Foam,* with its immense load of wealth, weighed anchor and headed westward into the Pacific.

[3]

Up to the part of Captain Brown's tale in which he described digging up the treasure from its Cocos Island burial ground, it might have been any sailor's yarn of hidden pirates' gold. Sutton had only to weigh the elements of credibility—the reasonableness of the story itself, the Captain's manner of telling it, and the points which seemed to conform with facts already known to Sutton. As he later told Walradt, "It all hung together." For example, there was the coincidence of the account given by young Henry Schmid about his father and the *Black Witch,* and the fact that the "ecclesiastical treasure of Lima" *actually was* loaded aboard a ship of that name, under command of a "Captain Henry Smith." All these served not only to lend conviction to the story, but whetted Sutton's appetite for treasure hunting to an enormous degree.

It was what followed after the treasure had been dug up and carried down across the Pacific to a remote island in the Low Archipelago that stirred strange apprehensions in Sutton's mind. The question of credibility was supplanted by a sense of horror and fascination, and possibly by a certain amount of fear.

"It may seem fantastic," he told Walradt, "but I began to feel that I was dealing with something malignant that seemed to hang over the old man—possibly the ghosts of the poor devils he shot or poisoned. By God, Arthur, the man struck me as inhuman—a kind of devil himself! When he sat there rocking in his chair, telling the story quite calmly, it seemed reasonable and sensible. It was afterward that I felt the horror of what he said. It was like talking to an insane man, who seems quite rational when he is talking, but afterward when you put it all together, it's the tale of a madman!"

There were two incidents in the course of the Captain's narration that particularly aroused Sutton's interest. It seemed almost as if he were dealing with two distinct personalities: the old man, hard and bitter but quite natural as he rocked back and forth in his chair and spun his yarn; and the other personality that grew out of the story itself—a wild, untamed youth, to whom shooting down sailors and murdering his partner far out at sea seemed quite ordinary experiences.

The first of these incidents that impressed Sutton occurred during Captain Brown's account of the voyage of the *Sea Foam* from Cocos down to the Low Archipelago. It was three thousand miles to Nuku Hiva, in the Marquesas, and another thousand miles past Tahiti to the lower end of the string of volcanic islands and coral atolls known as the "low islands." Some of these were populated by Polynesian natives, and others uninhabited. The *Sea Foam,* laden with its immense cargo of riches, made the voyage without touching at any port.

The Low Archipelago runs from below the Tropic of Capricorn northwest to within ten degrees of the equator. The islands spread over an area twice the size of New England, some rising sharply to heights of several hundred feet, others slabs of sun-scorched sand only a few feet above the sea, capped with coconut palms and low shrubs, and surrounded by thin strands of half-sunken reefs that form pale green lagoons around the coral formations.

These are the visible parts of the last ridges of the great undersea land mass known as the South Pacific Plateau, formed by the Austral and Tuamotu Ridges; and beyond this the ocean sinks way into the deep South Pacific Basin with only a few scattered shoals to mark the presence of land between the Low Archipelago and the Antarctic Continent.

Many of the islands are of volcanic origin, with a rim of coral around the jagged cone of an ancient crater, in the center of which there is often a small land-locked lake of fresh water. The smaller islands are usually coral, lying like scars on the surface of the sea, some of them as much as thirty miles in circumference but only a few feet wide. It is on these islands that the fierce tropical hurricanes, or typhoons, wreak their worst havoc.

Sutton had culled from such sources as Charles Warren Stoddard's *South-Sea Idylls* and the writings of Robert Louis Stevenson—who cruised through these islands in the *Casco*—stories of sudden and terrible storms that whirl out of the hot tropical air, spinning across the water with incredible force. No one really knows how they start, but the natives of the islands accept them as a fact of life. They rise quickly, preceded by a strange, pulsing hum in the air which may give as much as a half-hour warning; and then they rage across the islands, driving forty-foot waves over the atolls, smashing low barriers of coral and in some cases sweeping an entire island into the sea. Villages have been wiped out by these devastating winds, and natives tie themselves to coconut stalks while they watch houses and humans blown off into the unbelievable fury around them. Even the stalks of the palm trees, after the fronds are ripped off, may snap and cast loose their human appendages, which are then hurled far out into the raging water.

At one point, as Captain Brown was describing the course of the *Sea Foam*—omitting particulars as to the exact route of the vessel—Sutton interrupted to remark: "You must have been sailing in a dangerous season, Captain."

The old man stopped, and his eyes gleamed with a warning light. "What do ye mean—dangerous?"

"The typhoons," Sutton said. "You were in the typhoon season."

Captain Brown surveyed his visitor for a moment. It was an expression somewhere between astonishment and rage. When he spoke, his voice again was harsh.

"We buried the treasure, Cap'n! We buried it—that's all!" His big chest heaved, as if he were sucking in his breath for an explosion. "It's still there, and I'm the only man alive who knows where it is! Typhoons be damned . . . old women's tales, that's what they are!"

Having gotten this *non sequitur* off his chest, the old man continued with his rambling monologue, pausing now and then to glare at Sutton, as if he had injected some malignant or obscene notion into the situation, merely by his reference to typhoons.

Sutton had no idea what disturbed the Captain; but there was no doubt that he was disturbed. At one point he stopped, and edged forward in his chair, almost as if he were about to leap up and assault Sutton; and the latter found himself also sitting forward in his own chair, tensely, fearing he might have to stand up at any moment and fend off a physical attack if the Captain's strange ill humor should erupt into violence.

However, Captain Brown's inexplicable rage vanished as suddenly as it came; and he went on calmly reciting the events of the voyage. The *Sea Foam* sailed down among the islands; and sometime in late January of 1852 the vessel anchored off a small island, which Capatin Brown said was "well out of the way of trading routes."

The island was "about three miles long, and maybe a mile wide." It was apparently protected by a lagoon, which appeared dangerous for the *Sea Foam* to enter; and so the ship hove to in the channel outside two points of land and the beach was reached in the longboat. Captain Brown was fairly circumspect in describing the island. There was nothing to indicate specifically what the island looked like, except that there were cliffs of limestone facing the lagoon and the open sea, and behind that an irregular ridge, which was probably volcanic.

It was at this point that Sutton was moved to ask: "Would you recognize the island again, Captain? Could you describe it?"

He asked the question merely for assurance that the Captain could identify the island; but Captain Brown suddenly reared his huge body out of the chair, and stood for a moment, glaring at Sutton without speaking. It was the second time he had gotten out of the chair since Sutton arrived.

"Why in hell wouldn't I know it?" His ragged jaw parted in an expression of astonishment and anger—two emotions that he seemed to combine quite frequently. "Why wouldn't I know it? If ye think ye can get it out of me that way, Cap'n—we'd better stop this, right now! Nobody is going to cheat me—"

"For heaven's sake!" Sutton also was disturbed, and he too rose to his feet. "I've expressed no doubts, Captain—I merely asked if you would recognize the place if you saw it! No one is trying to cheat you!"

The old man grunted, and sat down. Sutton did the same.

"I would recognize it," the Captain said, shortly.

Then he continued, as if there had been no interruption.

"There were two entrances to the lagoon," he said. "Neither entrance was wide enough to risk the ship. We lay to and went in with the longboat."

After this it became evident to Sutton that Captain Brown's recital was becoming more guarded. He described places, and the actions of Captain Schmid and himself, in sufficient detail to lend validity to the story. It was apparent that he wanted Sutton to have enough information to take back to Walradt. But it was equally obvious that he did not intend to divulge any more information than was necessary to establish the "straightforwardness" of the story.

There was a cave, or cavern, in the cliff facing the lagoon, large enough for the treasure. The priceless relics of the Peruvian churches were ferried ashore in longboats and carried to this cave, where they were stored.

"How did you hide the treasures?" Sutton asked.

"Blasted the cliff down," the Captain said.

Sutton considered it rather notable that on this detail the Captain seemed to have no reservations or restraint; yet on the question of identifying the island itself, he had become almost choleric. This selective secrecy raised some interesting questions in Sutton's mind.

Captain Brown explained that the island was not likely to be visited by wandering ships, since there was no easily accessible landing area; and for this reason the treasure was considered safe from interlopers. However, he and young Schmid did not appear to have the same sense of security with regard to men in their own crew.

"Sailors can't be trusted, Cap'n," he remarked at one point, glancing at Sutton with a queer mixture of cunning and conciliation. This kind of mixed reaction was becoming familiar to Sutton; it seemed to open crevices in the old man's personality with which Sutton—something of a realist—knew they would ultimately have to deal.

"We had a hell of a fight on board ship one night—after we came back from a trip."

Captain Brown did not elaborate on what the "trip" was for, but Sutton had a notion that it was one of the things the Captain did not want to explain very fully. He had already received information, through Waldradt, from their San Francisco associates that parts of the

Captain's story, as told to Dr. Luce, had been connected with some rather vague reports of lost "gold ships" from Australia, which carried cargoes of bullion and silver from the newly discovered Darling River mine fields in Australia across the Pacific to England. It was widely believed that this shipping had been interrupted by freebooters who operated along the Pacific trade routes in the neighborhood of the Society Islands in the 1850s; and from some of Captain Brown's comments to Dr. Luce the suspicion had already been expressed in Green's letter to Walradt that Captain Brown might well have been one of these freebooters. Two ships in particular had been reported by Lloyd's of London as having been lost "east of Tahiti"; and at one point Captain Brown had confided to the doctor that he and Schmid had taken a few of their sailors into a port in Australia and "put them aboard a couple of ships leaving for England." The purpose of this was not clearly explained, but it seemed to the doctor it was a kind of seagoing "Trojan horse" operation in which men from the *Sea Foam* would assist in taking over the vessel from within the ship while the *Sea Foam* attacked from the sea.

One other point particularly interested Sutton, although he did not fully understand its significance at the time. Captain Brown told of a "large plant of oysters in the lagoon." Pearl fishing was a predatory pursuit in the South Seas, and places where oysters were found in abundance were visited frequently by natives living in the inhabited islands. Sutton wondered why they would have buried the treasure on an island likely to be visited from time to time.

Captain Brown's tale receded into sparseness as he approached the account of what finally happened. Sutton had the impression that all hands were to get a share of the plunder, in accordance with the unwritten code of ethics among pirates. At this point in the story, however, Captain Brown remarked that there were "too many people who knew about the treasure."

"You can't have fifty sailors knowing about that much gold—and not have trouble," he said. Sutton agreed with the improbability of this.

"What happened to your crew?" Sutton asked.

Captain Brown looked up as if to determine the motive for the question. Then he said: "Most of 'em died." The Captain's economy of words was most noticeable when he explained crucial situations. "Some of 'em were killed fighting. Others got sick and died."

It appeared that all this had actually happened in one night—the night they came back from the mysterious trip. There had been an uproarious celebration aboard the *Sea Foam* and Captain Schmid—either in excessive exuberance, or perhaps for some ulterior reason—ordered extra rations of rum.

"We usually kept a tight ship," the Captain said. "Not much drinking aboard. But this night we gave 'em plenty to celebrate with." The Captain chuckled.

Some of the sailors apparently detected a rather nauseous taste in the rum and a few began to vomit and roll on the decks in agony. Others crowded to the quarterdeck and shouted accusations at the Captain, charging him with putting poison in the rum. Captain Brown said he and Schmid stood at the rail and fired a few shots "to warn them," as Captain Brown put it. During the night quite a few of the crew died, and by morning the remainder, in an "ugly mood," as Captain Brown described them, again advanced on the quarterdeck. Captain Brown's comments at this point were fairly terse, but it appeared that when the shooting ended, only Schmid and Brown—and the cook—were left.

"We couldn't sail the ship—just the three of us," the Captain said. "So we sank the *Sea Foam* and rigged out a longboat."

They stowed some of the treasure—either from the ship or the cave—in the longboat and hoisted sail for the Australian coast, some three thousand miles west. For days they sailed westward; and somewhere south of the Tonga Islands, the cook became sick and finally died, and his body was dumped overboard.

After that, Captain Brown's story was even more sparse. Food and water were limited, and with more than a thousand miles to cover from the Tonga reefs to the Great Barrier Reef, it might require many days of sailing, particularly if they were to fall into calm weather.

"We watched each other," Captain Brown said. "There wasn't much to say. The steward hadn't counted for much, but Cap'n Schmid was different. He seemed to be going crazy, and I knew I had to watch him."

For days and nights, under the blazing sun and black skies, they sailed westward "watching each other." The winds were not steady; and the supply of sea biscuits and tinned food—and water—dwindled. The water had to be rationed a spoonful at a time.

"Men don't think straight in times like that," the old Captain vouchsafed, somewhat unnecessarily, stroking his beard as if he were trying to decide how much to tell Sutton—and how to tell it. "The sun gets into your skin and the thirst gets into your brain. Cap'n Schmid watched me, and I watched him. All the time. We had only one pistol aboard, and he had it. So I watched him."

At night Brown tied a line from his wrist to the gunwale so that any quick shift of the boat would awaken him . . . "in case Schmid moved forward." They sat there, hour after hour and day after day, Schmid in the stern sheets steering the boat, and Brown forward handling the sail. There was hardly enough water for a single man and Brown knew a final settlement would not be long in coming.

It came one night. They were still several hundred miles from land, probably south of New Caledonia. They had sighted only one island—probably Norfolk—since passing the Kermadecs, and for obvious reasons had not put in to shore. Brown, listening during the night and watching during the day, snatching only a few minutes of sleep from time to time, heard a scraping noise. He could barely make out the figure of Schmid in the darkness, but he knew he was moving forward.

"He had the pistol," the Captain said. "I knew he was going to shoot at me. So I jumped him first—before he was ready."

The two wrestled for the gun, struggling across the rocking longboat in the blackness of the night, hundreds of miles from land. Brown managed to get the gun, and he moved back to the bow of the boat and waited for morning.

"He was breathing hard all the time," Captain Brown said. "I could hear him breathe. I knew he'd gone crazy." Turning to Sutton and looking at him directly, with cold blue eyes, the Captain said, "When it was light enough to see, I shot him."

He continued, calmly and without any particular display of feeling, to describe the final stages of the voyage to Australia, after he had dumped the body of his dead partner into the sea. He sailed the longboat resolutely toward the west, chewing on small pieces of biscuit and drinking only enough water to keep his senses. He reached Australia safely and apparently converted enough of the treasure stowed in the longboat into English currency to be able to buy a "sheep station."

The rest of Captain Brown's story was fairly brief. He had lived in Australia for a number of years, working in mines and later on his sheep station, and finally traveled to England, where he married and settled down. During his time in Australia, he had returned once to the "treasure island," he said, and replenished his supply of riches. He felt that he could return for more any time he needed it, he told Sutton—until an unexpected stroke of adversity overtook him some ten years ago.

The Captain had moved from England back to America, bringing his wife with him, and had bought the house where he now lived near Providence, Rhode Island, which had been his boyhood home. He had enjoyed all the comforts he required, until he decided to put most of his resources into a "business" in Philadelphia.

"It was the shipping business, in a small way," he said, with a deprecatory wave of his hand. Something less than a hundred million, Sutton thought, and probably not requiring the Captain's exceptional talents in piracy and murder. As it developed, he was not entirely correct on this point.

"I had an interest in a company in Philadelphia," the old man went on. "We had two good ships—fast little converted frigates—which we used for running guns into Cuba."

This presumably was the freebooting venture to which Walradt had alluded. It was in the time when the notorious "Butcher" Weyler, the "devastator of haciendas, destroyer of families, outrager of women," to quote the Hearst papers of that day, was facing a rebellion of the Cuban populace against his bloody régime; and while the American people were somewhat sympathetic to the rebel cause, there was also an international restriction against shipping arms into the embroiled island.

Captain Brown's two ships sailed out of Chesapeake Bay with their cargoes of contraband guns and were unlucky enough to run into a naval patrol—an event that seemed to afflict the old man with a personal annoyance, in addition to the inconvenience of losing most of his financial resources.

"It was an outrage," he said, in a grumbling tone. "They were Americans and we thought they were on our side. I let them run up to us without firing a shot."

Sutton could not help wondering what the effect of "firing a shot" from small sailing vessels at the American gunboats would have been; but he also felt that Captain Brown would not have been incapable of trying to find out.

The two vessels were seized and confiscated, the Captain reckoning his losses at "several hundred thousand dollars." He then leaned forward and told Sutton in a confidential tone, and a somewhat lower voice, that he had revealed the "secret" of his original source of wealth to his wife.

"She wanted me to make a trip to get some more," he said.

As long as he had been in comfortable circumstances, he had not needed additional supplies from the cache of buried treasure, he explained, so he gave little thought to it.

There was also the possibility, Sutton reflected, that the Captain was not anxious to return to the scene of his piracies against the Australian specie ships, and thus arouse the attention of the British, who had maintained some interest in these matters over the years.

The Captain explained, however, that he was "getting along in years" and he decided to enlist the help of "partners," which was the reason he had gone to San Francisco, where he met Dr. Luce. There had actually been a "company" formed in San Francisco before he met the doctor; but this had not developed.

"I found I couldn't trust 'em," the Captain said, bitterness creeping into his eyes. "There was one fellow I didn't like, an' when I wanted to get rid of him, the others didn't want to. That's when I talked to the doctor."

Sutton knew something of the earlier group, from the letter Green had written to Walradt, telling how "the party broke up" because of trouble and dissension and Captain Brown's "inordinate suspicion."

At any rate, at the age of seventy-odd years—beyond the age when most men retire—this self-confessed ex-pirate was ready to set forth into the broad Pacific again to recover more of his "buried treasure," which he had first left on the remote island fifty years ago.

Sutton leaned back and sighed. He had absorbed quite a bit of information, much of it rather startling, in the past couple of hours. He felt it might take a little while to digest.

The Captain, glancing at him now and then from the depths of his chair, without changing his position very much, seemed to be measuring the effect of his story on his visitor. Once or twice he nodded at Sutton's reactions—a gesture which did not escape Sutton's notice.

Finally, at the conclusion of his story, the Captain called to Mrs. Brown, who came out on the veranda with a tray of tea. Sutton was agreeably impressed with her. She was tall and rather serene, with a calmness of expression that was belied, in a way, by the signs of worry around her eyes. She glanced at the Captain with a kind of affectionate concern, almost the way a mother would glance at her child.

Captain Brown, in spite of his rudeness, appeared to regard her with respect, and possibly affection—if the old man could be considered capable of harboring this emotion.

At one point, when the Captain arose and went inside to return the old leather case with the papers he had shown Sutton, Mrs. Brown leaned closer to Sutton and said in a low voice: "You must excuse the Captain's manners, Captain Sutton." She smiled in a way that eliminated any critical content in her words. "He is greatly concerned about this—he thinks of nothing else. He knows where the island is—I am sure of that." She hesitated an instant, and added: "He will do anything—anything to get it back." She paused again, as if to select her words carefully. Then she said, "He is a very determined man, Captain Sutton."

She looked directly at him; and Sutton could not help recalling the Captain's rather confidential attitude when he mentioned that he had revealed the "secret" to her.

"You must try to understand him . . . I think he likes you," she said.

This last cryptic remark left Sutton rather puzzled. Mrs. Brown went inside to bring out a tray of cookies to go with the tea. When Captain Brown returned, he looked at Sutton with what amounted to suspicion, but said nothing. At about six o'clock the setting sun had already left the inshore parts of the bay in a carpet of darkness, with lights beginning to glimmer on the far shore, and Sutton rose to say goodbye. The carriage which Sutton had ordered for six o'clock had already arrived and Sutton shook hands with the Captain.

"I'll write you as soon as I've discussed this with my associates," he said. "If we are agreed, we will develop plans for an expedition. We will need to raise a good deal of money."

Captain Brown nodded. In spite of his evident anxiety, he still did not materially change his general attitude, which was hard and rough. As Sutton looked at the old man, with the great mane of white hair surrounding his face, it struck him that the new adventure which the old man now wanted to undertake was indeed a rather remarkable affair. At an age when most men are about ready to die, this ancient mariner was preparing to set forth again over the wide ocean in search of a fortune in pirates' gold!

Sutton had time to weigh all the factors of Captain Brown's story on the return trip to New York on the night boat. Standing on the afterdeck, leaning against the rail, he watched the lights of Point Judith and Watch Hill sink astern, and the rising lights of Groton and New London glowing against the black Connecticut shore. His mind drummed with strange thoughts and counterthoughts.

Behind the ship, Block Island loomed against the southern sky, cold and dark and encased within a fiery framework of stars that might have been the Southern Cross—although, in point of fact, it was the Belt of Orion, blazing on the eastern horizon far down on the Milky Way.

Two things had deeply impressed Sutton: first, the remarkable coincidences of Captain Brown's story, conforming in all its grim details with what was known about the fabled "church treasure" of Peru. Even though Captain Brown seemed to have no knowledge—or interest—in the traditional history of Cocos Island treasures (Sutton doubted seriously that he even knew much about this history) his own tale fitted in so remarkably with known accounts of the lost "church treasure" that this could not be mere coincidence.

The second impression was less tangible. As Sutton stood at the rail for many hours, pondering over what he had heard, it was borne home to him with increasing conviction that the real problem that would confront the expedition was not proving out the Captain's story; Sutton was already certain of the "solid grain of truth" in the tale he had listened to. What he was not certain of was the extent of the risk they would be undertaking in the weird personality of Captain Brown himself.

Nevertheless, on his return to New York, Sutton was able to present what he considered a clear and favorable picture of the whole matter; and the upshot of it was that on May 20 Walradt wrote to Green giving a full account of his own impressions and those of Sutton, and agreeing to the plan now advanced by the San Francisco group that Sutton and Walradt travel to the West Coast with Captain Brown and organize an expedition there.

"Upon receipt of your confirming telegram," Walradt wrote, "we will proceed at once to San Francisco."

San Francisco: Storms in the West

[1]

San Francisco rose in precipitous glory toward the banks of swirling fog that lay above the city, mantling the Twin Peaks and the hills to the south with a gray shroud. Along the Embarcadero a forest of masts towered among the wharf sheds, and on the bay more ships lay at anchor. Looking across from the Southern Pacific pier, on the Oakland side of the bay, Sutton and Walradt dimly discerned the single cyclopean eye of the Ferry Building tower, facing them owlishly through the mist from the foot of Market Street.

A smallish man, wearing a brown bowler hat, hurried along the side of the train to meet them.

"Arthur!" he called, waving as he walked briskly toward them. This was Edmond F. Green, Walradt's friend. He shook hands warmly with Walradt and then with Sutton. Picking up one of their bags and talking all the while, he led them toward the slip where the ferry was waiting to transport the passengers on the last short leg of their journey.

Green gave them news of the Captain, who had arrived two days before. He had been met by Dr. Luce, and insisted immediately on "looking over some ships." Since then he was taking things by storm.

"The old boy is down at the wharves on the South Side now," Green explained. "Sent his greetings—wanted to meet you, but he wanted to look at the boats we are considering even more than meeting you. Can't wait to get started, can he? He's as spry as a young fellow of twenty."

These evidences of old Captain Brown's rejuvenation had already been observed by Sutton and Walradt. The three had left together on the train from New York, but when both Sutton and Walradt wanted to see Pikes Peak and stop over for a few days in Denver, the old man became restive.

"The poor old Captain couldn't stand the delay," Sutton had written from Denver, on June 10. "He begged to be allowed to proceed direct to San Francisco, so we started him off this morning for the city, which he sees in front of him all the time. The realization of years of waiting makes him eager to arrive at his destination . . . When we put him on the train, his joy was unbounded. . . ."

Green was a spry, bouncy sort of man, who seemed to jog along in a series of irregular jumps as he kept pace with Sutton's long strides and Walradt's shorter but even pace. He told them Captain Brown had impressed everyone with his energy and his obvious desire to be off for the southern islands.

"No stopping him—once he's started," he observed. "Quite an old fellow, isn't he?"

As Sutton looked up from the Ferry Building at the long, wide slot of Market Street coming in a straight line down from Twin Peaks, it seemed to him that Captain Brown had come to the right place. San Francisco radiated energy. This was the city before the Fire, with its glittering mounds of serrated buildings, rising like crystal cliffs against the gray banks of fog. Lorries and drays rattled along the Embarcadero, hustling boxes and bales in and out of wharf sheds. Saloons with gaudy 1890-style signs speckled the long array of waterfront with their glistening invitations.

This was the City by the Golden Gate . . . the gateway between the new West and the old East. Along the inner shore from North Beach and the Barbary Coast down to South San Francisco, the seagoing craft were packed into the docks. Stubby tugs mingled with black-hulled steamers and graceful sailing ships with ornate bows and slender stalks that reached up toward the hills behind the lower city. A few ships swayed gently at anchor out in the bay, but most of them lay alongside the docks. This was a windjammer port—one of the half dozen known to every sailor in the world . . . the golden port of the West, into which had poured the riches of Sutter Creek, the Comstock Lode, Goldfield and Rawhide . . . This was San Francisco, Queen of the West!

Sutton and Walradt followed Green across the loops of trolley tracks in front of the Ferry Building until he selected a streetcar painted green and marked with gold letters: "Market Street Railway." Car hawkers barked out the various routes . . . "Up Sutter!" . . . "Up Geary!" . . .

"All the way up Market!" Horse-driven hacks, with their own pitchmen, stood at either end of the loops of tracks, but Green steered the new arrivals unerringly past these toward the trolleys. They heaved their bags aboard one of the open-sided cars and climbed on.

Sutton felt the stimulation of San Francisco. It was incredibly alive—exactly the sort of place one would start looking for a hundred million dollars!

Sutton also became aware of a kind of suppressed excitement on Green's part. He was an active little man, prematurely bald, with sharp blue eyes and a ruddy complexion that seemed to blend with his enthusiasm. Once, however, he turned to Sutton, on the way up to the Palace Hotel, and asked curiously: "What is your estimate of the old man, Captain Sutton?"

Sutton was mildly surprised at the faint trace of concern in Green's voice. He had read Walradt's letter to Green, in which he said: "My friend, Sutton, has been over and seen the Captain and his wife and heard the story and is fully convinced there is something to it." He had assumed the San Francisco group also was "convinced."

Sutton began to wonder whether there had been some new development. He asked Green whether anything had occurred to revise their own estimate of the expedition. Green shook his head.

"No, nothing like that—although there have been some developments."

He went on to explain these "developments." For months San Francisco had been alive with rumors and reports about Cocos Island. A number of expeditions had been talked about, and even now one was reported to have sailed from Vancouver, in British Columbia, on the brig *Blakeley*. He admitted that in the face of all this activity, the San Francisco group had been rather anxious to see Sutton and verify his attitude toward the venture, which was based on the assumption that this one treasure was no longer on Cocos Island.

"The Captain is a rather unusual character," Green finally said, as if to sum up his uncertainties.

Sutton nodded. There was not much doubt about that. It occurred to Sutton, as he pondered Green's remarks, that he had not been alone in sensing that the success or failure of the venture might well hinge on Captain Brown's character and personality—rather than his knowledge.

During the early stages of the trip across the country, Sutton had observed the old man, sitting rigidly in his seat, saying almost nothing unless he was asked a question. It was as if his eyes were already fixed on

San Francisco . . . and the lonely island, far down on the horizon of the Pacific. The initial air of reserve, which had impressed Sutton at Auburn, and even up to the day of their departure for San Francisco (he had stayed in Auburn until the day they left, advising Walradt by note that he would be "ready when you want me"), had quickly dissolved once they were on their way. It seemed as if an innate suspicion of everyone held him fast to his anchorage until the expedition actually got started. Then wild horses could not have restrained him.

This sudden evolution of the Captain's spirits, which seemed favorable to Sutton, had disturbed Walradt, however. To his somewhat analytical legal mind, there might be reasons other than quickened enthusiasm that accounted for the Captain's suddenly aroused activity. It could have been possible, for example, that he felt he had already accomplished an objective which he had not necessarily revealed fully to Sutton and his associates.

"I don't know, George," he told Sutton, on the way to San Francisco. "These things don't just happen. I'll admit I was carried away at first—but now I'm inclined to reserve judgment. The whole thing could be an old man's dream."

Sutton nodded. "It could—of course. That's the risk we're taking."

Now that Green seemed to have introduced a somewhat similar reflection, it appeared advisable to consider this aspect—or possibility—more closely. Green went on to disclose some of the "new developments" which shed additional light on the matter. There was now in San Francisco, for example, a man named August Gissler, who called himself "Lieutenant Governor of Cocos Island" and claimed to hold a commission from the Government of Costa Rica. He had been on Cocos Island for many years, and was there, in fact, when Admiral Palliser of the British Navy visited the island in 1897.

A few days before Sutton and Walradt arrived, an advertisement had appeared in the San Francisco *Chronicle*. It read:

> WANTED: Twenty men with $300 each for a year's cruise, including four months sea voyage and prospects for a big future.

An address was given, and when curious newspaper reporters called at the office, they found a Captain John Ross, who said he was a partner of "Governor Gissler." Captain Ross was quite voluble about their plans.

"This day marks a turning point in the history of Cocos Island," Ross had exclaimed to the reporters. "It is a day when the charter of the South African Company of London expires—its option with the Government of Costa Rica is terminated. Now Governor Gissler will have the sole right to explore Cocos Island for the many treasures that are buried there."

Captain Ross went on to explain that the "South African Company" had been founded by the late Cecil Rhodes and held some kind of option for treasure hunting on Cocos Island, "in which the Government of Great Britain has been deeply interested."

Ross paused long enough to admit to reporters, according to the interview which had been published in the San Francisco *Examiner,* that he might be "disclosing too much—because Governor Gissler does not lean to publicity in these matters." Nevertheless, in order to encourage adventurers with three hundred dollars to invest, he felt it wise to divulge a few confidential bits of information.

"We are now organizing an expedition to Cocos Island," Captain Ross said. "We are building a schooner especially for the purpose. It will require about four months to build it. Meanwhile, we have organized a company with the sole right to search, under the protection of the Government of Costa Rica.

"We will have the Costa Rican gunboats, if necessary, to protect our right of search and keep all others off the island!"

Having delivered this dire warning, Captain Ross went on to expatiate in some detail on the personality of "Governor Gissler," who had spent some twelve years on Cocos and knew every excavation and cave in the pitted surface of the island. In response to a direct question by the *Examiner* reporter, Ross admitted, however, that the results of these searches had been negative, except for a number of old coins which seemed to be the standard reward for treasure hunters who invaded Cocos.

Ross then presented a rambling account of the "origin" of the Cocos treasures, which did not differ materially from the information Sutton had dug up in his researches at the New York Public Library, except for the usual amount of confusion and garbled accounts which made each story a little different from the others. He even offered as proof a copy of the Costa Rican *Government Gazette,* which described the rights given Gissler and his associates, and also described the treasure as consisting of "from $33,000,000 to $60,000,000 in money, bullion and utensils." In one excavation, for example, the description said, "There was buried 300,000 pounds of silver, 733 bars of gold, each four by three inches measure, and two inches thick." There were also "bejeweled swords, precious stones and several kettles filled with gold."

All this treasure, according to Ross, was buried on Cocos Island by "pirates from the West Indies, who were driven out by Spanish warships in 1820 and came around the Horn to prey on Spanish gold ships along the West Coast of South America." Ross noted that among the crew of one of these pirate ships "were two seamen, an Englishman named Thompson, and a Frenchman named Chapel." He said they escaped from the pirate ship and "gave information to the British Government which advised them of the existence of this treasure on Cocos Island."

Aside from its general similarity to traditional stories, all this still sounded like the euphoric utterances of a paranoiac on the loose; but Sutton, after reviewing the information with Walradt and Green, told them: "It is precisely because of this that I believe Captain Brown's story has the real ring of truth. He expressed no knowledge of these other treasures, which everyone seems to have known about. If he had come to us with the intention of deceiving us, he would have relied on the accepted accounts. Instead, he did not mention any of them, but spoke of the 'church treasure' of Peru—something that is rarely mentioned in any of the other accounts."

Green had another "bit of information" to disclose. It seemed that Dr. Luce had met a big, red-bearded man at one of the yacht clubs, and the latter—apparently unaware of the doctor's specific interest in Cocos treasures—showed him a number of Spanish coins, all dated between 1750 and 1790.

He said his name was Gissler, and he was organizing an expedition to go to Cocos Island and recover an enormous store of gold and silver buried there by Spanish pirates. He was soliciting backers and wondered if the doctor would be interested.

Dr. Luce, a tall, quiet man, was extremely deliberate and careful in his methods. He asked the red-bearded man to let him examine the coins. They seemed quite similar to coins Captain Brown had showed him when they first talked about the Cocos Island treasure several months ago.

Dr. Luce asked a few questions. He wanted to know where they had been found.

"On Cocos Island," Gissler told him.

"But on what part of the island?"

Gissler's face became rigid, and he closed his mouth tightly.

"You know about Cocos Island?"

"Of course," Dr. Luce said. "Everyone reads about it. There are maps showing the location of treasures. But no one seems to find the treasures."

Gissler shrugged.

"The maps are no good," he said. "I have many maps, but I have examined the island and I now know where the treasures are buried. It will require tools to reach them—to blast out the rocks that were poured over the front of the caves."

Dr. Luce tried to draw from Gissler the source of his information, but he would only say that he had maps, and that he had personally surveyed the place and knew where the treasures were buried. Dr. Luce gained the distinct impression that Gissler had become slightly unstable—perhaps due to the years he spent on the island; and this set him to wondering.

"What if old Brown is cracked, too?" he said to Green. "He could have picked up the coins, you know—anywhere. The same way Gissler got his."

Green reported this conversation to Sutton and Walradt, as they were getting settled in the hotel.

"George Luce is a very stable man," he said. "I believe he is beginning to wonder how far we can depend on what Captain Brown has told us. I can see you have great confidence in the Captain—and of course, you have put up a good deal of money."

Sutton shook his head slightly.

"As I told Arthur," he said, finally, "my confidence is not in Captain Brown, but in his story. It hangs together. I'm backing my own judgment—that's all." There was a touch of impatience in his voice. "Look here, Green—Arthur and I have started out on this, and I mean to see it through. As long as there is a strong likelihood that the Captain's story is sound—and I think it is—there can be no advantage in debating every step of the way as to whether we should have started out in the first place."

Green nodded, and smiled.

"Of course, Captain Sutton. We are in the middle of it all out here. The papers have been full of reports and rumors about Cocos Island. It sets your head to ringing and that may account for our uncertainty." He became brisk again. "All right—let's go meet the others. They are expecting you at my office. It's over on Montgomery."

At Green's Montgomery Street office, several men were assembled.

They had obviously been talking prior to the arrival of Sutton, Walradt and Green. They looked curiously at Sutton as he entered. John Chetwood, a rather slight man with sandy hair and a perpetually puckish smile, came forward to shake hands. Sutton instinctively liked him.

Dr. Luce was also there, sitting a bit apart in a large chair. Donzel Stoney, a San Francisco lawyer who had been in New York during the "investigation" of Captain Brown's story, and had met both Sutton and Walradt, seemed to be the spokesman.

He got to the heart of the matter without delay.

"We've all agreed to go ahead with this. You gentlemen"—he indicated Sutton and Walradt—"have put up a good share of the money, and we can easily raise the remainder among our group here. Now, none of us is a professional at this sort of thing. If anyone wants to back out, now is the time to do it."

Sutton wondered if this had been the topic of discussion before he and Walradt and Green arrived; but he said nothing. No one said anything.

"All right," Stoney said. He was short and abrupt in speech, and possessed a certain air of assurance that was readily construed as authority. "We've got our eyes on a good boat. Ninety-foot schooner. Captain Brown is out looking at it now and if he is satisfied, we can get it on charter, with the owners participating in the venture only to the extent of the charter. The principal thing I want to get over is the need for keeping all this among ourselves."

He paused and produced several clippings from newspapers, which he laid on the table.

"The town is full of rumors. As soon as we charter a vessel, we'll be up to our necks in it. We don't want to talk to newspapermen—I've told Captain Brown that, too. If any of us are pinned down, we'll say we're going on a long fishing trip."

Stoney turned to Dr. Luce.

"Tell Walradt and Sutton about your talk with this fellow Gissler, will you, George?"

Green had already given Sutton the story; but he listened carefully to Dr. Luce. When the doctor finished, he asked Sutton: "What do you think of it? If Gissler's coins are from Cocos, as he says—does that make Brown's story sound any better?"

Sutton shook his head. He explained that there were a half dozen fairly well-known reports of treasures on Cocos Island, and even if

Captain James Brown, as photographed by George Sutton, strolls beside the *Herman*.

Left. At a pier in the San Francisco harbor, the *Herman* is shown before her purchase by the syndicate.

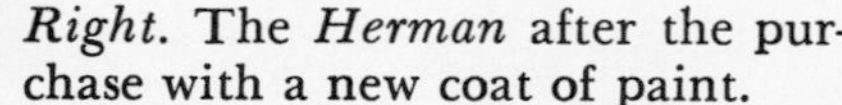

Right. The *Herman* after the purchase with a new coat of paint.

the old coins were from these treasures—which would be hard to verify—it only proved that somebody had been on the island and picked them up.

Sutton leaned forward, his usually mild expression becoming quite serious.

"Look, gentlemen—we are all in this together. None of us can be sure whether Brown's story is authentic or just his imagination—or a hallucination. If it is a hallucination, it is one of the most sustained I've ever heard of. He's over seventy—and if he just wants another sea trip, he is going about it in an extremely complicated way.

"But—" Sutton's voice became very firm. "It isn't going to do us any good to debate this over and over. I, for one, would like to get on with the business. It's a risk. We know it. Arguing how much of a risk it is won't change it one iota. I'd like to feel that we've got the debate behind us and are ready to concentrate on the work ahead of us."

Chetwood, who had been listening without saying anything, suddenly stood up and began to walk around the room, twisting the ends of his mustache. Finally he stopped and looked at the others.

"I agree with Captain Sutton," he said. "It's no use now to question Captain Brown's story. We have decided to put up the money—and we did it because we believed there was enough possibility to warrant taking the risk. Our task is to get a boat that will satisfy the Captain, and get on our way. This city is humming with rumors, and sooner or later somebody is going to find out about our search. I move we get on with our plans and stop playing cat and mouse!"

Stoney laughed.

Sutton wondered whether this kind of thing was a good omen or a bad one. He glanced at Dr. Luce. The doctor was smiling, and he nodded. Sutton did not realize it at the time, but this was the beginning of an understanding between Chetwood, the doctor and himself that would have to last for more than a year—and in the final stages of the "search," it would be its determining factor.

There was a certain conspiratorial character to the meeting that Sutton found a bit difficult to understand. At one point he asked Stoney—who seemed to be the unofficial chairman—how many were now involved as contributors to the venture.

"About thirty," Stoney said. Sutton shuddered, mentally. A "secret" among thirty people was only a bit short of publishing it. Stoney had turned meanwhile to Chetwood who sat on the arm of a heavy leather chair, pulling at his pipe.

"By the way—Ogden Hoffman called," he said. "He told me he would meet with us as soon as we decide on the boat."

"What does that mean?" Sutton asked.

Chetwood answered. "Hoffman represents Louis Mooser—who represents the buyers of the schooner *Herman*." Chetwood turned to Stoney again.

"Has Ogden put up anything?"

"Not yet—that is, not Ogden. But Mooser and his group will put up the purchase money if we take the *Herman*."

Chetwood nodded, still drawing on his pipe. As Sutton looked around the room it struck him that this would be an odd combination for a sea trip—on a ninety-foot schooner! There seemed to be more cross currents and shoals than he had expected, even before the search for Captain Brown's treasure island was under way.

"Who is Mr. Hoffman?" he asked. "I hadn't heard of him."

Stoney laughed again, looking at Sutton out of the corner of his eye.

"You will," he said. "I think he'll be on the boat—if we take the *Herman*. He's what the newspapers here refer to as 'a wealthy clubman.' What that means frankly I don't know. Ogden is from an old San Francisco family. . . . His uncle was a distinguished judge. Quite well thought of."

Sutton suspected that Ogden Hoffman was not so well thought of, but he decided to bide his time and ask questions of Green later on. The meeting ended on what seemed to be a solemn pledge. Stoney said, "We're all sticking together, that's it, isn't it?" Sutton was not certain to what—or whom—they were "sticking." But he nodded with the rest.

On the way out, Chetwood linked his arm in Sutton's, guiding him down the stairway to the building entrance.

"It isn't as all-fired confusing as it sounds, Sutton," he said, grinning. "The thing is—none of us are exactly sure what we're looking for. I've seen Walradt's letters to Frank Green, and Don Stoney has talked with you, of course. We are more or less relying on your judgment. I think we all feel that way."

The reasons for this reliance did not seem too apparent to Sutton; but he did not pursue the matter. He finally said, "I think our real problem is the Captain. He seems to have a lot of force in his make-up, and I'm not always sure how it will be applied. He's a rather explosive type, you know."

Chetwood grinned and nodded.

"Explosive," he repeated. "I think you've put your finger on it."

[2]

Captain Brown's first "explosion" was not exactly a detonation; it was more like the low rumbling of an incipient volcano, not particularly devastating in itself, but conveying a hint of things to come. It was directed at a small squad of newspaper reporters who had gathered on the afterdeck of the *Herman* to ask some questions.

Sutton and Chetwood had come down to the wharf at the foot of Howard Street the following morning to inspect the new craft. They saw the group of men clustered about the Captain on the afterdeck. He stood, legs apart and baggy trousers blowing in the breeze, the personification of Viking fury. His hair and whiskers were furled over his ears by the wind, surrounding a face that was a mask of trembling rage.

"Ye'll get off this ship, damn ye!" he was shouting, as Sutton and Chetwood clambered over the rail. Captain Brown hardly noticed them. With his legs spread solidly athwart the afterdeck, he was berating the reporters and brandishing his fist.

The situation obviously was not critical. Some of the reporters were grinning, and one turned to Sutton and winked. Finally noticing his two partners, Captain Brown turned and shouted over the heads of the reporters at Sutton:

"They demand particulars, Cap'n Sutton! Demand, mind ye!" It was difficult to tell which was the more agitated: the Captain's coat and pants, flapping in the wind, or the Captain himself. Sutton edged his way through the group.

"Are you skipper of this ship?" one of the reporters asked Sutton. "If you are, we've got some interesting news for you—and we'd like to get some information from you."

"What sort of information?" Sutton asked. He sensed that Captain Brown had not fully revealed his own position aboard the *Herman,* and so he did not answer the first question directly.

The reporter, a young man with a good-humored face, explained that the "Governor of Cocos Island," a certain August Gissler, had announced through the press that very day that he had full knowledge of the purpose and intention of the mysterious voyage of the *Herman.* The ship's company were treasure hunters, and they were planning an expedition to Cocos Island to recover buried gold that was pretty well known to be there!

The "Governor" also had announced that he had a hundred years' concession from the Government of Costa Rica giving him the right to "develop the island of Cocos as an agricultural community, and to find treasure." He said a Captain John Ross was his partner and he and Ross were in San Francisco to raise funds for the venture.

"Gissler plans to return to San Jose on the Pacific Mail liner *Para* and get the Government of Costa Rica to detail a gunboat to intercept the *Herman*," the reporter said. "He said they would shoot you out of the water, if necessary. What do you say to that, Captain?"

Sutton said nothing at first. The group had agreed on a story that might serve to divert attention from the real purpose of their expedition, if it became necessary; but Sutton did not feel authorized to reveal it. This bit of fiction involved a Japanese steamer on which Captain Brown had supposedly sailed years ago and which presumably had been carrying some millions of dollars worth of specie. The crew was supposed to have mutinied, seized the treasure and buried it on an island in South Pacific waters. Captain Brown alone knew the location of the island. However, it occurred to Sutton that the announcement of "Governor Gissler" might be sufficient to divert attention, without resorting to the fabrication of the Japanese ship.

The reporter went on to explain that Gissler had apparently put in a pitch for his own expedition in the course of his warning to the *Herman*. He showed Sutton a clipping from the morning San Francisco *Chronicle* which said (quoting Gissler):

> I will leave on the Para on the 29th and will secure a gunboat from my government to head off the Herman. I am asking $300 from each person who joins our expedition. This is to pay for hydraulic machinery. We have to divert the course of a small river.
>
> I can say that I have recovered some of the treasure already, and it only requires machinery to get the rest.

Another reporter, identifying himself as representing the *Examiner*, told Sutton they had a report that the *Herman* was sailing for the South Sea Islands. "We understand you expect to recover some gold specie stolen from a Japanese ship and buried on an island, Captain," he said. "This fellow"—he indicated Captain Brown, who was still standing in the stern sheets, at times lifting his fist—"this fellow is supposed to be the man who knows where it is."

Sutton looked at Chetwood, who was grinning. The slender lawyer had said little, but now he shrugged. "I'm John Chetwood," he said. "Some of you know me. All we can say is that we are sailing on a pleasure trip. We have no further statement. What we do is our business, and what this man Gissler does is his business."

After a few ineffectual questions, the newspaper reporters departed. Captain Brown, his wrath subsiding almost immediately, turned to an inspection of the ship, with Sutton and Chetwood following him. The cabins were being turned out nicely. A pair of staterooms adjacent to the captain's quarters had been cut through into one large room; and two other staterooms for passengers were of ample size. The crew, Captain Brown explained, would be ten: himself and two officers, a cook and a steward, Dr. Luce as the ship's physician, and four sailors. In addition, there would be Sutton and Chetwood and a San Francisco mining man, Frank Sharratt, who was a partner in the venture. Sharratt was Donzel Stoney's brother-in-law, and would, in a sense, represent the interests of Stoney, who informally spoke for the committee.

"And Ogden Hoffman," Chetwood said. "He will be along."

Captain Brown turned and led them into the enlarged stateroom fitted out for Hoffman, he said—at Hoffman's request. It was ample, even luxurious, with teakwood finishing on the walls, ornate suspended lamps and a gun rack.

Before they left the schooner, Chetwood spoke to Captain Brown about his future attitude toward newspaper reporters.

"They are going to ask questions, Captain. We can't very well throw them off the ship, you know. We live here in San Francisco—that is, most of us do. Perhaps we should be more tolerant of their questions, even if we don't tell them anything."

Captain Brown regarded Chetwood for a moment; then he said: "These men were insolent, Mr. Chetwood. I will not tolerate insolence aboard my ship."

Sutton studied the Captain as they talked. He began to understand the qualms of his associates, to whom the old man, with his history of piracy and murder and his domineering and arbitrary manner aboard ship, must be disturbing. A voyage of perhaps many months with Captain Brown might turn out to be something of a problem.

The schooner itself was ideal for the kind of voyage they had ahead of them—strongly built, with a flaring bow and ample beam aft to assure both stability and speed. She would probably run eight or nine knots in an average wind.

Her rigging was complete, with two full suits of sail—two mainsails, two foresails, two staystails, pairs of inner and outer jibs and an added main staystail. With all sails set she would be a thing of beauty carving through the long Pacific swells. She carried two dinghies and a launch set between the main and foremasts, with enough cargo capacity in the launch to effect a lightering operation from the beach.

Captain Brown had scrupulously overseen the entire refitting operation. He was the first on the ship at daybreak each day and the last to leave. He examined each bit of refitting as if the safety of the vessel depended on it. At one point he ordered a complete reworking of the master's cabin because two shades of paint had been used.

The morning after Captain Brown's abortive press conference on the afterdeck of the *Herman,* San Francisco was seething with rumors and reports. The *Chronicle* and *Examiner* took opposite views of the situation. The former held to the position expressed by "Governor Gissler" and at one point in the story the writer reported:

> Captain Brown, when questioned, said he was bound for an island in the Pacific where the mutinous crew of a Japanese ship had buried $70,000,000 in gold and silver specie. A roseate and misleading story to that effect appeared in a morning paper, stating that the Herman had a Boston expedition of fifteen men all told, fitted out at a cost of $25,000. . . .

The story then stated that it was "known that he is bound for the Island of Cocos, with charts which will direct him to the spot where the treasure is buried."

The "controversy raised by Governor Gissler, of Cocos Island," was referred to in some detail, with the statement that "the Governor, who has been very reticent about his mission," had threatened armed intercession by Costa Rican gunboats. The *Chronicle* asked, with rhetorical anticipation: "Will a battle be fought in tropical waters as a result?"

The *Examiner* leaned to the view that the purpose of the mysterious voyage of the *Herman* was to recover the buried treasures of the Japanese ship. In the flamboyant journalese of the day, the *Examiner* said:

> Here is a mystery of the South seas—a real romance of that misty region below the equator, so prolific of poetical yarns. . . . There is for instance a set of men of furtive manner, a trim-built craft in gleaming white, . . . strange whisperings among its crew and a still stranger story of treasure buried deep in some distant island. And such a treasure as buccaneer of the main never conjured in his wildest dream of wealth—a matter of $70,000,000, within the reach of those on board. . . .

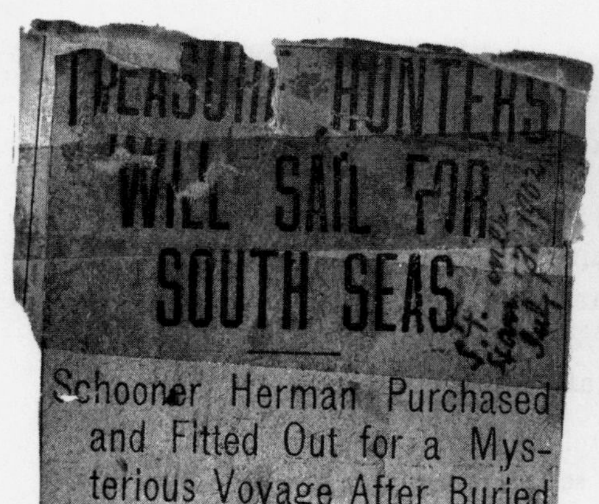

TREASU HUNTERS WILL SAIL FOR SOUTH SEAS

Schooner Herman Purchased and Fitted Out for a Mysterious Voyage After Buried Millions in Cocos Island.

Here is a mystery of the South seas—a real romance of that misty region below the equator, so prolific of poetical yarns. Being a mystery, and romantic, it must of course be a secret at the outset. It has all the essentials of those imaginative tales of the seas that read well in books. There is for instance a set of men of furtive manner, a trim-built craft in gleaming white, the color associated in nautical fancy with the tropics, strange whisperings among her crew and a still stranger story of treasure buried deep in some distant island. And such treasure as buccaneer of the main never conjured in his wildest dream of wealth—a matter of $70,000,000, within the reach of those on board.

That there is an expedition almost ready to sail to the South seas on this vessel is not denied. Indeed an admission was made yesterday afternoon by one of the crew that she was bound for Tahiti and Samoa on a treasure hunt, but there the information stopped. The craft is in readiness for the venturesome voyage. She is lying at Howard-street wharf, taking in ballast and may be distinguished, even by landsmen, by the contrast she presents with trading vessels. The name on her bows in gold letters is "Herman." To all appearances she is a schooner yacht prettily rigged. Her hull is painted white, her gunwales are covered with shining brass, and her decks and cabins are as neat as those of a private yacht.

Her master is Captain Brown, an elderly man who came here recently from Boston, and is mentioned as the instigator of this treasure trove adventure.

Somehow the secret of the Herman got out at some clubs. As told by clubmen it is this: Captain Brown of Boston when a young man was a member of a crew of a Japanese treasure ship conveying treasure to the amount of $70,000,000 from Japan to another country. Most of the crew mutinied and took the ship to an island in the South seas, where the treasure was carried ashore and buried. Dis-

Y 21, 1902. Examiner

TREASURE SEEKERS SAIL IN QUEST OF LOOT

Schooner Herman, Captain Brown Commanding, Goes Out With Morning Tide to Find Fortune In South Seas.

Five Stockholders, Provided With Proper Implements for Unearthing Long Buried Millions, Accompany Expedition.

Ballasted with hope, freighted with dreams of wealth untold, and trimming her sails to catch the landward breezes of El Dorado, the rakish little schooner Herman made her offing yesterday morning and was running down the trades on her long voyage to the treasure isles of the summer seas.

Captain James Brown was in command and five mysterious passengers leaned abaft the binnacle as the trim little craft tossed across the bar. These passengers are supposed to be stockholders in Captain Brown's tale of treasure trove, and Judge Daingerfield is believed to be another, although he did not venture upon the sea quest. He was aboard the vessel yesterday, however, and seemed much interested in all that was preparing for the voyage.

The Herman carried provisions sufficient to sustain crew and stockholders a year. On deck was a gasoline launch, and in the hold were stowed wheelbarrows, handtrucks, pickaxes, shovels and other implements of modern make especially adapted for unearthing buried treasure and conveying it to a safe deposit for the future use of its new possessors.

There is now no doubt that the Herman is the embodiment of a speculative desire to test the accuracy of Captain Brown's memory concerning the place where the mutinous crew of a Japanese treasure ship buried $70,000,000. If the treasure is not found where Captain Brown saw it buried he will tell the stockholders that some of the mutinous crew who stole it originally have probably stolen it again. If it is found intact the treasure seekers will unquestionably return it to its rightful owners, the Japanese Government, minus the legal sal-

These two stories appeared in the *San Francisco Examiner*. The one on the left is dated July 3, 1902, and the one on the right, July 21, 1902—the day the *Herman* sailed.

The story went on to describe the *Herman,* "lying at the Howard Street wharf, the name 'Herman' painted on her bows in gold letters. To all appearances, she is a yacht, prettily rigged out for a long voyage. But. . . ."

The story got down to fundamentals.

> Her master is Captain Brown, an elderly man who came here recently from Boston . . . Somehow the secret of the Herman got out at some clubs. As told by clubmen it is this: Captain Brown of Boston when a young man was a member of a crew of a Japanese treasure ship conveying treasure to the amount of $70,000,000 from Japan to another country. Most of the crew mutinied and took the ship to an island in the South seas, where the treasure was carried ashore and buried. Dissentions among the mutineers followed. Each man feared his companion, and so the party in time scattered far from the scene of the mutiny and the cached treasure, and one by one, they dropped off.

The story did not disclose how they "dropped off," but Captain Brown was portrayed as one who somehow survived—a curious similarity to his own story of his exploits in the South Pacific with Captain Schmid and the *Sea Foam.* In any event, the Captain was now organizing an expedition to return to the island and dig up the buried money.

Several things about the report aroused Sutton's curiosity. It did not seem likely, in view of the Captain's treatment of the reporters on the ship, that he had divulged this story. Yet it coincided so closely with the account the members of the group had agreed to use as a "diversionary tactic" that it must have come from someone among them. Sutton recalled Stoney's reference to Ogden Hoffman as "a well-known clubman."

On the way down to the wharf that morning, he spoke to Chetwood about this.

"How do you suppose it got out? The Captain doesn't seem to talk very much, and he was ordering the reporters off the ship."

Chetwood nodded. "I don't suppose it makes much difference how it got out, except that Hoffman should keep his mouth shut. We'll have enough problems before we leave, without deliberately stirring up rumors."

The Captain had a different view. In fact, he was furious.

"From now on, I'll handle these reporters. I would have ordered the whole parcel of them off the ship and told them nothing. This is a very dangerous thing—giving this kind of matter to the papers. They will try to destroy us."

While Sutton was puzzling over this remark, the Captain leaned forward and spoke in a low, almost conspiratorial voice.

"There's other matters, Cap'n. Things I mean to find out about."

Sutton looked at the Captain, surprised at the sinister tone.

"What kind of matters?"

"Gravy," the Captain said. "Cumshaw! Somebody's getting gravy out of this business. It's either Green or Stoney—I don't know which. Somebody got a commission on the sale of the boat!"

Sutton stared at the Captain. Chetwood had gone forward, and had not heard anything.

"This is a pretty serious charge, Captain," Sutton said finally. "I think you should be sure about it. If we can't trust each other—at the start of the trip—"

"I don't trust anybody, Cap'n," the old sailor interrupted in an explosive voice. His pale eyes narrowed and glittered for an instant —as they did when Sutton had mentioned typhoons in the South Pacific, back in Auburn. "Not anybody." He raised his huge fist. "I've killed men who tried to rob me—and I'll do it again!"

This sweeping statement startled Sutton; but he was due for an even more astonishing disclosure. Captain Brown leaned closer, and in a whisper that seemed to reverberate from the depths of his massive chest, he asked: "Do ye believe in ghosts, Cap'n?"

Sutton could see that some strange emotions were at work in the old sailor. He was also taken by surprise. The question whether he did or did not believe in discarnate creatures was usually a matter for table talk; it had never been put to him quite so bluntly.

"I—I don't think so," he managed to remark. "Why?"

"Well!" The Captain glanced to one side and then the other, as if to apprehend the possible approach of an incorporeal eavesdropper. Then he leaned even closer, presumably to avoid a single word escaping into the ethereal spaces surrounding them. His mouth twisted into a wolfish smile.

"Ye will, Cap'n—mark that! Ye will before the trip is over! There's ghosts of a hundred men watching every move we make. The treasure was buried in blood, Cap'n—buried in blood! And dead men can hear—mark that, too! That's why blabbin' things around won't do any good. Men who talk too much can't be trusted!"

Sutton instinctively thought of Hoffman—whom he had yet to meet. He had absorbed quite a few surprises thus far, during his brief stay in San Francisco; and this rather illogical correlation of "blabbing" to newspapermen, shakedowns on commissions—or "cumshaw," as it was called—and the allusion to ghosts was a series of *non sequiturs* he found difficult to digest.

This latter element also introduced a disturbing possibility that perhaps the Captain was a bit cracked. At his age, a man who had led a life of raw adventure—including piracy—might be expected to have collected a few oddities of character. But to have such a man lead an expedition, which was fundamentally perilous in itself—if it proved successful, they might have several tons of gold aboard!—was a disquieting prospect.

"We're shapin' up the crew this afternoon, Cap'n," the old man said, breaking into Sutton's thoughts. Sutton looked up and Captain Brown's eyes seemed to be penetrating his own with astonishing intelligence. Did the Captain know what he was thinking? His expression—the old man was smiling slightly—seemed to indicate that perhaps he did. "Do ye want to be here?"

Sutton had to shake himself physically. He looked at the Captain a moment, and then said, "The shape-up? Oh, yes. Certainly, Captain—I'd like to see the kind of men who are shipping with us."

"Two o'clock," the Captain said.

When he returned with Chetwood to the hotel for luncheon, Sutton had some more surprises. Donzel Stoney was waiting for them, and his face was set in hard lines. He was undoubtedly quite angry.

"Louis Mooser called me," he said. "He's purchasing the *Herman*. He wanted to know if I had been present when we signed the charter after he made the initial payment. I said I had."

"You were authorized to represent us," Sutton said.

Stoney nodded.

"Mooser asked me some questions. At first I didn't get the drift of them. Finally I found out what was on his mind. He said there was definite information that someone had picked up a commission on the transfer of the *Herman*."

Stoney paused. He was actually breathing hard, from the effect of anger.

"He thought at first that I had taken the commission. Fortunately, the man who gave him the information straightened this out. He did not know who it was, but he knew I had nothing to do with it. That satisfied him—as far as I was concerned. But it doesn't satisfy me."

"Nor me," Chetwood said. "Who do you think it was?"

"I've got a pretty good idea," Stoney said, grimly. "And I mean to find out. Incidentally, Frank Green's name came up, too. It was about the insurance—there was some idea that a broker's commission had been paid to him, but I asked him, and he didn't handle it. What I want to know is, who is doing this? It's a hell of a way to start off on a partnership!"

Sutton thought a moment and finally said: "Did either of you talk to Captain Brown about this?"

Both Stoney and Chetwood indicated they had not.

Sutton shook his head and sighed. Everything seemed to be going bad—and the ship was not yet out of the harbor!

"Brown talked with me—this morning," he said. "He knew about the report of the commission. He was pretty mad about it, too!"

Sutton did not pursue the seemingly unrelated matter of "ghosts," which Captain Brown had brought up in connection with the information about the commission, largely because he had been unable to figure out the connection himself.

"If there's a nigger in the haystack," Stoney said, with some disregard of the metaphors involved, "I'll find it."

They agreed that nothing would be said for the present; but all would keep their eyes and ears open.

Sutton left immediately after lunch to watch the "shape-up."

[3]

The shaping up of the crew in the days of sailing ships was an important and interesting event; in the case of the *Herman* its importance was critical. The men who comprised the original crew would in all probability be the men aboard when the treasure—if it was found—would be loaded aboard the schooner and carried back to San Francisco. For this reason Sutton was quite interested in the selection of the sailors who would make up the crew.

Captain Brown stood beside a table, on which the ship's articles were placed, on the afterdeck, which was raised perhaps thirty inches above the main deck, his arms akimbo, glaring at the human specimens below him. They stood in varying attitudes of attention—about a dozen sailors. One man, half his teeth missing from his face—possibly lost in some barroom skirmish—and a looseness of lip and gaunt look about the eyes that made him hardly seem to be the stuff of which hardy sailors are made, was slouching against the small deckhouse which led down to the passengers' staterooms.

"Here—you!" Captain Brown leaned over and roared at him, not a foot from the man's face. The sailor jerked himself erect. "What's your name?"

"Johnson. Johnson, sir." The man spoke like a Swede. It seemed to Sutton, as the man stood erect, that he looked taller than he appeared at first.

"Go forward with Mr. Hendrickson," the Captain almost snarled. Mr. Hendrickson was the first officer. He was a quiet, orderly sort of man, whom Sutton had met earlier. The sailor muttered, "Aye, sir," and slouched off after Mr. Hendrickson. Sutton would have regarded him as probably the lowest in the order of selection, and he wondered whether the first mate would simply shove him off the ship, or afford him the courtesy of asking a few questions before he got rid of him.

The second man addressed by Captain Brown was a small, unshaven fellow with a ratlike face and a rather scrawny beard.

"You!" Captain Brown did not even ask his name. "Pick up that gear and get it out of the way." He pointed to several coils of cable. The man looked at it, without moving, and finally looked up at the Captain. His eyes were shining and he looked as if he might break out in tears.

"Go to hell," he finally said. "I wouldn't ship with the likes of you—if I was starving."

"Ye damn well will—before ye sign on this ship! Get off!"

The man shambled toward the gangway, and Captain Brown seemed almost on the verge of taking off after him and physically assisting his departure; but the sailor, glancing around at him, quickened his pace and a few seconds later Sutton saw him moving slowly down the wharf, probably glad that a sudden intervention of temper had spared him from shipping with the *Herman.*

The shaping up continued. Sutton was unable to determine the basis, or formula, upon which the Captain relied. Each selection seemed to be wholly different. One tall, red-haired fellow, who was very quiet and respectful in his answers, was sent forward to join Mr. Hendrickson on the forward deck. Sutton would have liked to go forward and watch the process of screening which the first mate employed, but he was more interested at the moment in Captain Brown's methods.

In a few minutes, to his considerable surprise, the Swedish sailor, Johnson, returned and said: "Mr. Hendrickson said to sign me on, sir—if you agree." Captain Brown nodded slightly, and pointed to the table. "Sign the ship's articles on there. Ye know the agreement—one year, or thereafter if we are in any other port."

Johnson nodded, and went inside.

Another man approached the Captain, touched his hat respectfully, and said, "Willie Peterson, sir. You told me last night to report in."

Captain Brown nodded again, and pointed to the table. Thus, by two utterly dissimilar maneuvers, two of the four sailors seemed to have been signed on. Sutton watched in fascination. It seemed that the Captain must employ some sixth sense, an alchemy of thought processes, by which he pierced the unprepossessing exterior of each man and determined, by secret formula, the inner character of the applicant. Except for Willie Peterson, whom he accepted without further examination, he sent each one who appeared to have favorable characteristics forward to Mr. Hendrickson.

The red-haired sailor came back and was the third man accepted. He also gave his name as "Petersen" —spelled with an "e." After several rejections, a fourth man, who gave his name as "John Smith," was approved. Captain Brown waved away the rest, and they slouched off the deck and down the gangway. Later Sutton found that all had been sent by an agency which prescreened the applicants so that their actual seamanship—except for Willie Peterson—was pretty well established before they came aboard.

Nevertheless Sutton marveled at the procedure by which the Captain had made his selection of the crew. Had it been an ordinary cruise, this would have been important only from a standpoint of discipline; but on the mission which the *Herman* was to undertake, there were many other factors, including personal reliability and some verification of the sailor's reputation for honesty.

Captain Brown lumbered down from his elevated position, and waved amiably to Sutton.

"They aren't the best," he said. "But they'll do. We'll knock out any bad ones before we reach Honolulu."

The steward and the cook—both Japanese—had already been selected; and except for a second mate, the crew seemed ready for sailing.

"Half of 'em will be so drunk the night before, they may not show up," the Captain said. "We'll have a couple of standbys from the seaman's agency, just in case."

Sutton remained a short while aboard the *Herman,* and then left to join Chetwood and Dr. Luce uptown. It was only nine days before

This is one of the clearest photographs of the *Herman* that appear in the records of Captain Sutton. It was taken in San Francisco before the voyage began. The extra rigging is that of a larger vessel which can barely be seen on the far side of the *Herman*.

sailing—this would be on the following Sunday, if all went well—and there were many threads of problems still to be brought together. Stoney had been working feverishly to collect all the money that had been subscribed by some thirty "sponsors" in the venture. The agreement with Captain Brown had to be restated; he was to get a quarter of the proceeds plus expenses, but the latter was proving a variable item, and a more specific understanding was necessary.

After working on the agreements, Sutton returned that evening to the *Herman* in hope of finding Captain Brown still aboard. He wanted to discuss the final arrangement for expenses which he and Stoney had worked out; but there seemed to be no one on board.

After a quick look along the deck, he was about to leave, when he heard the sound of voices from behind the covered entrance to the aft companionway. One of the voices was a deep rumble, which he recognized as that of Captain Brown; but the other was of a higher pitch —not musical, but certainly female.

Sutton was startled, and a bit hesitant about investigating further. Finally, with several coughs to indicate his presence, he moved toward the afterdeck. The captain was sitting comfortably in a deck chair, and beside him was a lady, also in a deck chair. She was not young—probably in her late forties; and at first glance she seemed to fill the chair quite amply.

"Oh—good evening, Captain!" Sutton nodded to the lady, not knowing what else to do. She smiled with ready amiability, and the Captain —who apparently had not heard Sutton's preliminary coughs—seemed almost to eject himself from his chair.

"Cap'n Sutton! What the hell—" He glanced around, as if expecting others to crop up suddenly, with Sutton. He finally nodded toward the lady, who was still smiling. "Mrs. Samson," he muttered; and then waved at Sutton, "Cap'n Sutton—my associate."

Sutton was able to observe by this time that Mrs. Samson had a rather plump face, a row of bright, well-exposed teeth, and hair that seemed in the early evening light to be somewhere between a magenta and burnt orange. Her hat, a wide-brimmed straw affair, well decorated with ostrich plumes, lay on her lap.

"Sorry to interrupt," Sutton managed to say. "I had a few things I wanted to discuss, but they can wait." He turned to leave, but the Captain said, "No—wait," and followed him back to the gangway.

When they were out of hearing distance of the lady, the Captain said, almost apologetically, "Just an old friend—of my wife, Cap'n. She'd heard about my being here, and wanted to see the ship."

"Of course," Sutton said. "Please extend my regrets to her, Captain." He waved at the woman, who was staring after them, bowed and left. He observed Captain Brown moving toward the deckhouse as he walked down the wharf; and Sutton could not help wondering what all this portended. Was the lady a "friend of his wife," as Captain Brown had explained with unnecessary secretiveness; or was this some association that had developed during the Captain's stay in San Francisco?

This was July 10. The departure originally had been scheduled for July 13, but due to many obstructions—settling on the vessel to be purchased, arranging for the provisioning of the ship, and the succession of other problems—it had been decided to delay leaving until July 20.

Sutton was fearful that if there were any further interruptions, the typhoon season, which sets in late in the year in the Low Archipelago, might cause an additional six months' delay. Walradt was planning to return to New York, by way of Seattle; and Sutton needed to get his own personal affairs straightened out with Walradt before he left. He arranged to meet Walradt in Green's office the following morning. When Sutton arrived, Green was furious.

"The old fool has practically accused me of picking up a commision on the insurance," he said. "He braced me with it, down at the ship."

Sutton found out from Green that he knew nothing of the other matter of the commission on the sale of the boat. So he told Green what had happened.

"The trouble is," Walradt said, "the Captain is suspicious of everyone and everything. I don't envy your problem, George. You've got your work cut out."

"What do you know about this fellow Ogden Hoffman?" Sutton asked Green.

"He's a bastard," Green said. "He thinks he's a seaman—which makes it worse. But Louis Mooser insists he go along to represent his interests."

Sutton finally met Hoffman in Donzel Stoney's office a few days later, when they were making last-minute preparations for departure, which was now definitely scheduled for Sunday, July 20. He took a quick dislike to the tall, rangy "clubman." Hoffman, leaning indolently against the back of his chair, was indulging in what amounted to a cross examination of Captain Brown, and the old man was not taking it easily.

"Who ordered the smelter?" Hoffman asked. His sharp gray eyes, set narrowly over a predatory nose—the shape frequently referred to as "aristocratic"—were fixed directly on the Captain.

"The doctor," the Captain said. Dr. Luce, who was listening, nodded slightly.

"I didn't realize it would take so long to operate," he admitted, in a quiet voice.

Hoffman snorted. "Why in hell should a doctor handle the selection of a smelter—and for that matter, what in hell do we want with a smelter, in the first place?"

Captain Brown straightened in his chair, glaring at Hoffman.

"It was my decision," he said. "I gave the instructions. We need the smelter to reduce the metals to a solid state for stowage. And we do not want them identified, if we should be taken by a French patrol ship."

"Or maybe the English," Hoffman said, his thin lips curved in a slightly sneering smile. "We know why you want those coins melted, Captain—the ones from the Australian ships, I mean. The British Navy has a long memory, Captain. . . . They might want to know how you got them in the first place." Hoffman's voice had acquired a nasty twang. "Piracy is like murder, you know. . . . There's no statute of limitations!"

The Captain was becoming choleric, and Sutton—who had arrived late—decided it was time to intervene.

"Look here, gentlemen," he said. "I've brought this up before and I'm going to bring it up again. I have as much as any invested in this venture, and I don't like to see our efforts imperiled at the start by a lot of petty squabbling. If Dr. Luce made a mistake in the smelter, that's too bad—but it's not fatal. We can ship another to Honolulu and pick it up there."

Hoffman was not ready to drop the matter, however.

"I believe we should give this information to our customs officials—that we are taking a smelter along as part of our equipment. Then there won't be any questions raised."

Stoney looked sharply at Hoffman.

"You've given out enough information already, Ogden. Why don't you drop it?"

"If you take the smelter along, there may be presumed an intent to violate the law. I won't be a party to it—and I won't have the ship libeled."

Chetwood, smiling as usual, broke in.

"You're not a lawyer, Ogden."

"No, but I'm a mining man and I know the laws on metals."

"Raw metals," Chetwood said amiably. "There is no law against taking a smelter on a treasure hunt. The list of equipment is on the ship's manifest, and there is no intent to conceal anything. The only mistake was in buying a smelter that will require a long time to do the work. We can't wait that long."

Hoffman grumbled a bit, but finally changed to another subject. "What about guns?" he said. "Each of us must be armed. The crew isn't likely to sit idly by while we recover several millions in treasure—if we find it." He looked at Captain Brown, whose bewhiskered countenance was still twitching with suppressed rage. "The Captain ought to know something about that, eh?" He uttered a nasty laugh, and for an instant Sutton thought the old sailor, in spite of his seventy-odd years, was going to lunge at Hoffman. The latter, who had a reputation as an athlete and a crack rifle shot, continued to grin in a nasty way, leaning against the back of the chair. He seemed to lounge rather than sit, stretching his legs out in such a way that he looked as if he might spring into action.

"We will have a dozen pistols and three Winchester rifles," the Captain said. "All arms will be locked in the master's cabin, and will be issued as needed. That's the rule of the sea."

"It isn't mine," Hoffman said. "We're on a treasure hunt—not a pleasure cruise, Captain. The crew certainly is going to find out what we are doing—and I, for one, do not intend to be unarmed. We'll have to divide watches among the six of us—the Captain, Sutton, Chetwood, Dr. Luce, Sharratt and myself—if we recover the treasure. Each of us must be armed."

Sutton again interposed a comment, in an effort to reduce the tension.

"Once we get into a danger area—that is, once we have the treasure on board, we can simply set up a system of mustering all arms in the captain's cabin daily. That will give us a daily check on the guns, so that if one is missing, we can search for it. I'm inclined to agree with Hoffman," he said to the Captain. "We must each have arms, and the rest should be locked up, as the Captain says. Certainly we can trust each other."

Captain Brown's features had assumed the pre-explosion expression which Sutton by now had come to recognize; but he glanced at the others and apparently decided there was no point in making an issue of this. It was evident from this exchange between Captain Brown and Hoffman, however, that there was bad blood brewing. Sutton wondered whether they would reach Honolulu without open warfare.

It ocurred to Sutton that perhaps he should have gone along with the Captain, and agreed to all guns being locked in the Captain's cabin, at least for the early part of the voyage.

The Pacific: Trouble at Sea

[1]

The departure of the *Herman* from San Francisco at high noon on Sunday, July 20, 1902, had been planned as a quiet event, with only immediate friends and associates of the voyagers to be on hand, but it was anything but that.

To begin with, the presence of the trim little schooner with her bowsprit tucked against the corner of the shore end of Pier No. 2, at the foot of Howard Street, had not passed unnoticed. Some of this was due to plain curiosity, but the greater part could be attributed to the running series of conflicting stories about the vessel that had appeared in the *Chronicle* and the *Examiner,* the latter linking the voyage to a search for a fabulous treasure of a Japanese ship buried on a South Sea Island, and the former—presumably goaded by the "Governor of Cocos Island," August Gissler—contending that the purpose of the expedition was to raid the treasure troves of Cocos Island itself.

Much of the shoreside commotion connected with the sailing of the *Herman* was personally stimulated by the red-bearded "Governor Gissler," who chose to come down to observe the departure; and the rest was furnished by Captain Brown himself.

When Sutton arrived at the dock at midmorning, preparations were already in progress aboard the schooner; and a considerable crowd had gathered at the dock, around Gissler, a tall, powerfully built man whose reddish beard vied with the white whiskers of Captain Brown.

An hour or so before sailing time, Gissler had stood on the dock, addressing his comments to newspaper reporters and others who clustered around him. Sutton and Dr. Luce were on the afterdeck, near the taffrail, and they could hear occasional fragments of Gissler's remarks. "We'll see!" he shouted at one time, gesticulating directly toward Captain Brown, who was directing operations from amidship—seeing to the laying out of lines, deckhouse lamps, the state of the furled sails—in fact, almost everything.

"I'm leaving on the *Para* for San Jose this week," Gissler told the reporters. "We'll see what happens to these robbers! I've already advised the government."

"Ye'll see what?" Captain Brown suddenly roared, apparently unable to endure the running commentary in silence. He strode to the rail. "You red-haired Dutchman—I was on Cocos before ye was born!"

This, of course, interested the gentlemen of the press. They moved forward to the edge of the dock. "Can we come aboard and get a statement, Captain?" one of them called out. The Captain shook his head and fist at the same time.

"Not a damn one of ye!" he said. "A pack of lies—that's what you put in your dirty sheets! I'll see ye in hell first!"

Sutton shook his head. It was hard to know how to keep the Captain under restraint. He looked at Dr. Luce, who was grinning.

"That's old Gissler," he said. "The fellow who had the coins at the yacht club. He's got them all figuring we are going to Cocos—and from all I can see, that should be fine with us."

Sutton turned toward the Captain, intending to speak a word of caution, but the old man had disappeared. Sutton went to the rail and looked down the dock. Captain Brown was striding along the wharf, his nautical cap perched squarely on the top of his flowing white hair. Even in the hot July morning, his coat was neatly buttoned over his chest.

At first Sutton thought he was going to accost Gissler and was on the point of following him to the dock; but then a rather heavy-set woman of middle age burst from the crowd, and waddled toward the Captain. It was Mrs. Samson. The Captain extended his hand to greet her, and then suddenly embraced her.

"Good heavens!" Sutton muttered. Dr. Luce, who had moved up beside him, seemed to be enjoying the scene.

"It's one of the Captain's weaknesses," he said. "We noticed it shortly after he arrived. He's probably promised her a trip to Honolulu —in Ogden Hoffman's stateroom! We'll see what happens."

Sutton shuddered. With all the other complications, they now had a seventy-two-year-old Lothario on their hands—and possibly a female fellow passenger! The doctor, observing the expression of dismay on Sutton's face, laughed sympathetically.

"There isn't anything to worry about," he said. "It's not an unusual affliction—quite harmless, I think."

The Captain had momentarily disentangled himself from the attentions of Mrs. Samson, and turned toward some of the newspapermen who had followed him. One had a news camera and was about to snap a picture of the Captain and Mrs. Samson. The Captain, with a single sweeping stroke of his hand, knocked the fellow spinning.

"Oh, my God!" Sutton groaned. "He's done it now. Come on—let's get him out of there!"

Sutton and the doctor ran down the gangway and sprinted up the wharf. By the time they arrived at the scene, things seemed to have settled down. Two wharf policemen had come up and the reporter who was knocked down was dusting off his camera. Apparently it had not suffered any damage.

Captain Brown stood solidly. Apparently the affair was regarded as an accident. Mrs. Samson was holding one arm and screaming, "Goodbye, dearie!"

The Captain smiled and waved appreciatively, as if responding to plaudits of the crowd. One of the reporters, from a safe distance, called out: "Is your ship armed, Captain? Do you carry guns?"

The Captain, now in a good humor—apparently as a result of the farewell he was receiving—waved to the reporter and shouted: "We'll give a good account of ourselves! That's all I can tell ye now—we'll give a good account!"

Sutton managed to get the Captain's attention. "They are getting ready to cast off, Captain. I believe they want you aboard."

The Captain accomplished a final embrace with Mrs. Samson—his wife's friend—and turned and strode back toward the gangway.

Dr. Luce, watching Sutton's face as they came up the gangway, slapped him on the back. "Cheer up, George! Nobody's gone over the side yet, and we haven't split a sail." Then, apparently sensing Sutton's mood, he added: "Things will settle down, once we get under way."

Sutton shook his head morosely.

"We have to agree on a method of handling the old boy," he said. "Otherwise this expedition is going to founder."

The first mate's hail—"Make ready to cast off!"—interrupted them; and Sutton moved forward to watch the operation. Mr. Hendrickson, the first officer, was at the forward capstan. The spring line was taken in and the bowline cast loose, leaving only the stern line. The *Herman* fell off slowly, the bow swinging around while the little tug, chugging restlessly some sixty or seventy feet offshore, was paying out towline. The stern lines were slacked and the weight of the cable drew the vessel slowly from the dock, until the stern was clear.

Captain Brown, with one of his chameleon shifts of temper, was now all business, standing amidships, watching the proceedings calmly at both ends of the vessel. He signaled Mr. Hendrickson when the stern line was ready for casting off, and quite suddenly the *Herman* was free of the dock and nosing gently into the mist-covered bay. The cable straightened out, and within a matter of seconds the dockshed was only faintly visible in the fog. The only evidence of those behind on the dock was a murmur of "Goodbyes," accented by the shrill scream of Captain Brown's lady friend: "Goodbye, dearie!"

Sutton smiled wanly as he walked forward to watch the passing wharves and the clear water that opened as soon as they rounded the North Beach point. Behind, on the starboard side, was Alcatraz; ahead lay the Golden Gate and the wide reaches of the Pacific.

The *Herman* dropped its cable, after raising sail, well beyond the bar off Baker Point. The Cliff House could be seen, brown and snug against the cliffs; and behind lay the misted fortress of the city itself, now almost out of sight in the fog. The little tug gave a farewell blast of its whistle, turned and headed back toward the Golden Gate while the schooner, with full main- and foresails, staysail on the foremast and both jibs set, nosed off to the southwest into the gray Pacific swells.

Sutton received a letter later in Honolulu from Donzel Stoney—who had driven to the Cliff House to watch the schooner raise its sails—in which he had written: "We went out to the Cliff House and saw your boat break out its sails and drop the tug. Then we felt a great relief from the strain of the last few days. These days were very trying to me and it was a great relief to see your boat plowing toward Honolulu. What a glorious time you will have when you get there. . . ."

Sutton, watching the receding contours of San Francisco and the Marin shore, felt a similar relief. It seemed ages since he had first taken the train from New Rochelle into New York to see Arthur Walradt on a "peculiar matter." Actually, it was a scant four months ago, but it seemed to Sutton he had lived a lifetime since then.

John Chetwood, coming aft to join Sutton, put his hand on the taller man's shoulder. "The doctor spoke to me about the problem that worries you," he said. "We both agree that you must be the man to handle the Captain, if it becomes necessary. We'll back you to the limit—but you seem to be the one he listens to."

Sutton was not sure whether this was an accolade or a sentence. He stood for some time with Chetwood, watching the actions of the crew —and Captain Brown. A small vessel shakes down very quickly—as to the character of both the ship and those who are its inhabitants, for the time. The crew of the *Herman* seemed to be doing very well, in spite of the haphazard manner of selection.

Sutton watched the set of the new sails, as the schooner heeled over on a starboard tack. Bristling gusts of a sharp northwest wind lashed the water across her foredeck as she rose and sank into heavier and heavier seas. There was a metallic grayness to the water, broken at the crest by whiskered strands of foam that seemed to be blown off the surface.

Captain Brown came aft to join them. He stood glaring about a bit, and then broke into a rumbling laugh.

"At last—we're on our way! Eh, Cap'n Sutton? The crew's working in —and those that don't, I'll knock 'em into shape! Eh?" He laughed jovially. "What do you say to that, eh?"

Sutton was watching the crew, quickly bringing the deck rigging into running order. He was impressed with Captain Brown's selection of the sailors. Mr. Benton, an Australian who was the second mate, had only joined the crew on Saturday—although he had been hired a week earlier by the Captain—and Sutton had had little opportunity to judge his worth. The others seemed to be admirably adjusted to the work aboard a cruising yacht. Sutton was observing Willie Peterson, the sailor who had simply come aboard and presented himself at the shape-up with a deferential tip of his cap, and was accepted and signed on forthwith. He felt moved to ask: "How did you pick that fellow, Captain? Peterson, I mean. He just came aboard while you were selecting the crew, you remember?"

Captain Brown seemed to scowl momentarily. Then he said: "Willie Peterson is the bosun. He's an Aussie—like Benton. A good man on rigging. He'll hold the job as long as he can do the work, and if not— off he goes! Is that what ye wanted to know?"

Sutton nodded, and then went on with mild persistence: "I was just interested in the way you arrived at your judgment, Captain."

The Captain's scowl deepened. "Let's say it was my decision, Mister Sutton." It was the first time he had addressed Sutton as anything but

"Cap'n." "Don't worry about the crew. That's my worry. I know how to handle things."

He spoke with such finality that Sutton looked at him in surprise. The Captain turned abruptly and walked forward. Chetwood looked at the Captain's retreating back, and then at Sutton.

"You seem to have touched a nerve, George," he said. "The old boy seemed right testy at your cross examination. What did happen with this fellow Peterson?"

Sutton shrugged. "Nothing in particular. He came aboard and said the Captain told him to report, and he was signed on. That's all. I wondered why he wasn't put through the screening with Hendrickson —but I guess, as the Captain said, that's his worry. He's responsible for the crew."

"I know." Chetwood nodded. "But he seemed damned testy, all the same."

Sutton had found himself quite interested in Chetwood; and during the first few days of the voyage this interest deepened. Due to an epidemic of *mal de mer* among the passengers, not many showed themselves on deck—with the exception of Chetwood and Sutton himself. Chetwood was slender with a kind of birdlike agility, which at first seemed slightly effeminate; but Sutton quickly discovered that there was considerable resilience in Chetwood's activities, a kind of wiry quality.

He had taken to following Sutton around the deck, clambering over coiled lines and running gear along the gunwales, stepping over these obstacles on the smooth, scrubbed deck of the schooner with mincing agility. It always seemed a bit of a hazard to the slim lawyer, as the ship rolled forward and sideways, sliding over the long swells in a continuous and rhythmic cycle; but Chetwood never lost his footing.

The length of the deck was about ninety feet, furnishing the course for a brisk walk from the topping bar over the transom across the downward slope of the afterdeck to the break of the poop, and then across the waist, along the midship rail and up a small two-step ladder to the rise of the forward deck, which slanted upward into the slope of onrushing water. The small ladder was at the foot of the mainstays, and Chetwood invariably grasped the rigging and swung himself up to the foredeck level.

"Don't you ever get tired walking, John?" Sutton asked him at the end of one of these journeys, clutching the rail and puffing from the effort. Chetwood grinned.

"I always liked walking," he said. "Used to take long walks on Sundays through Golden Gate park and sometimes I'd go across to Sausalito on the ferry and walk up Mount Tamalpais just for the fun of it. I like walking."

Sutton grunted. "You must," he said. He realized he was a bit overweight and slightly paunchy from the weeks of inactivity in San Francisco. He felt he had picked up at least ten pounds, and although he was fairly big-framed and over six feet, he liked to stay as trim as possible.

"Small fellows—such as I am—have one advantage over you big fellows," Chetwood went on agreeably. "We don't carry so much weight, and we can keep going for a long time. Have you noticed that distance runners are usually small fellows—with a lot of stamina?"

Sutton hadn't noticed. "We're going to need stamina on this trip—plenty of it," he said, leaning on the rail and gazing off into the wide sweep of rolling waters, now losing some of the murky gray and becoming more and more the characteristic indigo of the Pacific. The waves, washing against the flared bow of the schooner, created a hissing noise, mingled with the rumble of breaking crests, that was quite pleasant. "It's nearly six thousand miles out, you know—and five thousand miles back."

"We're going straight back to San Francisco—if we find the treasure?"

"That's the Captain's plan. No use arousing curiosity anywhere. You know, John"—Sutton's expression became quite serious—"that's where the real problem lies. Getting back. There are only five of us—six with the Captain. Several million dollars' worth of treasure is quite a temptation. We may be in danger of an attack."

"You mean from somebody else—or aboard ship?" Chetwood asked curiously.

"Both. There are only six of us—and six of the crew, not counting the Captain, of course . . . or the two Japanese. It's pretty damned important that we be able to count on all six of us."

"What do you mean . . . all six of us?"

Sutton shook his head.

"I'm not sure what I mean, John . . . But there's Sharratt, for example. He seems lazy and fat. What could he do in a fight?"

Chetwood nodded.

"We'll have the guns under our control, of course. The Captain has that responsibility. You know the doctor isn't too well—he's been in poor health for some time. But Hoffman is strong, of course—he's lean and wolflike. I imagine he can give a good account of himself. Sharratt's pretty fat, but he ought to wear some of it off."

"Not if he keeps eating and sleeping in his bunk all day." Sutton had tried to develop a liking for young Sharratt, since he was Don Stoney's brother-in-law; but he found it difficult. Sharratt seemed to be completely immersed in his own affairs, spending most of his time in his cabin, reading or sleeping. This was understandable at the beginning of the voyage; most of the passengers had either stayed below or hung over the rail in the process of getting used to the sea. But they were now several days out, and Sharratt had not displayed much interest in anyone except to chat now and then with Hoffman.

Sutton said nothing about Hoffman; but he had observed the lean, broad-shouldered "clubman" with graying hair and a constant expression of bored disdain on his angular features, and he wondered how well Hoffman fitted into the solidarity of the group. Hoffman had paced up and down the deck fairly constantly, since coming topside, stopping to chat now and then with sailors, which was a source of annoyance to Captain Brown. He liked to run what he described as a "tight ship" and on one or two occasions he had suggested that Hoffman avoid "fraternizing" with members of the crew.

Hoffman had rather airily dismissed this initial reproof.

"The old man is as suspicious as a coyote," he said.

"We know that, Hoffman," Sutton had told him. "We agreed that it's one of the conditions we've got to live with. But he's in control of the ship and I don't think any of us should in any way challenge that authority."

It became evident as the *Herman* plunged through the long swells on its southwest course that Captain Brown was fully in control of the vessel and planned to keep things that way. He put the whole crew to work sprucing up the ship on the third day out, when the *Herman* was well out of the coastal drift, clipping off eight to ten knots into a northwest wind which had lightened as they passed beyond the choppy waters just off the California coast.

The first instance of Captain Brown's ability to "knock 'em into shape" occurred after a week or so at sea. The red-haired sailor—whose name, Petersen, had been shortened to "Pete" for handy reference—was working on the launch when the Captain called out an order from the stern. Pete apparently did not hear the order.

Captain Brown strode forward suddenly from the deckhouse and placed himself directly behind the man. Then he bawled the order again —which was to release the gunwale gripes and prepare the launch for a test of the lowering gear.

"Swing the davits and make ready to lower the launch!" he roared.

The sailor jumped up.

"Sorry—I didn't hear you," he said.

"Sir!" the Captain bawled, even louder. Pete touched his cap, and said, "Aye, sir."

The old man raised his huge clublike fist and Sutton and Dr. Luce, who had been at the afterrail when this happened, both moved involuntarily forward. Clubbing a sailor was no longer lawful, as it had been in the raw days of the earlier sailing ships. However, the Captain lowered his hand.

"Don't ever look at me like that again," he said, in a voice that seemed to be choked with anger—in spite of the apparent inconsequentiality of the incident. "It'll be your last look—and mind that sharply!"

Pete was almost as tall as the Captain, and his anger at this unprovoked action seemed to be almost as great as Captain Brown's. But he nodded, muttered, "Yes, sir," again, and went about the business of releasing the fastenings of the launch. Benton, the second mate, and the Swede, Johnson, also came forward.

They went through the procedure of lowering the launch almost to the water's edge—the *Herman* being partly hove to in order to slow her speed for the maneuver—and Sutton marveled at the quick efficiency of the crew. It seemed that the Captain, by some process of seamanship not discernible to an outsider, had worked the crew into shape more rapidly than might have been expected.

The *Herman* laid a southwesterly course until the twenty-first parallel was reached, some twelve hundred miles off the coast of Baja California; and then the schooner veered to a more westerly course, picking up easterly trade winds which blow almost constantly along the belt of the Tropic of Cancer. When the vessel was ten days out of San Francisco, the winds died and there were stretches of light winds and calm in which the *Herman* logged less than thirty miles a day.

On one occasion, when the Captain ordered a shift to a new tack, he took the wheel himself and the second mate, Mr. Benton, sprang to secure the tackle on the main boom. As he did so, one of the lines flipped across and hit the Captain on the side of his head. There was hardly any injury in the blow from the rope, but the effect on Captain Brown was electric.

With a roar of rage, he reached for Willie Peterson, the bosun, and jerked him over against the wheel. Then he strode forward to confront Benton. The latter was so astounded by the Captain's fury that he stood for a moment, his jaw open. Then he walked a step closer to the old man, fists clenched. Benton was a short, stocky man, squarely built as a full-rigged ship; and his eyes met the Captain's without any indication of being cowed.

Sutton was sitting on the afterdeck with Dr. Luce and Frank Sharratt, playing chess with the former, when the sudden altercation occurred. All three rose, and stood listening to Captain Brown's jawing.

"You strike your captain again and I'll have ye in irons, Mister Benton," the old man bellowed, his whiskers trembling in the sheer frenzy of rage. "Do ye understand that, ye damned scum! In irons!"

"Oy didn't strike you—it was an accident," Benton was saying. "But it won't be no accident if you talk to me this way ashore—and be damned to yer white hair!"

The Captain turned and walked back to the wheelhouse while Benton stared after him. He glanced once at the three men standing on the afterdeck, and finally turned to make fast the sheet on the main boom as it swung out on the new tack.

Captain Brown went below, and when Sutton came down to his stateroom a few minutes later, he found the old man daubing iodine on a scratch across his face. "Damned insolence," he muttered, when he saw Sutton at the door of his cabin.

"Do you want Dr. Luce to attend to you?" Sutton asked, and the Captain shook his head. "No—not for this." He sat down on the edge of his bed—an elaborate four-poster with the upper ends of the posts fastened to the roof of the cabin. The old man then took off his hat and for an instant his big frame seemed to sag with weariness.

"It's the fevers coming back on me," he finally said. "Maybe the doctor *could* give me something for them." Sutton nodded and went forward to advise Dr. Luce. The doctor grinned in a kindly way and shook his head.

"I checked his pulse and his temperature last night and this morning," he said. "He may have recurrent attacks of malaria, George—but that isn't what's worrying him now. Something else is, and I'm damned if I can figure out what."

Sutton agreed. His mild expression was almost settling into a perpetual frown; it seemed with each passing day new things occurred that were disturbing and puzzling. There was a great deal about old Captain Brown that he, like Dr. Luce, was finding harder and harder to explain to himself.

[2]

Among the varying characteristics Captain Brown displayed—from hearty good humor and downright joviality at times, to unreasoning anger and petty truculence over trivial incidents—the thing that worried Sutton most was the instability of his moods. This concern was not due to the inconvenience of these chameleon changes; it was with a view to the future. The voyage thus far was quite tolerable, in spite of these annoying interludes; but what would happen on the long voyage homeward—*after* they found the island and the treasure, if, indeed, they should find it? The need for stability would become enormously greater.

He broached this to Dr. Luce as they sat on the afterdeck playing a game of chess, which had become a kind of after-dinner habit. The *Herman* had rounded off to a westerly course and was running down the latitude toward the Island of Hawaii (or "Owyhee," as it was frequently called), the most southerly island of the Sandwich group. Behind the little schooner trailed a frothy wake speckled with phosphorescent plankton that bounced through the roiled water like incandescent bulbs.

"Our problem isn't now," Sutton said. "But what will happen after we reach the island? Do you think the Captain can control things—with the possibility of millions of dollars' worth of gold bullion in our hold? We've got five thousand miles of water to cover, back to San Francisco. That's when the trouble is going to come."

Dr. Luce paused and concentrated on his next move. Then he looked up.

"I understand what you mean, George. I've puzzled over that, too."

"Do you know what paranoia is?" the doctor finally asked. Sutton nodded.

"Well, there is a less serious form of the disease known as 'paranoiac dementia,' " Dr. Luce went on. "Its symptoms are sometimes associated with senility. I think the Captain may be afflicted with this."

"Is it dangerous?" Sutton asked.

Dr. Luce shook his head.

"Not necessarily—only in extreme cases. It mainfests itself in sudden suspicions—delusions and sometimes hallucinations." Sutton thought immediately of the Captain's discourse on ghosts, the day he went aboard the *Herman* in San Francisco. "Mostly they are delusions of persecution and grandeur. The victim of the disease usually regards himself as someone of great importance, and he suspects everyone else of plotting his undoing."

"Do you think his story of the treasure is an halluciation?" Sutton asked.

Dr. Luce smiled. "I don't think I'd be aboard if I did," he said. "If we had relied only on what the Captain said, perhaps I would have regarded it as such. But there was your investigation, and ours out here. We know his ship, the *Sea Foam,* was on the West Coast in the early 1850s. We also know that the 'church treasure of Lima' disappeared, as he says it did. We know there was no real record of what happened to it, until Captain Brown came forward with his story. No—I think the story stands on its own. Whether Captain Brown is still in a mental condition to remember the island—or actually knows where it is—is a problem that will not be answered until we get down there.

"But your concern about the trip home is very real, George—and quite important. The Captain seems to have changed even in the short time I've known him. He's become much more irascible and quick-tempered, and shows less regard for the judgment of anyone but himself."

Sutton sighed.

"It's a hell of a way to start out, isn't it?"

Ogden Hoffman interrupted their colloquy, coming up from the aft companionway. He had not spent much of his time on deck, having been afflicted longer than the others with the *mal de mer* incident to their departure. Now his rather long face, with its expression of bored sophistication, seemed even longer.

"Glad I found you two together," he said, pulling up a deck chair. "I've been going over the ship's documents—Louis wanted me to look them over. Then I got Jimmy to help me check the supplies against the shipping lists. Here—" He laid down a sheet of paper on the table, pushing aside their chess board. "Look here," Hoffman said, running his finger down a list on a sheet on which "Ferry Drug Stores, No. 8 Market

Street" was emblazoned on the letterhead. It showed a long list of medical items, including "blue ointment" and "quinine pills." One item was "rat poison."

"We found that," Hoffman said. "We also found a can of strychnine—which can be used for rat poison. The rat poison labeled 'Rough on Rats' is on the list of supplies, but this strychnine isn't listed. Before I ask the Captain about this, I want to talk with you fellows. Having a can of strychnine aboard—without listing it—is dangerous procedure, don't you think?"

Dr. Luce looked over the list carefully, and then said: "The medicine must be locked up in my chest, in any event. Why don't we put it in there and say nothing? I'll have the key."

Hoffman nodded.

"All right," he said. "But I don't like it. Everything else has checked out—except this. There's enough to poison us all—including the crew."

Sutton and Dr. Luce went below with Hoffman and saw to the locking of the medicine cabinet in the doctor's cabin. The doctor took the key, and carefully fastened it to a key ring.

It became evident, following this incident, that Hoffman's attitude toward the Captain had grown more hostile. At times he seemed almost to hold the old man in contempt. Captain Brown was oblivious of this; but Sutton was not.

He mentioned it to Chetwood and Dr. Luce. (Frank Sharratt, who was younger than the rest, stayed pretty much by himself, watching the sea from a deck chair and reading books on mineralogy, which he had brought along.)

"Hoffman doesn't like the Captain—and he won't give an inch," Sutton said. "If we've got to live together for six months or so on this boat, we've got to learn to get along with each other."

Both nodded. Sutton turned to the doctor.

"George, why don't you talk with him? Hoffman, I mean. Try to get him to water down his feeling of hostility. If he opens up with what he's thinking about the Captain—hell's likely to break loose."

It broke loose, sooner than they expected.

Hoffman had gotten into the habit of talking to the first and second mates—particularly to Willie Benton—more than seemed necessary. He even talked a good deal with members of the crew. He began to tell them how to perform the various duties Captain Brown had assigned; and at one point Willie Peterson turned to him and said, in an Australian twang: "Oi'm sorry, sir, but the skipper 'as tol' me 'ow to do this bloomin' job and that's the wy Oi'm doin' it, with all respeck to you, sir!"

Captain Brown was standing near, at the rail; and now he came over.

"Get on with your work, Peterson—and don't be swappin' yarns with the passengers."

Willie Peterson looked over his shoulder and touched his cap—as they all had learned to do.

"Oy wasn't talkin' to 'im, sir—'e was talkin' to me," he said.

Captain Brown turned toward Hoffman.

"Please keep to yourself while you're aboard this ship," he said, his white whiskers trembling with the familiar bristling effect while he worked his jaw in what seemed to be a physical effort to suppress his anger.

"You expect me to sit by myself?" Hoffman asked, in a drawl. "Hell, why don't you put me in solitary?"

"You've passengers to talk to," Captain Brown said, visibly restraining himself. "This vessel is at sea, and while it is, my orders will be obeyed. I'm responsible for the conduct of the crew."

Hoffman gave a short laugh and turned and walked aft. Sutton, who had watched the scene from the forward rail, shook his head. He hoped Dr. Luce would talk with Hoffman soon. In fact, it might be advisable for all of them to talk with him. Everyone had a stake in the venture, and it would be entirely unreasonable for Hoffman to put his own personal antagonism toward the Captain above the interests of the group.

Hoffman had stopped to look at the binnacle, then turned to the charts. Willie Benton was logging the course, and Hoffman leaned over his shoulder.

"Too far to the south'ard, eh?" he muttered, in a voice loud enough for Captain Brown to hear. "I thought we were laying a course too far down."

The second mate turned and said over his shoulder: "We're not too far down, Mr. Hoffman. The wind was nor'west and we've pulled down into easterly trades. This will hold up all the way to the Sandwich Islands."

Hoffman snorted. "This boat will foot faster on a beat than a run," he said. "Any damn fool knows that!"

Captain Brown strode up. "Any damned fool knows better'n to listen to a landlubber that ain't been out of sight of land in his life,

Mr. Hoffman," he said. His eyes were mean with anger and his voice shook with rage. Sutton and Dr. Luce, who had been sitting aft of the deckhouse, rose from their deck chairs.

Hoffman shrugged in a way that conveyed complete disregard of the Captain's opinions. He sauntered back to the companionway and went below, while the Captain stood watching him, his hands clenched in anger. Finally, with a prodigious shudder, as if to shake off the spell of his enormous rage, he turned and observed Sutton and the doctor, still standing on the afterdeck. He walked toward them, and as he passed Willie Peterson at the wheel, he leaned over and said something. The bosun nodded.

"We'll run down our westing," the Captain said as he approached them, apparently by way of explanation. "There's usually a southerly wind off the island of Hawaii"—he pronounced it "Hav-ai"—"and we'll run up the windward coast to the channel. We should raise the peaks of Mauna Kea and Mauna Loa by tomorrow morning."

This was good news. Sutton and Dr. Luce walked to the rail, looking forward off the port bow. The *Herman* was now steering a bit to the northwest. The position on the chart that morning showed 21° 39′ north and 153° 37′ east, some eighty miles due east of the northern tip of the island of Hawaii. The schooner was rolling in a strong southeast swell, and making about seven knots. Full sail was set, including staysails on the fore- and mainmasts. The canvas, billowing out in the following wind presented a beautiful sight to those aboard.

The Captain, coming up behind Sutton and the doctor, indicated a direction a few points off the port bow. "The peaks should come up there early tomorrow," he said.

Sutton glanced at him.

"You've made this run before, Captain?"

He shook his head.

"Willie Benton—Mr. Benton—has been on the run before. I've never been in these waters. But the sailing directions are very complete. Mauna Kea rises almost fourteen thousand feet. It is the tallest mountain in the Pacific. Mauna Loa, to the south, is only a bit below that. It should be a grand sight."

The Captain seemed to have completely forgotten his altercation with Hoffman. His manner was calm and pleasant.

However, that night when the Captain was topside seeing to the running lights and the pumps, Sutton got Dr. Luce and Chetwood together in the former's cabin. Hoffman's attitude toward the Captain, he told them, might imperil the entire expedition, and he felt there should be an organized effort on the part of the rest to persuade Hoffman to change his conduct.

While they were discussing the matter, a bellow issued from the Captain's stateroom, and they all hurried aft to see what had happened.

The Captain was standing in the middle of the room glaring at Ogden Hoffman, who was sitting in a chair. Hoffman's lips were curled in his customary smile of disdain, which Sutton had come to dislike on any occasion. On the bed was a scattering of papers.

"These are instructions, Captain Brown," Hoffman was saying. "They represent the wishes of the owner of this vessel."

"Owner be damned!" the Captain was roaring. "They are insulting! I am to get your approval on any decision? You're insane!"

"Regardless of which one of us is insane," Hoffman continued, in a deliberate drawl that was calculated to push the old man to the brink of frenzy, "they are the owner's instructions, and I mean to follow them."

Chetwood walked to the bed, picked up the sheets and glanced over them.

"These are your instructions, Hoffman?" he asked, rather slowly. "They are not the basis of our agreement with Captain Brown. This ship is under charter, as you know."

Sutton also glanced at the papers. They seemed to be a set of orders to Hoffman from the owner, Louis Mooser. They required periodic reports on finances and other matters, chiefly pertaining to the security of the vessel, to be obtained from Captain Brown by Ogden Hoffman.

"Why in hell didn't you talk with us about this, Ogden?" Chetwood asked. "We're involved in this expedition, too, you know."

Captain Brown, to whom the elements of command seemed to be a highly sensitive matter, stood for a moment still glaring at Hoffman, and finally he said: "I am captain of this vessel. I will report only to the owners, and that after the ship has returned to its port. These papers have nothing to do with me—and they are not part of my agreement!"

Sutton, fearful that the Captain might break into violence at any moment, persuaded them to leave the matter in abeyance until they arrived in Honolulu. Then, he pointed out, the entire matter could be ironed out by a letter, if necessary, to Donzel Stoney in San Francisco.

This finally was acceptable to everyone, although the Captain, who seemed to be suffering more from the challenge to his authority than from the new requirements imposed upon him, dismissed the whole matter with a wave of his hand, and turned his back on the group.

Chetwood, for the first time, was angry. His usually good-humored smile had been completely erased by the incident; and when they went on deck, he turned to Hoffman.

"If your idea is to break up this expedition at the outset," he said, "you are certainly going about it in the right way."

Hoffman shrugged. "I am doing what I was instructed to do," he said. "I represent the owner. The rest of you are investing your time and some money, but Louis Mooser is risking his boat. It's my business to see that confidence in Captain Brown isn't misplaced—and I'm beginning to think it is."

The *Herman* plowed steadily westward and just after dawn the following day—August 7—when the black morning clouds were beginning to lift into the lightening sky, those aboard caught their first glimpse of land. It was high land, a sharp, glistening island in itself, which seemed to rest well above the mass of fleecy clouds that spread across the horizon.

Sutton, in a letter sent home from Honolulu, wrote:

> Our first sight was the Mountain of Mauna Loa on the Island of Hawaii—some 13,000 feet high. It was a magnificent spectacle, a chain of towering peaks that seemed to be suspended far above the clouds. First there was the light blue sky, then the chain of dark peaks and the mass of fleecy clouds, growing lighter as the sun rose behind us, with the clouds extending right down to the dark blue water itself. Later we saw the peak of Mauna Kea, sharper than the other, rising to the north of Mauna Loa; and then we saw the island itself. But the peaks always appeared far above the clouds, like islands in the sky.
>
> As we gradually approached the land, other islands came into view—first Maui, with its towering crater of Haleakala, some 10,000 feet above the sea; and then Molokai, with its line of rising cliffs as we rounded the end of that island and turned into the long channel between Molokai and Oahu. . . .

At this point, an additional difficulty had developed. Dr. Luce, watching at the forward rail as the spectacle of the islands unfolded itself, was late for lunch. The Captain, who had initially expounded the doctrine of promptness at meals aboard a ship, apparently regarded this as an opportunity to discharge his pent-up wrath—presumably suppressed during the Hoffman incident—and he let loose the full force of it on Dr. Luce. He said he regarded lateness at meals as an insult to his own person!

The doctor apologized, but the Captain—under a full head of steam—rose abruptly and left the mess table in the main cabin. Sutton and

Chetwood exchanged glances with the doctor. Sharratt went on eating. Hoffman smirked and remarked: "You gentlemen want to treat the old fool with kid gloves. Go ahead—this is your opportunity."

Dr. Luce and Sutton went aft for their usual game of chess. It was evident that the Captain knew he was under discussion, because he scowled when he passed them; but even though Dr. Luce greeted him affably, as if nothing had happened, the Captain walked by without speaking.

Sutton had observed a growing chumminess on the part of the Captain and Willie Peterson, the Australian sailor. Whenever he paused to look at the chart which Peterson logged when he was on watch, he appeared to chat with him. This was not his habit with the other sailors, and Sutton recalled the circumstances under which Peterson had been recruited. The Captain probably had run across him ashore, Sutton decided, and found out enough about his seamanship to warrant his judgment of the man.

Hoffman, it appeared, had noted the same difference in attitude. He came up alongside Sutton as he was taking his regular promenade along the deck for exercise. Timing his stride to Sutton's, he said: "Have you noticed our Captain's behavior toward the bosun—Peterson?"

Sutton glanced at him in some surprise, and nodded.

"Yes, I noticed it. He seems to have a lot of confidence in him. Why do you ask?"

"Peterson is the only member of the crew who was not pre-picked by the Seaman's Agency," Hoffman said. "That was the understanding with Louis Mooser. The agency was to review the records of each applicant before he was screened by Brown. The Captain had the final say—but only as to applicants approved by the agency. He gave Peterson's name to the agency—said he knew him—and the agency checked his record and found nothing bad about it. So he was hired on Captain Brown's say-so."

He paused a minute, as if to let this information sink in. Then he said: "I don't like it! I'm going to see that Peterson is discharged from the crew in Honolulu. I'd like your help on that."

"But you can't do that!" Sutton exclaimed. "The man signed for the voyage. Unless he's discharged for a reason, he'd have a claim on the ship."

"There's a reason." Hoffman grinned, with a curiously expectant expression. "Look here—" He led Sutton to the chart box against the wall of the wheelhouse. The red-haired sailor, Pete, was at the wheel and did not seem to be observing them. Hoffman lifted the lid of the box.

"Look at that!"

There was a pistol lying at the back, partly covered with charts.

"It's the Captain's gun," Hoffman continued. "It was agreed each of us would retain one pistol, and the second pistol and Winchesters would remain locked in the Captain's cabin. I saw Peterson put this gun in the chart box."

"What do you suppose it's here for?" Sutton asked.

Hoffman shrugged.

"Probably the old man told Peterson to put it there—so he'd have it handy, in an emergency. That isn't the point. It's there, and its a violation of ship's rules for a member of the crew to have firearms. I expect Captain Brown to enforce those rules—and that means he has to fire Peterson when we get into port. I wanted you to see the gun."

Sutton looked for several seconds at Hoffman, before he spoke. Then he said: "I think you're playing a dangerous game, Hoffman. This isn't anything for you to decide. If you think there's any infraction of the rules, take it up with the Captain or the rest of us. That's the proper course."

[3]

The Captain's gun, lying in the wheelhouse chart box, became a matter of more than academic importance before the *Herman* reached port in Honolulu. In fact, it attained a measure of significance that Sutton—had he been a superstitious man—might have regarded as an omen of trouble to come.

The schooner worked its way on a beam wind up the windward side of the islands until it rounded the eastern point of Molokai, passing almost under the stubby white tower of Hamakuapoko Light, which stood on the craggy bluffs of Halawa Point, spreading its comforting beam to seaward.

The schooner wore full main- and foresail, a triatic staysail on the mainmast and forestaysail and both jibs set as it eased off for the run along the Molokai coast; but even at that point it had become evident that in spite of more than a hundred and fifty miles logged since midnight, the *Herman* would not clear Diamond Head by nightfall. This would require entering the harbor after dark, and Captain Brown

The first mate, Hendrickson, and the second mate, Benton.

Doctor George Luce on board the *Herman*.

Three photographs taken from the schooner while on the way to Honolulu.

seemed unwilling to risk this. Shortly after sundown he gave orders to Mr. Hendrickson to clear the gear on the afterdeck, heave to in the channel and ride out the night under close-trimmed sail.

The first indication of this decision that reached those below occurred with the sudden change in the pitch of the ship, from long, gliding rolls across the swells through which the *Herman* had been plowing gracefully all day long, to sudden abrupt leaps into high walls of water that came crashing across the foredeck.

Sutton heard the familiar ring—"Hard alee!"—and started to go up on deck. The grinding clash of the sheet-blocks on deck and the sudden snapping of the main- and foresail as the sheets were taken up, alerted him to what was happening. It apparently also alerted Hoffman. He came striding out of his cabin and took the after companionway steps three at a time.

"What in hell are we doing now?" he demanded. "Going back to San Francisco? Who ordered this, Captain?"

Captain Brown, standing rigidly on deck aft of the wheelhouse, was calling out orders to Mr. Hendrickson. "Ease off on the jib sheets—you want to rip the canvas off her?" he roared. "Move fast! Make ready to set up the la'board shrouds as soon as we shorten sail. Mr. Hendrickson, see that all sheets are properly slacked for'ard so she can come around. That's it, Mr. Benton—hard alee and easy does it. Let the wind bring her around . . ."

During a pause, Hoffman—standing only a few feet from the Captain—again bawled out: "I asked you what in hell is going on?"

Captain Brown ignored him.

"Make ready to take up the topping lift on that foreboom," he called out. "Slack the peak halyards, Mr. Hendrickson—see that it's eased off so you can drop the gaff and shorten sail." He suddenly looked at Hoffman; and Sutton once more was aware of the blazing intensity of the old man's eyes. "Get the hell out of the way—go below, Mr. Hoffman, or I'll have you put there!"

The waves were rising now in massive surges of water, huge walls of glassy green that seemed to pour directly down upon the forward deck. The dark cascading seas roared across the deck, washing aft everything that had not been secured. Captain Brown suddenly leaned down and caught hold of a passing bucket that seemed on its way to Honolulu in spite of the fact the *Herman* was now aiming the other way. He tossed it down the companionway, narrowly missing Hoffman.

"Who in hell are you throwing at?" Hoffman shouted.

The Captain continued to take little notice of him, directing his attention to the rapid handling of lines and the quick reefing of the foresail as the vessel came smartly around, bearing off a bit south of east to hold some headway until the sails could be shortened.

Hoffman turned angrily to Sutton, who stood near him.

"We'd have been in Honolulu now if the damned old fool hadn't tried to sail halfway to the South Pole," he snorted, crossing in front of the Captain as he spoke, so the Captain would hear his words.

It seemed to Sutton that Captain Brown, standing with legs braced against the sharp roll of the deck, stiffened slightly; but he gave no other sign that he had heard Hoffman's comment.

Sutton wished devoutly that Hoffman would shut up. He had even less taste for Hoffman now than at the start of the voyage; and as a result of his approach in the afternoon on the matter of the Captain's gun and Peterson, he was not only disgusted but worried. He had not had an opportunity to discuss Hoffman's remarks with Dr. Luce or Chetwood, but he meant to do so at the first opportunity. It was becoming apparent that Hoffman's senseless hostility toward Captain Brown was not only creating a problem that might become as acute as the Captain's own mercurial attitudes, but it threatened the entire future of the expedition.

Sutton was awed at the impressive spectacle, as the *Herman* rode close-hauled into a rising northeast wind. Mountains of green water seemed to rise before them and descend upon the ship with fanatical fury. The frothy crests blown off the waves cast long strands of white foam across the foredeck. The *Herman* rose to meet each new challenge and then dived into a seemingly empty abyss beyond. The sky had settled into a canopy of star-speckled darkness, the gleaming brightness of the scattered lights blending with the growing blackness of the sea below; and above, the white sails, now slanted over to port, showed in ghostly outline against the darkened sky as the schooner pointed to the northeast.

It would have been frightening, Sutton thought—far out at sea, and this sudden challenge of the little schooner against the overwhelming force of the massive waves—except for the comforting spots of light gleaming from settlements along the Molokai shore, which showed they were near land.

Hoffman apparently had subsided, finding no particular reception for his dissenting remarks; and Sutton turned to watch the activities of the crew as they took in sail on the main- and forebooms, hauled in the mainsheets to keep the vessel as close to the wind as possible and avoid making much headway to the eastward.

The lighthouse on Makapuu Head now shone faintly astern, a tiny white dot in the darkness, and far to the north another light—this one probably from Kahuku, on the northeast tip of Oahu—spread its sudden flashes periodically across the water. Sutton knew the city of Honolulu itself lay beyond the black cape of Makapuu, nestled under the curving ridge of mountains which were obscured by huge banks of clouds; and the city would not be visible until they rounded Diamond Head in the morning. Almost everything, at the moment, was covered in velvet darkness.

Sutton spent some time on deck, watching the waves in their successive assaults upon the ship, the huge walls of water rising under the dim glow of the forward running lights, driving past the glistening white sides of the *Herman* only to fall away astern under the pallid illumination of the binnacle light and the faint glow cast from the after ports.

"Quite a spectacle, isn't it?" Dr. Luce had moved up beside Sutton in the darkness. Sutton nodded, and said: "The old skipper seems to know his business. I found a good deal of comfort in the way he brought the ship about and trimmed her into the wind. We'll have a pretty wild night of it, but I guess we've all got our sea legs. Where's Hoffman?"

"Below," the doctor said. "He said he had spoken to you about Peterson, the bosun. Wants him fired when we land. What's his reason?"

"He thinks Peterson has possession of a gun. Captain Brown told Peterson to keep it in the chart box. We agreed no one but the Captain and each of us would have arms—but this was more or less a precaution for later on, wasn't it? I intend to speak to the Captain about it, however."

"Why do you think Captain Brown wants a gun on deck?" Dr. Luce asked. Sutton thought it over; there really wasn't much point in it. Perhaps they should try to persuade the Captain to keep his firearms in his cabin, and this would satisfy Hoffman. Since there seemed to be no particular urgency, Sutton decided to wait until they were in Honolulu to take it up with Captain Brown.

Meanwhile he watched with fascination this interplay of forces between man and sea. It seemed to be a game at which Captain Brown excelled. He moved from one point of observation to another, his bewhiskered face turning now aloft to watch the bend of the double-reefed mainsail, now forward to check the slant of the inboard jib, the other jib having been lowered as the schooner came about. The old man not only seemed to know what he was doing, but he was enjoying it.

The *Herman* lay smartly on a northeast course, and the wind seemed to have abated slightly once they had come about in the channel. The wind was perhaps two points to starboard, so that whatever leeway the vessel attained would be in the direction of the open sea. Although the faint lights of the Leper Settlement at Kalaupapa could be seen dimly abeam, they were ten to fifteen miles offshore and it was unlikely that the channel drift would carry them any closer during the night.

Hoffman, after a time, came back on deck and threw in his customary dissenting vote.

"I've been watching those lights ashore, Captain," he remarked, standing beside Sutton and Dr. Luce.

"Looks like we might back into the rocks before daybreak."

Captain Brown turned his head, but said nothing. Sutton glanced at his hands, swinging at the sides of his dark, baggy trousers; they seemed to clench and unclench spasmodically, as if the whole enormous violence of the old man were pouring out of his hamlike paws, like escaping charges of electricity.

At one point he raised his arm, and since he was within striking distance of Hoffman, Sutton thought he was going to hit him. But instead, the Captain turned and walked a few steps in the other direction, bawling some order to one of the sailors. Finally he turned and called all hands aft. They stood there—Willie Peterson, John Smith, Pete (the red-haired sailor), and Johnson, the mournful Swede. Mr. Benton stood at the wheel, while Captain Brown detailed his orders for the night.

Mr. Hendrickson was to take the watch at four bells, with all hands except Mr. Benton, who would go below until four bells of the dogwatch. Then Mr. Hendrickson and all but Peterson would go below; the Captain, Mr. Benton and Peterson would maintain the early-morning watch.

"We will come about at four o'clock," the Captain said. "We should clear the Head in four hours."

"Unless we're on the rocks," Hoffman muttered, in a voice loud enough to be heard. Sutton turned to him.

"I think we'd better go below—now," he said, rather sharply. "Doctor—we have a game, you know."

Dr. Luce nodded. His usually placid expression had become tightly drawn. Since the Captain had dressed him down for not showing up at lunch, the doctor's usual equanimity had undergone some signs of change, and now he turned quickly, glaring at Hoffman as he passed him and started down the companionway. Sutton followed the doctor into the main cabin, where they set up a chessboard.

Hoffman followed them into the large room, which served as a mess hall and general social room for the passengers. His elongated features, with their perpetually bored expression, betrayed no awareness of the animosity which he appeared to have provoked on all sides.

Sutton was becoming so disturbed with Hoffman's conduct that he hardly acknowledged his greeting. Hoffman leaned his elbows on the table where the chessboard was being set up. Sutton turned suddenly and looked at him.

"Why don't you drop this, Hoffman?" he asked. "There are others on this trip, as you know—and you're in a fair way to wreck the whole thing at the start."

Hoffman shrugged in a way that seemed to achieve a deliberate balance between indifference and insolence.

"Drop what?" he asked, in a slow drawl. "My job is to take care of the ship."

Sutton stood up, knocking over some of the chessmen. Whatever he was about to say was lost, however, because at that instant, as he glared at Hoffman, there suddenly arose the most awful clamor on deck. Someone shouted—probably Mr. Hendrickson—"Stand clear—she's coming down!" There was a rending sound, the rattle of shackles and blocks, and then a terrific crash.

Sutton sprang for the companionway, with Hoffman and Dr. Luce in close pursuit. They arrived topside to witness what seemed a mass of inextricable confusion. Several of the crew were amidships where the foresail gaff lay across the pile of canvas. The shrouds were vibrating under the sudden change of tension, and the peak halyards and foresheet were twisting and whipping in the wind, like live things.

"All aft—every damn' one of ye!" the Captain roared to the three passengers who surged up from the companionway. Sutton saw Chetwood's face, puckish and sleepy-eyed, protruding from below. Sharratt, who was fat and a bit lazy, was the only passenger who had not showed. He was probably sleeping.

"For'ard and clear that rigging amidships," the Captain roared. "Get that canvas furled, Mr. Hendrickson, before it goes overside."

Willie Benton, whose strength was prodigious, was hauling the boom to the windward side with a single effort, clearing the area around the launch for furling the sail, which was now blowing in every direction. Willie Peterson was at the wheel. Captain Brown leaned forward to call out to him, "Hold her steady as she goes—keep into the wind, damn it, or we'll have the foreboom torn out!"

The red-haired Pete, John Smith, the Swede, and even Jimmy, the Japanese steward, were working feverishly to haul in sail so it could be furled on the lee side of the vessel. Meanwhile Mr. Hendrickson was examining the yoke, which seemed to have given way when the peak halyard parted.

In a few minutes Pete went aloft on the port stays to rig a new peak halyard, and Mr. Benton—an expert rigger—made a quick repair of the broken yoke. Sutton moved forward to the lee side of the deckhouse to observe the operation. Suddenly he found his attention wrenched from the scene by a hoarse cry.

"Stand back—or I'll heave ye over the side!"

It was the Captain; and he was roaring at Hoffman. The latter had gone forward, in spite of the Captain's orders, and had been directing Mr. Benton and the others as to what they should do. He then apparently turned his attention to Willie Peterson at the wheel. For an instant Sutton found himself actually transfixed by the spectacle. The running lights and the lantern on the foremast cast enough light to make the midship area look like a stage, encircled with a feeble spotlight. But such a stage as he had never seen before! The wild heaving of the waves threw up moving walls of glassy water at either side; the sea itself seemed about to swallow the whole scene momentarily. In the center were the sailors, working like gnomes. And at the near side of this stage setting stood Hoffman, his long, pale face suddenly arrested in an expression of incredulity as he stared at the Captain.

Captain Brown himself was standing just forward of the wheelhouse, his nautical cap lost in the shuffle, his encircling mane of whiskers and hair blowing over his ears as he faced the wind and Hoffman.

It was as if the entire tableau had been frozen for an instant in time, so clear and distinct was the impression in Sutton's mind. Two massive forces—the Captain herding and driving his crew to action, and the sea swirling in rising fury around them—seemed to enclose the tableau; and in the center stood Hoffman, the troublemaker. For the few seconds that Sutton watched him, Hoffman's usually cynical face seemed to betray uncertainty and possibly some fear.

Captain Brown broke the spell. With another hoarse cry that was unintelligible—just a roar of rage—he turned and reached into the chart box on the after side of the wheelhouse.

"Oh, my God!" Sutton muttered, and started for the Captain. Before he could reach him, Captain Brown came out with the pistol which Hoffman had showed Sutton earlier in the day.

"Stand back, damn your hide—or I'll drill ye!"

Hoffman stared at the old man, who stood like an angered Viking, his head bare and his white hair blowing about his face. Hoffman suddenly turned and darted down the companionway.

"Stand aside!" the Captain roared again. Almost automatically the work on the midships deck had stopped. The sailors ducked for cover behind the launch. Holding the pistol at his side, Captain Brown presented a formidable picture; and Sutton was almost sure he had gone mad.

At that moment, Hoffman reappeared. He also had a pistol in his hand.

"Put that gun down!" He spoke in a high-pitched voice that seemed almost on the point of cracking. "I can shoot better than you, Captain—put that gun down, or I'll drop you!"

Captain Brown started to raise his pistol and suddenly Sutton stepped into the light which shone above the binnacle, and stood between them.

"Stop this!" he said. Hoffman, half crouched in the companionway, looked at Sutton with a startled expression. For an instant, Sutton realized that both of them might shoot, and he was directly in the path, either way. The Captain finally lowered his gun and Sutton continued in a quiet voice: "Put your guns down—both of you!"

He turned to Hoffman. "Hoffman," he said, "you know as well as the rest of us that Captain Brown is master of this ship while it is at sea. If you go below, I will talk with him—and try to see that nothing happens. Otherwise, I will personally prefer charges against you when we reach port!"

For a few seconds no one said anything. Dr. Luce and Chetwood stood near Sutton; and finally Chetwood spoke up.

"We'll see that Hoffman goes below, Captain—so he can't interfere with your operations," he said, quietly. "Put the gun away, and I promise you there will be no more trouble tonight."

He turned to Hoffman. "Hoffman, I don't know what your arrangements are with Mooser. But I know the law as it pertains to ships at sea. Unless you go to your cabin without delay, I will also bring charges of mutiny against you. Now, do you understand that?"

Hoffman looked down at his gun and then at Chetwood. His face was dead white—whether from anger or fear, Sutton could not determine. He licked his lips once or twice and then without speaking turned and descended the narrow steps of the companionway.

Chetwood turned to Captain Brown. "You have had your troubles, Captain—we all understand that. You have handled this ship in a way that seems to me thoroughly competent. I think Captain Sutton will agree with me on that. I'm sorry for this unnecessary disturbance, and we will take steps to see that it isn't repeated."

The Captain grumbled some kind of acknowledgment, and then stepped over and shoved his gun into the chart box. Sutton shook his head and sighed; then he said to Dr. Luce: "Let's go below and finish our game, Doctor. I don't feel like sleeping."

Dr. Luce grinned wryly and put his hand on Sutton's shoulder. "Damned if I would have walked between those two men."

Sutton shrugged. He still felt slightly weak from his experience, and even a bit dizzy as he and Chetwood followed Dr. Luce down to the main cabin. It seemed to him that the *Herman* was freighted with several kinds of human dynamite which might blow the expedition—and its human components—into fragments at any moment.

[4]

Sutton spent the night sleeplessly pondering the problems presented by the unusual character of Captain Brown and the intransigent attitude of Ogden Hoffman. He was not at all certain of Hoffman's motives, and he intended to take this up with Chetwood and Dr. Luce as soon as possible.

He came up on deck early, a bit tired and shaken by the night's happenings, hoping to be alone and able to think by himself; but Dr. Luce and Chetwood were already at the forward rail, both smoking their pipes, which gave off a strong, sweet fragrance. They nodded as Sutton joined them.

It was about five o'clock and the *Herman* had already worked off the windward beat and was now running a westerly course, heeled over on a port tack as she nosed through Kaiwi channel toward the southern tip of Oahu. The island loomed in the gathering light, a dark mound covered with masses of heavy clouds that showed rosy tints on the upper fringe from the first shafts of the sun. The sea was running in long, smooth swells in contrast to the black turbulence of the previous night.

Dr. Luce looked at Sutton's drawn face a moment, and said with a kindly smile, "You had more courage than I would have had, George—to step between those two fellows last night. They are both arrogant men."

The word "arrogant" struck Sutton as odd. He asked, "Where's Hoffman? Is he on deck?"

They looked around, but only members of the crew could be seen, with Captain Brown lumbering about on the afterdeck. Willie Peterson was at the wheel. Hoffman apparently had not come up, for which Sutton inwardly composed a word of thanks. He intended to bring the matter of Hoffman's actions and attitude to a head, but he wanted to talk it over with Chetwood and Dr. Luce before saying anything to Hoffman.

Chetwood, pursing his lips as he drew on his pipe, seemed to have read Sutton's thoughts. He nodded, and without looking at Sutton, remarked, "It isn't over yet, by a damn sight. I'm not sure we'll want to go on until this thing's settled, one way or another."

Dr. Luce grunted, and Sutton said, "We'll have a chance to get things squared away in Honolulu, won't we? I want to know where Hoffman stands." He looked at the doctor. "What did you mean, Doctor, by two arrogant men? I'd hardly call Captain Brown arrogant. He's responsible for this ship and I don't think I'd like to have some damned fool always interfering with the command of the ship."

Dr. Luce, puffing slowly on his pipe, nodded.

"Captain Brown is arrogant in a different way," he finally said. "He has lived a hard life and he's a hard man by nature—and by the kind of life he's led. He wants respect, which all older men want . . . for the things he's done. They may not be respectable to everyone, but they are to him. But Hoffman's arrogance is different. He wants to prove something about himself. He wants to demonstrate that he's superior to the Captain. In my judgment, this is a very dangerous kind of arrogance."

Chetwood nodded agreement. Sutton felt drawn to both these men. Dr. Luce was the oldest of the group—older than anyone aboard except the Captain. He had a kindly tolerance that Sutton realized would help to balance some of the differences between the members of the party. Chetwood was more volatile; and Sutton had already observed a certain possessive characteristic in the man, as if he wanted to hold not only the good will but the physical presence of those around him. Sutton had written in a letter to his wife: "John Chetwood is a lawyer, and strange to say, an old classmate of mine at St. Paul's when I was there, although I do not remember him very well, since he was in the upper class when I first went there. He has strange moods; at times he seems to want to dominate, and at other times he cannot do enough for me. We often go out on the deck at night and we may sit for a half hour without talking, but he seems annoyed if I get up to leave."

Chetwood suddenly remarked in a low voice, "I wish Hoffman would keep his damn mouth shut. We all know the Captain is inclined to be pompous. It's his nature. Why not let him?"

Dr. Luce laughed, his gray eyes twinkling. "That's what I decided—early in the game," he said. "But it won't do to overlook his arrogance, either. It can cause trouble."

"Have you talked with him this morning?" Sutton asked.

"Only to say 'Good morning.' He seemed quite cheerful when I came up with John a few minutes ago. Waved his hand and asked how we slept—almost as if he'd forgotten about that foresail gaff coming down!"

"He handled it well," Sutton said. "There was no trouble—until Hoffman butted in." Sutton realized that his dislike for the tall athletic "clubman," with his constant air of bored sophistication, was almost at the point of an obsession. This irritation was rendered more acute by his worry about what might happen if the Captain and Hoffman should meet again in a head-on collision of authority.

The *Herman* by this time was slanting northwestward on a broad reach, coming off the following wind; the breeze seemed to have veered around to the southwest. They were close enough to the shoreline to see a few scattered houses, apparently fishermen's homes, almost obscured in clusters of coconut palms and large spreading trees, some of them flowering in a blaze of red and purple. Directly off the beam was a long, loaflike promontory, stretching out into the sea, with shelves of black rock at its tip that looked like claws. The bursting of waves against these ragged outcroppings of land threw clouds of spray into the air, reminding Sutton somewhat of the rocky shores along the New England coast. However, the long, rolling swells of the Pacific and the deep blue of the water created a certain aura of perpetual calm that was unlike anything he had seen in the East. The constant battle between sea and land seemed to have settled down here in the Pacific to a more stable contest, unmarred by the irregular battering of waves against the rocks so characteristic of the Atlantic.

"It's like a new world, isn't it?" Chetwood remarked. Standing a head shorter than Sutton, he glanced up at him, his mouth bunched in its customary puckered smile. "By God, that's what we're coming into, George—a new world!"

Sutton thought, with a twinge of misgiving, that Chetwood was probably more nearly right than he imagined. They were sailing into a strange, new world—with some strange, new people to deal with! When he had made the decision to leave the comparatively sedentary life of the Chairman of the Board of Sewer Commissioners of New Rochelle, Sutton had hardly envisioned that he would find himself standing between two men, each with a pistol in his hand, in a wildly rocking ship far out at sea in the middle of the night—trying to stop them from shooting each other!

The ridges of Oahu were now clearly defined, sloping up from the westward and dropping sharply off to the east, so that they seemed to be sheer cliffs, hanging in folds like giant purple drapery.

"That's the rim of an ancient volcano, from what I'm told," Chetwood said, again seeming to read Sutton's thoughts. "What we see is the western rim of the crater, with most of the eastern half sunk into the ocean." He pointed to the north, where Diamond Head was visible from the rear, lying like a massive breastwork facing to the west.

The *Herman* was now running before a freshening offshore breeze, plowing swiftly up the coast, having rounded Koko Head and now slanting off toward the yellow promontory of Diamond Head. Sutton wondered idly whether those who feared the rise of the "Yellow Peril" might find comfort in the presence of this craggy crater, facing the yellow hordes some seven thousand miles distant—now that Hawaii was a territory of the United States. The islands, annexed by the American Congress only a half dozen years before, had already been referred to as America's "fortress in the Pacific."

The beauty of the island and the freshness of the wind already seemed to have erased recollections of the happenings of the night before. Sutton felt an increasing excitement as the magnificent panorama of Oahu unfolded, its sloping ridges now extending almost to the water's edge, coated with gray lantana and algarroba trees. The beach showed in a glistening white curve, like a collar along the land; and nearer to them was a rim of frothy surf, rolling over a reef perhaps a mile from shore, like a rugged necklace strung around the island. Along the beach slender coconut palms with feathery green tops could be seen clearly, leaning gracefully against the perpetual offshore breeze.

Captain Brown walked by, his baggy pants flapping in the wind, and stopped to tell them they would pick up the bell buoy off Diamond Head at about eight o'clock. By the time the *Herman* made the turn toward Diamond Head, the dark blue-green of the island had changed to more brilliant hues, with yellow scars plainly visible along the ridges, where heavy rains and avalanches had washed off the outer layer of earth and shrubs. The clouds had changed from deep purple to fleecy white and they seemed to have been pushed back to the east, exposing the sharp ridge of the mountains, towering several thousand feet into the air and running the length of the island, like the jagged backbone of an enormous prehistoric monster.

The schooner was under full canvas, with the triatic staysail rigged on the mainmast, staysail on the foremast and both jibs working. Sutton, looking aloft to observe the fill of the sails, thought it must be a wonderful sight to anyone on shore. He was greatly impressed by Chetwood's remark that it was "like a new world."

The Captain, looking robust and in good humor in spite of the fact that he had hardly three hours' rest during the night, finally came forward to join them, his eyes crinkling as he waved smilingly at the island.

"We've made it, Cap'n—and done well! Eighteen days at sea. A good run."

The turbulent events of the night before seemed to have vanished from the Captain's thoughts. Sutton, looking at him narrowly, wondered what strange mentality inhabited the old man's being. He seemed, for the moment, to have lost all the uncontrolled rage he had displayed the night before, even his air of pompousness. With a clap on the shoulder of each, he turned and shambled forward to see to the lines when the tug would take the little schooner in tow. Chetwood turned toward Sutton with a whimsical smile.

"You'd think it was all his island," he said. "Yet he's never been here before." His expression became serious. "George, this really is entering a new kind of world. In San Francisco we live closer to the Islands than you people in New York, and even though I've never been in Honolulu, I've met quite a few people from the Territory. The white people—haoles, they're called—are as proud of Hawaii as they are of being American. You won't find color lines as sharply drawn here as you have it back East. If I were an older man, I wouldn't mind staying here."

Sutton laughed. It struck him that the South Seas fever—the languor and *laissez faire* of the tropics—had already captured his friend.

"Better wait until we find the treasure," he said. "Then perhaps we can all come back."

The shore was now so close that the houses and trees that fringed Diamond Head could easily be seen. Chetwood, turning to catch the scented wind off the shore, stretched his neck and remarked as he sniffed at the breeze: "If we're lucky enough to get home, George. We're just starting."

This rather ominous forecast was punctuated by the arrival of the other two members of the treasure-hunting party, Ogden Hoffman and Frank Sharratt. The latter was much younger than the others, and even at this early age was inclined to weight. He had taken little part in the social life aboard the *Herman,* except to show up promptly at mealtimes; and Sutton had no real idea of what sort of man he was. His reason for being aboard seemed to be chiefly that he was familiar with mining and metallurgy, and was also a brother-in-law of Donzel Stoney. He had stopped to have breakfast before coming up on deck, and after a cursory glance at the shoreline, he went below again—possibly for an after-breakfast snack, Sutton thought. Hoffman stretched his long frame, leaned back and drew in several deep draughts of air, as if this were a morning ritual. Then he nodded in a friendly way to both Sutton and Chetwood, and took a place at the rail beside them. He, like Captain Brown, seemed to have forgotten the events of the night before.

"Fine town," Hoffman remarked, with a proprietary air, almost as if he were the host. "Excellent stock here—both whites and the Hawaiians. They intermarry, you know."

From his superior manner, he might have been discussing the inbreeding of cattle or sheep. Sutton, in order to show some semblance of courtesy, asked Hoffman if he had visited the islands before this trip.

"Why, of course!" He laughed in a way that annoyed Sutton. "I've made several trips—even before the annexation. We'll have some good times ashore. I've quite a few friends here—old families, you know."

The four stood at the rail while the *Herman* came smartly up to the buoy and shifted to a starboard tack. Ahead, perhaps three or four miles to the north, they could see the smokestacks which indicated the presence of the city; and south of the town they could clearly see a row of combers and a single white structure, apparently a hotel.

"Must be Waikiki beach," Chetwood remarked.

"Of course," Hoffman said. "That's the Moana Hotel you see on the beach. One of the finest hotels in the Pacific."

Hoffman's continued proprietary air gnawed on Sutton's nerves, but he restrained himself. The problem of reducing Hoffman's ego to something reasonably below his own concept of his importance was going to be difficult enough, without creating unnecessary friction.

Shortly before nine o'clock they approached the bar outside the harbor, and the little tug *Fearless* chugged around the southern end of the breakwater and met the schooner off the bar, putting a pilot aboard and taking the vessel in tow.

By this time the center of Honolulu was visible, a few tall stacks rising along the edge of the harbor and a few larger buildings standing out against the green background of the foothills. Aside from the square white block of the Moana Hotel, the single impediment to the natural beauty of the coastline, there seemed to be only sparsely inhabited areas between the beach and the cluster of buildings that formed downtown Honolulu.

As they cleared the breakwater and headed into the channel, Hoffman remarked sententiously, "The Paradise of the Pacific!"

Chetwood glanced at Sutton and grinned. Looking up at the hills, with the rising tiers of beautiful homes scattered along the lower levels, surrounded by huge trees and stately royal palms, Sutton could not help thinking that while it might be paradise for some, it could easily prove to be hell for the small group of adventurous men on the *Herman*. He knew they had reached a point where matters must be settled with Hoffman—and the Captain—before they cleared the port of Honolulu for the South Sea Islands.

Honolulu: Problems in Paradise

[1]

Chetwood's "new world" began to unfold before Sutton's eyes with startling swiftness, as the *Herman* slowly passed the breakwater and entered the harbor, trailing behind the *Fearless*. Honolulu, at the turn of the century, was a place of strange contrasts: a full-grown, if rather small, city, against a background of tropical extravagance of nature. It was a small replica of San Francisco, spawned in the brawling days of sailing ships and whalers; but it was the tropical character of the place that intrigued Sutton.

The waterfront was plainly visible from the rail of the schooner—a mixture of ship's chandleries, small stores and mills spread along a wide muddy road behind the wharves. Two larger structures—Lucas' Mill and Hopper's Cooperage Shop—loomed clearly above the smaller Chinese stores and shops. Tall-masted ships were moored at the back of the harbor, alongside freighters. A single passenger steamer—the *Sierra,* which was to become quite familiar to Sutton in the months ahead—was nestled at the main wharf.

Behind the lower city were signs of Honolulu's new mercantile affluence, which had arrived with the advent of missionaries and the discovery that sugar could be grown profitably in the Islands. Palatial homes, surrounded by luxurious gardens, could be seen in the lower foothills.

To Sutton, this spectacle had the elements of romance and mystery. As he stood with Chetwood and the doctor at the afterdeck rail, he could literally smell the city. At first it was the fragrance of flowers, wafted down from the hills; then, as they neared Fishmarket Wharf, where the *Herman* was to be tied up, he began to smell the more pungent fragrance of Oriental markets, musty odors of strange vegetables and spices, and the more familiar aroma of the fish market, which sprawled just beyond the wharf.

Sutton had expected to go ashore as soon as the *Herman* docked, but he realized that this was a short-lived hope. Captain Brown, striding from one end of the ship to the other, bawling orders and cursing the sailors at the slightest provocation, came aft and announced that they would meet on the afterdeck, where the awning had been spread, as soon as the schooner was made fast. Sutton wondered whether he was going to give them instructions as to their behavior ashore; and Chetwood, glancing at Sutton with a wry grin, must have had the same thought.

The Captain meanwhile had taken a position midships, standing by the launch, and was bellowing orders in stentorian tones—even though Mr. Hendrickson and Willie Benton, assisted by the longshoremen on the dock, seemed quite capable of handling the rather simple procedure of throwing lines and making them fast to the Samson post and bits. Captain Brown wore his full panoply of command—nautical hat and tightly buttoned dark jacket, in considerable contrast to the naked torsos of the men working on the dock.

After tying up, the Captain mustered all hands aft and in a voice that could be heard the length of the wharf he assigned two men—Willie Benton and Pete—to remain aboard while the rest would have liberty until six bells, which would be at eleven o'clock.

The crew would lay to until five o'clock with a full watch, to clean the decks and leave everything shipshape; and after that they would have shore leave except for a standing watch consisting of the Captain and Willie Peterson.

A small crowd had gathered on the wharf. Sutton observed that all were dark-skinned or deeply tanned—small, round faces that looked up with friendly, shining eyes. A few waved and shouted unintelligible greetings. Most of those on the wharf wore only shirts and trousers. A few were barefoot, and two or three white duck coats were in evidence. Sutton noticed that the only dark coat worn by anyone in the area was Captain Brown's.

A man wearing a white Panama hat with a brilliantly colored feather band approached the edge of the dock and called out: "United States inspector. May I come aboard?"

Mr. Hendrickson was ordering the gangway maneuvered into position when Captain Brown stepped forward.

"I'm Captain Brown, master and owner!" he shouted. "What is it you want?"

"United States Immigration Service," the man repeated. "May I come aboard?"

By this time most of the crowd on the wharf was clustered around the foot of the gangway. The pilot, a short, swarthy man—apparently Hawaiian—walked down the gangway waving a greeting to the Immigration inspector as he stepped on the dock. The man in the white hat approached across the gangway and stepped down on the deck of the *Herman.*

"What port are you from—and what's your destination?" the man asked.

"San Francisco—bound for Sydney, Australia," Captain Brown replied.

"Any Chinese in the crew?" The Captain shook his head.

Sutton was surprised, and glanced involuntarily at Hoffman, who had been standing back under the awning. He had the impression that a look of surprise and some displeasure crossed Hoffman's face, replacing momentarily his customary expression of bored disdain, at the mention of Sydney, Australia.

After the official amenities had been completed, the Immigration man left. Sutton noticed that he stopped to ask something as he passed Hoffman, and handed him an envelope. As soon as the members of the expeditionary party gathered under the awning, Hoffman burst out: "Why in hell did you say Sydney, Captain? We're not bound for Sydney!"

The Captain looked at Hoffman deliberately, before replying. Then he said abruptly, "It's always customary to name the farthest port, Mr. Hoffman. Possibly you did not know that since you are not familiar with the sea." He paused to let this comment sink in. Then he said in a growling voice, "As master, I will determine the sailing routes. We sail from here to Tahiti—that is, Papeete; or to Apia, Samoa. It will depend on the weather."

Hoffman's face seemed to harden, and Sutton stepped closer so that he could place himself between the two men if necessary.

"Let's not get into a discussion of this now—there are people within earshot, and there is no reason to explain our purpose to anyone," he said, trying to keep his voice under control. His anger at Hoffman, which had been simmering since the events of the night before, was at the point of explosion and he was not sure how well he could control himself.

"Captain Brown's procedure is entirely normal," Sutton went on, looking at Chetwood and Dr. Luce. "The farthest port should be designated as our destination. We can put into port anywhere we wish en route."

Hoffman seemed to have subsided on that point; but then he raised another question. "I'd like to know why in hell you said you were the owner, Captain?"

"This vessel is chartered under my name—as master and owner," the Captain said, his pale eyes now conveying the warning of erupting anger, which Sutton had learned to recognize.

Chetwood broke in, his voice quite mild. "Captain Brown is correct about that, Ogden. The agreement of the committee with Louis Mooser specifies that Captain Brown will act as master and owner during the voyage. This was to avoid any complication in a foreign port if ownership should become a factor. After we return to San Francisco, the vessel reverts to Mooser, of course—that is, unless we have to sell it."

For a moment Hoffman was silent. It was evident to Sutton he had not read the details of the agreement. Finally he shrugged and said, "My job is to see that the ship gets back safely—and that's what I aim to do."

Captain Brown considered this remark for a moment; and then he said, "My purpose in calling this meeting is to explain what I have decided to do in the event I am disabled. I have made arrangements so that the expedition can continue." He drew himself up, unable apparently to restrain his compulsion for a certain kind of dramatic pomposity. "I have prepared an envelope which I will deliver to Cap'n Sutton, to be held by him until it is necessary to open it. It will have instructions and information as to the location of the island." He looked directly at Hoffman, and Sutton had the horrid notion that the Captain might be preparing deliberately for a fatal showdown with the tall San Franciscan. However, Captain Brown continued: "I've had more attacks of the fevers—as you know. In San Francisco and on the voyage." This was largely an overstatement, as Sutton knew from remarks Dr. Luce had made. The Captain's moments of despondency often seemed to be interpreted by him as "the fevers."

The Captain's statement came as a surprise to Sutton. He had been mulling over the possibility that the Captain might be put out of commission, in some way or another; and since he was the one indispensable member in the expedition, Sutton had intended to present this problem to the Captain and suggest that he provide some kind of alternative plan. The increasing hostility between the Captain and Ogden Hoffman had made some solution practically imperative. Without Captain Brown there would be no point in continuing the voyage.

At that moment Sutton happened to glance at Hoffman, and it seemed to him an expression of naked hatred flashed for an instant in Hoffman's eyes. Sutton did not have time to consider this at the moment; in the activity and excitement of their arrival he forgot the incident, or perhaps attached no real importance to it. He was not even sure whether Hoffman's glance was directed at Captain Brown or himself.

"We must remain in Honolulu at least a week for repairs," the Captain went on briskly. "We need a new yoke for the foresail gaff. The sails are not damaged, but we will need a spare jib and that must be fitted. The vessel also makes too much leeway and will require about six tons of ballast.

Hoffman, with expansive cordiality in curious contrast to his earlier behavior, interrupted to say, "I'm authorized to dispense sufficient funds for everything we need. Don Stoney arranged that with the committee. You can draw on me for everything you need, Captain Brown. I am holding five hundred dollars in cash for necessary repairs, and I have a thousand-dollar letter of credit."

Sutton wondered whether this showing of accommodation was designed to ameliorate Hoffman's feud with the Captain or was simply another of Hoffman's gambits designed to achieve personal importance. He said in a low voice to Chetwood, "Why don't you and the doctor and I go uptown together—if you have no other plans? I'd like to talk with both of you about all this."

Chetwood nodded and a few seconds later Dr. Luce glanced at Sutton and he also nodded. To Sutton's way of thinking, matters had come to such a head that some definite plan must be devised for containing some of the conflicting attitudes and personalities aboard the *Herman,* or they might as well turn back to San Francisco.

Hoffman had meanwhile pulled from his pocket the envelope which Sutton had seen the customs man pass to him.

"I've a note from a very good friend of mine—Angus MacGregor. He's quite influential. He'd like to arrange a party—reception, you know—" He glanced at them as if to assure himself that they understood the significance of the word "reception," and then went on. "He'll arrange it at our convenience." Hoffman looked deliberately at Sutton. "What do you say, Captain Sutton?"

Sutton looked over at Captain Brown, who had stepped away and was supervising the laying of lines on the afterdeck.

"Of course—if it is satisfactory with Captain Brown. I assume he will accept for us all."

Captain Brown heard this. He came back, drew himself up, and seemed to consider the matter gravely for a moment. Then he nodded.

"I think so." He paused. "I am also considering holding a reception aboard the *Herman*—for some of the government people, you know."

Captain Brown then launched into a small speech, in which he set forth certain "rules" for going ashore. He even cautioned them about associating with people who might be of questionable moral character, particularly "women of the port." Sutton was not certain who the "women of the port" might be, but he supposed from what he saw of Captain Brown's affiliations in San Francisco—with Mrs. Samson, the "friend of his wife" for example—that he must know something about them.

Hoffman and Sharratt were first to leave the vessel, taking small bags with them. Both apparently had made plans to stay with friends or relatives in Honolulu. Sutton, Chetwood and Dr. Luce left soon afterward, the Captain having decided to remain aboard to "tighten things up." A crew of hack-callers shouted out their offers of transportation services —which, in each case, consisted of a single-seat carriage with a doleful-looking horse standing drowsily in the traces; but the three voyagers decided the walk uptown would do them good.

Fort Street in that day extended from the docks to the upper limits of the city proper—a distance of about six blocks—and was a fairly wide road, covered with packed coral surfacing from which the frequent rains readily drained off. A single-track trolley ran down to the dock, where the big Matson and Oceanic steamers came in. Beyond the end of Fort Street the sloping foothills of Pacific Heights could be seen from Fish-market Wharf. A few large homes were visible along the winding road that traced a zigzag course up the heights. This was the residential area of the Scottish merchants and American planters who, a scant dozen years before, had financed and carried out the Hawaiian "revolution," overthrowing Queen Liliuokalani.

To the north and south of Fort Street the "business district" spread, with the better-looking buildings to the south. The rambling frame structure of the old Royal Hawaiian Hotel faced an area of government buildings where Iolani Palace, home of Hawaii's deposed royalty, stood with its imposing façade of balconies and tall spires. To the north the streets became narrow and crooked, spreading out toward Honolulu's notorious red-light district, which had been a haven for sailors long before the coming of the missionaries in the early part of the nineteenth century. This was known as "Iwilei," a low-lying area sinking away into swamps and rice paddies; and it already bore a startling resemblance to the slums of some of the more civilized cities of the world.

Sutton, Chetwood and the doctor were directed to the post office, a two-story frame building about three blocks from the wharf. They proceeded up Fort Street at a leisurely pace, fascinated by the strange kaleidoscope of colors and scenes—the faces of the people with their many racial origins; the garments they wore; and perhaps above all, the abundance of flowers. Everyone seemed to wear flowers, strung around their necks, tucked over ears, or coiled around hats. The three were easily identified as *malihinis*—newcomers—and everyone stared at them. Yet Sutton was aware of a friendliness and eager curiosity that seemed to radiate from the faces of those who passed them on the street. Many nodded a cheerful greeting—*Pehea oe,* meaning "How are you?" The atmosphere of the place was one of warmth and a natural and graceful hospitality which was strange to anyone coming from the States.

Sutton had only a short time in which to absorb these pleasant impressions, however. At the post office they found mail awaiting them. The first letter Sutton opened was from Donzel Stoney and it contained some rather astonishing information. After briefly telling of the drive out to the Cliff House, in San Francisco, to watch the *Herman* drop its tow and break out sails, Stoney's letter went on:

> I thought as we turned for home yesterday that the annoyance and trouble I had was a thing of the past, but today (the day after the *Herman* sailed from San Francisco) I learned some things that made me madder and sicker than anything I had known while you were here. Louis Mooser was in today, and after congratulating ourselves on the successful start, we began recalling a few things . . .

The letter, in a restrained way—probably, Sutton thought, to avoid a direct accusation against any member of the party—detailed the circumstances under which the *Herman* had been chartered, and the basis of the suspicion previously expressed that a "commission" had been paid for the arrangement of the original sale of the vessel to Louis Mooser.

> I thought Mooser was inquiring about the purchase, to assure himself that the money had been paid, but it seems that he had been told by one who knew that a commission had also been paid to the person who arranged the sale. At first he suspected me, but fortunately he was not satisfied that such was the case and asked his informant, who told him it was not I. There is no question but that a commission was paid, and the only question is: to whom? I believe I know, and if my suspicion is right, the end is not yet . . .

The letter went on to explain that Captain Brown had known of this, and at first had suspected Fred Green, "but Green is not the man, which I am glad to know." Stoney added significantly: "There is actually only one person who could have been involved."

> I wish the Captain to know what my feelings are in the matter, since I have found out these things and knew that the Captain had heard of this when he was here. I cannot blame him for thinking we were a lot of grafters from start to finish. It explains many things that happened here which I could not understand. I thought I was dealing with gentlemen. Please show this to the Captain so that any impressions he may have will be removed.

Sutton passed the letter to Chetwood and Dr. Luce, and when they had completed reading it, he said: "I think you know the only person, besides Stoney, who was involved. This may explain the animosity between the Captain and Ogden, don't you think?"

Chetwood sighed and nodded.

"It explains a hell of a lot of things. Hoffman—as you all know—was appointed by the committee as custodian of funds. They will naturally expect an accounting, and this is a joint responsibility of all of us. I'm not just sure how to handle it. We've really nothing to go on now, and I don't like to promote trouble."

The three men stood for some time on the steps of the long veranda, which covered two sides of the post office building. Overhead the sky was clear and blue; this was August and the "dog days," but the midday heat was cooled by the constant trade winds which blew down from the Koolau peaks sending random clouds across the sky and now and then dampening the streets with a quick burst of rain which was known as "liquid sunshine."

Sutton finally struck his fist against the palm of his hand.

"I know what I'm going to do," he said. "This thing has got to be straightened out before we sail out of here—and I mean to have it out with Hoffman. I don't intend to accuse him of anything, because we have nothing really to go on. But his presence and attitude toward Captain Brown is creating an impossible situation. It's got to be stopped."

He looked at Chetwood and the doctor. It occurred to Sutton that perhaps he was the only one of the three who recognized the gravity of the situation created by Hoffman. Dr. Luce had nodded gravely, but Sutton had a feeling that he would not be inclined to make a real issue if it could be avoided. Chetwood, on the other hand, was a lawyer, and he must be aware of the predicament in which Hoffman's conduct and attitude toward Captain Brown was placing them. But Chetwood was also cautious. Sutton went on: "Look at it this way. Hoffman has put nothing into this venture, and yet he is risking the whole thing by his belligerent attitude toward Captain Brown. I'm not certain about the Captain's reasons for providing me with information about the island . . . but he hasn't provided it yet, and he may not. Until he does, we'll know nothing. Even then, it will be only for use in case of emergency—and I don't think any of us want the Captain lost to this expedition. As matters stand, Hoffman must accept certain conditions, including the Captain's temperament."

Dr. Luce's kindly face was creased into a deep frown. Chetwood seemed less perturbed, yet Sutton felt he understood the situation perhaps more accurately than the doctor.

"What do you suggest, George?" the doctor finally asked.

"That we agree among the three of us to put this squarely up to Hoffman. Either he drops this constant harassment of the Captain, or he gets off the ship."

"What about the funds? And Louis Mooser? Hoffman represents him, you know."

"Hoffman has funds to pay for repairs in Honolulu. He said so. We'll put it up to him to get squared away, or leave him here and write Stoney to have additional funds forwarded to Papeete—or Apia. Wherever we make our next port. Either that, or the three of us return to San Francisco and get this thing straightened out! All of us would have to go to convince them."

The trio plodded along the streets, wandering through the lower section of town, discussing the matter for perhaps an hour. Finally both Chetwood and the doctor agreed to Sutton's plan. By the time they returned to the *Herman,* Captain Brown had gone ashore. Willie Benton, the second mate, greeted them with the news that the Japanese cook and two sailors—Johnson and "John Smith"—had also gone ashore, and taken their duffel bags with them.

"Deserted, you mean?" Sutton asked.

Benton nodded. "This is a bloody good port to desert in. They figure they've worked their way down here and the pay they don't get ain't enough to hold 'em. Bloody rats, that's w'at they are—but there's nothin' any bloomin' skipper can do that'll hold 'em, except lay 'em out with a marlin spike an' see they can't go ashore." He grinned, exposing a row of rotten teeth, and walked forward to attend to some of the deck gear and check the mooring lines.

Dr. Luce had gone below to his cabin, and a few minutes later he returned and signaled for the other two to join him below. "You recall that small can of strychnine we found in the medical supplies?" he asked Sutton. The latter nodded. "It was locked up in the medicine cabinet, as we agreed. As far as I know only the Captain and I have keys. Last night I checked the medical supplies to see what we need to get here in Honolulu. Quinine for the Captain's malaria and such. Well—" He shrugged. "About half the can of strychnine is missing."

Chetwood drew in a quick breath. "Are you serious, George?"

The doctor nodded. "I checked the supplies very carefully—particularly that can of strychnine. I intended to get rid of it here—we don't need the stuff aboard, actually. Now I can't really say what to do about it."

"Have you mentioned this to Captain Brown?" Sutton asked.

"I asked him this morning if he had opened the medicine cabinet for any reason. He said he hadn't, but he sent the Jap cook to get some pills —for his 'fevers.' I just checked again when I heard the cook had gone, and half of it is missing. I don't like this, gentlemen! First it's the matter of the gun in the chart box—and now some poison has been taken. By God, I don't like it! If we start out this way, what's going to happen when we get down in the South Sea Islands?"

"We're certainly getting off in fine shape," Sutton remarked, pacing up and down the doctor's cabin. At that moment there was a sound of footfalls on the deck above. Sutton looked out and saw Hoffman coming down the companionway.

"Glad to find you fellows," he exclaimed, heartily. "Angus is quite anxious to have that party. Told him we'd only be here about a week and he'd like to set it for Thursday night. That would be a day or so before we leave. How's that with you?"

Sutton looked at Hoffman. He would have liked to dispose of both the party and Hoffman without further delay—right there in the cabin; but to refuse the invitation would probably be rather churlish and would lead to an argument. Besides, a party might be something of a relief from shipboard life and the complications of conflicting personalities. So Sutton nodded. "If it's all right with George and John—and the Captain."

"You'll meet some fine people," Hoffman continued. "Fine people!" He had the air of a Chamber of Commerce spokesman extolling the virtues of the city.

"Have you mentioned this to the Captain, Ogden?" Dr. Luce asked.

Hoffman shook his head.

"Haven't seen him. He isn't aboard. I hadn't planned to ask him—he's not exactly the type for this crowd. Something of a boor, you know . . . But I suppose we'll have to ask him."

Chetwood glanced at Sutton, his mouth puckered in a slight grin. "I should think it would be appropriate, Ogden—after all, he is the Captain, you know. It would be practically an insult not to ask him, and I don't think I'm in favor of insulting Captain Brown at this stage of the game."

Hoffman pursed his lips, as if in deep thought, and nodded.

"Probably not . . . Look here, that brings up something I want to talk to you fellows about." He paused, as if to choose his words. "He's such a confounded ruffianly sort," he went on. "Crude as all hell. But I suppose we'll have to stand it. I'll brief Angus in advance on what to expect. There'll be ladies, of course, and I'm not sure . . . but as you say, we'll have to make the best of it."

"I didn't say that," Chetwood said, dryly, but emphatically. "I said we certainly don't want to offend the Captain—particularly when we're just starting out."

Dr. Luce coughed slightly. "Look here, Ogden—we've all agreed the Captain is a bit pompous at times, and perhaps a bit arrogant. That's his nature. We've all agreed to make the best of it—"

"That's exactly what I said," Hoffman interrupted; but the doctor went on:

"Yes—but I think it requires more than just saying it, Ogden. We've all suffered from his temper and arrogance—I perhaps more than the rest of you. I don't exactly like being dressed down for showing up late for lunch. But this sort of thing last night—we can't afford to have these things happen, Ogden! Without Captain Brown there isn't any expedition. We simply go home."

Hoffman, draped casually against the end of the bed, bit his lips and then smacked them. "That's just the point I want to talk to you fellows about. I'm right with you as far as catering to the old fool is concerned. But do we have to?" He looked directly at Sutton. "The Captain mentioned he was turning over some dope to you—about the location of the island, I suppose. He seemed to be confiding in you, Sutton—putting it on paper. This would appear to be a matter for all of us. After all, if he gives us the information—we don't really need the Captain, do we?"

Hoffman laughed shortly, drawing his lips back and exposing his teeth in a way that infuriated Sutton. He looked steadily at Hoffman for several seconds before saying anything. Then he ran his finger through his collar, to loosen it. Sutton was fairly tall, as tall as Hoffman; and he was somewhat heavier.

Chetwood reached out and put his hand on Sutton's knee, as if to restrain him. Sutton leaned forward sitting on the edge of Dr. Luce's bed. His mouth was set in a straight line and his eyes were hard and bright.

"I'm not sure I understand your suggestion, Hoffman—but if it is what I think it is, I'm sorry you made it," he said, spacing each word carefully. "Whatever information Captain Brown gives me in confidence will be kept in confidence. He hasn't given me anything yet, and perhaps he won't. But you can be sure the envelope won't be opened until an emergency requires it. Do you understand that, Hoffman?"

It was not often that Sutton let his temper boil to the surface; and he knew that on the few occasions when this had happened, he usually regretted it. He had a feeling this was going to be one of those times. For an instant, he had an almost irresistible urge to smash his fist in Hoffman's face.

Hoffman, who seemed singularly impervious to what might have been passing through Sutton's mind, laughed again. It was hardly a laugh—just an exhalation of air. His angular features were entirely relaxed. However, he shifted his balance forward slightly, his weight resting on his feet rather than on the bed.

Chetwood, acutely conscious of Sutton's rising anger, broke in calmly. "George is certainly right, Ogden. If Captain Brown is willing to provide us with an alternative—in case of an emergency—and puts information into George's keeping, this confidence must be respected. I, for one, would not want this matter brought up again."

Hoffman lifted his shoulders slightly. "Just a thought," he said. "Well"—he arose from his leaning position, as if nothing much had been said—"Thursday night will be okay for the party then—if the Captain is agreeable? We'll have a wonderful time." He nodded to

CAPTAIN BROWN IS VERY INDIGNANT

Evening Bulletin Aug 29 1902

Captain James Brown of the schooner Herman, about whose treasure hunting plans there has been so much talk lately, is very indignant over the statement of the morning paper that citizens of this town put up the money with which he paid the claim of the Wilder Steamship Company yesterday.

"I want to say," said Captain Brown this morning, "that there is not a word of truth in the statement that I got money from people here. I do not have to borrow money from any one. I myself wanted to fight the Wilder company but as my friends advised me to settle the matter out of court, I paid the bill yesterday. I haven't tried to interest anyone here in treasure hunting plans."

Captain Brown further stated that he intended to leave this port as soon as his mail from home should reach him. As near as he can calculate, his letters will reach San Francisco August 28 and he will expect them on the first steamer leaving San Francisco after that date.

AROUND THE WORLD

SCHOONER HERMAN WILL MAKE INTERESTING TRIP

SMART LITTLE VESSEL WILL VISIT TAHITI, AUSTRALIA, MANILA, SAMAR, INDIA AND MANY OTHER PLACES.

When the spick and span little schooner Herman made her appearance in the port this forenoon but few of the waterfronters knew who she was and what she came for. The Herman is a trim little schooner of 100 tons register. On her fore she flies the pennant of the Providence Yacht Club of which her master and owner, Captain James Brown is a prominent member, while the Stars and Stripes are flying from the main.

The Herman is at present on a voyage around the world. Her owner, Captain Brown, is a veteran mariner. Some time ago he met with quite a serious accident, which impaired his health to such an extent that he decided to take a small jaunt around the world to see if a sniff of salt air would give him back his health. Accordingly Captain Brown with a friend, George W. Sutton, left New York for San Francisco where Captain Brown purchased the two-masted schooner Her- ... which he is now the sole own-

THE SKIPPER OF THE TREASURE SCHOONER—Thanks, kind lady.

In Honolulu the secret of the trip was kept—at least for a while. The article at the upper right appeared in the Honolulu *Evening Bulletin* on August 8, 1902. The story at the upper left is a later one from the same paper. The satirical cartoon at the left, which roused the ire of Captain Brown, appeared in the *Commercial Advertiser* of Honolulu on August 29, 1902.

the others and started for the door. "I'll have particulars for all of you—how to get there," he called over his shoulder. "See you later, fellows."

Sutton's face was white. He looked first at Chetwood and then at the doctor. "I think I'll kill that son of a bitch before this trip is over," he said.

[2]

The work on the *Herman* progressed rapidly during the next three days, and Captain Brown announced with some pride that "if all goes well" they would be under sail on Sunday. This, as things turned out, proved to be an ambitious estimate.

Meanwhile Sutton composed a letter to Donzel Stoney, to be posted for the next steamer to San Francisco. After consulting with Chetwood and Dr. Luce, he wrote:

> Things have reached a state aboard ship that requires a definite commitment by you or the Committee as to Ogden Hoffman's status on the expedition. As you know, he has not put anything of his own into the venture. He claims to represent Louis Mooser and has a letter to that effect. The result has been a direct clash of authority between Hoffman and the Captain, which, as you will readily understand, cannot continue if the venture is to succeed.
>
> Unless we can establish a basis for the unhampered exercise of the Captain's command, Chetwood and I would have to prefer charges against Hoffman and have him removed from the ship. This will be disturbing to the members of the Committee, and probably to Louis Mooser. Therefore, as an alternative, in lieu of all other efforts to avoid unnecessary friction, the doctor, John and I will return to San Francisco by steamer and present these matters to you and the Committee.
>
> I do not know why we were not advised more fully on the matter of Hoffman's status before we left, but that is now water under the bridge. Believe me, this is not a reflection on your conduct of these arrangements, but is something that has arisen by virtue of the conflicting personalities of some of those aboard ship. We three are agreed firmly on this course; and I would call to your notice your own statements in your letter of July 21st.
>
> If John and the doctor and I return to San Francisco, we will arrange to intercept the *Herman* at Apia, in British Samoa, rather than Tahiti, since Apia is on the regular run of the Oceanic Steamship line. I do not believe there will be imminent danger of serious trouble for the

present, providing Hoffman does not press the Captain too far. We hope to reduce that tension by a direct appeal to Hoffman. However, this is a risk that must be taken.

Sutton purposely avoided any reference to the near-shooting affair on the *Herman* just before the arrival in Honolulu. Chetwood had pointed out that this would create a legal as well as a disciplinary problem. He and Sutton had examined the ship's log and found no reference to the matter in the journal, and assumed Captain Brown did not intend to press charges.

"We ought to wait until after Mr. MacGregor's party," Dr. Luce pointed out, "before we talk with Ogden. In that way there may be a better feeling between all of us . . . that is, we may be able to get Ogden to understand the whole position."

Sutton was of the opinion that it would be impossible to get Hoffman to understand anything he did not want to understand; but he agreed to let the matter rest until Friday before sailing.

The party—or "reception"—as it turned out, was all Hoffman had said it would be—"a wonderful time." Although Honolulu's social life was under the general influence of "missionary families," it was also a place of lively moods and warm hospitality, and the MacGregor home on Pacific Heights was no exception.

Captain Brown had given a rather regal assent to the more formal invitation, transmitted by Sutton and the doctor; and he showed up in full regalia, with nautical cap and blue jacket, in striking contrast to all the other male guests, who wore white linen suits. The Captain established himself in a large chair in the corner of a spacious room, filled with red koa furniture and numerous ferns and other plants. The veranda, leading from the main room and covering three sides of the house, had the appearance of a greenhouse with baskets of hanging plants, including many varieties of orchids suspended from the eaves.

Sutton had gone out on the veranda and then walked down to the terrace overlooking the city. The air was cooler and the fragrance of flowers and delicate perfumes was not as heavy in the night air. Behind him, drifting in tinkling waves of sound, came the soft strains of Hawaiian music—the ukulele and steel guitar. Below lay the "downtown" part of Honolulu, glittering with gaslit stores and streets, and the soft glow of harbor lights in the background. Around and behind the MacGregor home were other equally spacious residences that seemed to increase in splendor, as a measure of affluence, the higher they rose on the slope. The abundance of flowering plants and trees was intoxicating, with their many exotic colors and shapes. Below Pacific Heights, to the north, lay Nuuanu Valley, where the kings and queens of Hawaii had lived in stone mansions, surrounded in some cases by yellow coral walls.

Sitting on a stone bench, with the muted sounds of music drifting from the open windows behind him, Sutton found himself wondering why anyone would leave such a place. New Rochelle and his family, which he had temporarily deserted for this strange voyage into the South Seas, quite suddenly became a distant memory, half forgotten in the beauty of a new and exciting tropical paradise. Even the trade winds blew away from the land where his home had been and he wondered musingly whether they ever blew anyone back home again.

"You are the *malihini* Captain?"

The soft voice behind him was so musical he did not at first recognize that someone was talking to him. Then he jumped to his feet.

A fairly tall woman, wearing a long, flowing dress gathered at the neck in a ruffle made fashionable by the missionaries and their religious concept of feminine decor, was standing near, smiling at him. At first glance, in the semidarkness, Sutton was unable to determine whether she was a young woman or more matronly; but even in the dim light he knew she was strikingly beautiful, in a way that seemed entirely new to him. Her hair and eyes were dark. Her features were small and regular and seemed to be chiseled out of old ivory. While her skin was darker than most women Sutton had known, her face had a natural glow, a translucent coloring that seemed to shine from her cheeks as she turned toward him, her features partly revealed in the light from the veranda. She was smiling, exposing white, even teeth; and Sutton, standing awkwardly, said nothing in response to her greeting.

The woman laughed with a soft, tinkling sound. "I am Mrs. Davis," she said. "Mapuana Davis. You are Captain Sutton?"

"Good heavens!" Sutton finally exclaimed. "I'm sorry." He felt his face suffused in a flush at his own rudeness.

"You are Captain Sutton, aren't you?" She spoke in a low, melodic voice, with what seemed to be a trace of accent, although Sutton could not immediately identify it. Perhaps it was French, he thought; but the woman—Mapuana Davis—decidedly was not French.

"Yes—and I really am sorry." He took her hand and shook it rather awkwardly. "I was admiring all this beauty—" He waved toward the lights below. "Suddenly when you spoke—your appearance seemed a part of it."

Sutton had not meant to say anything so extravagant; but the woman's rippling laugh, like the sound of tiny bells in the wind, made him aware that she enjoyed the extravagance.

"Your surprise is quite charming," she said. "I am sorry—I must have disturbed you. I am sort of half-hostess—Mrs. MacGregor's sister. I was not here when you arrived and that is why I took the liberty of introducing myself. May I sit down?"

Sutton racked his mind for some recollection of what Mrs. MacGregor looked like. She had not seemed to be Polynesian when he was introduced to her, although she was rather dark; but this woman evidently was Polynesian—in a very exotic way. Mrs. Davis laughed again, and Sutton found himself wondering what he might say to keep her laughing—it was such a delightfully musical sound.

"You are puzzled," she said. "Because my sister and I do not look alike. Well, we are what we call *calabash* sisters. That means we have different fathers, but the same mother. My sister's father was a Scotsman, and mine was Samoan—which accounts for our being sisters, and I Samoan."

Sutton nodded. He assumed this *calabash* relationship was something peculiar to the Polynesian people; and furthermore, he was so enthralled at the sound of her voice that he did not pay particular attention to what she was saying. Mapuana Davis had seated herself on the stone bench and motioned for Sutton to sit beside her.

"You are going on a great adventure into the islands, I understand. That is where I lived as a little girl—and since your great Captain Brown is telling everyone inside the house everything he knows about the Islands, I thought perhaps I should come out here and tell you something, too."

Sutton felt an inward twinge of embarrassment; the old Captain was undoubtedly in form—talking about himself!

"He does get carried away by himself," he observed.

She nodded.

"But not in a bad way. Not like your Mr. Hoffman." Sutton was aware of a sharper note in her voice and he looked at her in surprise. "He is a friend of Angus—my sister's husband—of course. Perhaps I should say nothing about him that is unkind, but I really do not like him."

She had inclined her head toward Sutton and her voice was low and confidential. The scent of her hair, only inches from his nose, almost caused Sutton to sniff, an act which he instinctively felt would have compounded his rudeness.

"Your old Captain loves to talk about himself. . . . But of course, he has done many things. Some of the things have been terrible. . . . We know a great deal about such men down in the Islands, because they are the first *haoles* who came to the place where my people lived." Sutton observed that she seemed to choose her words carefully. "I think I may know something about your old Captain—or rather my *tutu* did, long before I was born."

"Tutu?"

"That means 'grandmother' in the Samoan language."

Sutton's interest had quickened. "You mean your grandmother knew of Captain Brown—in the Islands?"

"I think so." She nodded. "One cannot be sure, of course . . . it was such a long time ago. My *tutu* came from a group of islands called Paumotu." Sutton almost started, because he knew quite well where the Paumotu Islands were; they were at the northern end of the string of islands called the Low Archipelago . . . and this was the area where it seemed, from Sutton's study of the maps, that the "church treasure" of Peru had been taken in the *Sea Foam* and buried!

"You are a princess, Mrs. Davis?"

"Yes . . . that is, my father was a chief. We do not talk much about our fathers' titles in the Islands, but they mean a great deal to us. The old high priests were very great men . . . but now we are all Christians, and we have forgotten the things they did."

"Why are you telling me this, Mrs. Davis?" Sutton suddenly asked. She smiled, and looked at him.

"Perhaps it is not important. . . . But my people are different from yours—that is, the people you have known." Again she seemed to choose her words carefully, to avoid being misunderstood, or offending Sutton. He was beginning to understand the characteristic gentleness and kindness of these people.

"You do not believe in many of the things we do—even though we are now Christians. We still believe in the old ways, which you cannot know about. When the great lava flow from Mauna Loa was coming down toward the village of Hilo many years ago, the queen of Hawaii —even though she had become a Christian—still firmly believed in Pele, the goddess of the volcano; and she built a little *heiau*—a church— just above Hilo and the two streams of lava separated there, and the village was not burned. You can see the place today—at Olaa—where the streams parted. This does not mean anything to you, but it does to us."

Sutton was not sure what it did mean to him. Sitting on the terrace, with the sounds of music coming through the window, he began to wonder if he was really here—in person—at the beginning of the twentieth century. It seemed there were a lot of things about Chetwood's "new world" that he was only beginning to understand.

"These forces are quite real and strong to our people," Mapuana Davis continued. "They are stronger than those of us who are living . . . but not as strong as the spirits of the *haoles* who came here. We know that."

Sutton had an uncanny feeling that he was being confronted with something that bore a vague resemblance to something he had heard before . . . Captain Brown's unexpected question in San Francisco: "Do you believe in ghosts?"

Sutton had heard many odd stories of ghosts of dead men who supposedly sat on chests of pirates' gold, stained with their own blood. The Captain had mentioned "the ghosts of a hundred dead men . . ." Was it possible, he wondered, that this beautiful woman was trying to tell him the same unbelievable thing, in a different way?

"You spoke of—knowing Captain Brown," he said.

"Yes . . ." He noticed that her face seemed relaxed and extraordinarily calm as she talked, in spite of the disturbing thoughts her words evoked. "The thing I wished to tell you was that when I was a little girl my *tutu* told me of a ship that came to the island where she lived when she was a girl."

She stopped, apparently to recapture these recollections.

"The men were rough—like your Captain Brown—and they took some of the young men from the island where my *tutu* lived and made them work on the ship, to take the places of men who had been killed. The ship went away to another island, and some of the young men were killed in fights with other ships, but others came back and told what happened. They took a lot of gold money in cases, and then sank the other ships."

The story bore such a close resemblance to some of the tales Captain Brown had recited that Sutton finally asked, "How did you know we were going to sail down into these islands?"

Mapuana Davis laughed. "Your Captain has told everyone. . . . He said you were looking for some treasure from a Japanese ship, but he says so many things anyone can see he is lying—and nobody pays attention to his lies. But I think if you were to ask the Captain what he knows about the ship that took the young men away from the island of my mother's people, you will probably find out he knows about it."

She hesitated an instant, and then said, "Perhaps it is not important?"

"Oh, yes, indeed it is! Quite important . . ." Sutton still was not certain why she was imparting this knowledge to him. "Captain Brown has told us a great deal of his sailing days—as a young man—but of course he did not say exactly what he was doing, or where he was—"

"He was a pirate," Mapuana Davis said, calmly. She got no further, however, as Ogden Hoffman came up at that moment, and stood beside them. Sutton inwardly cursed him for his ubiquitous presence.

"Wonderful place—isn't it, Sutton?" He waved at the city, with an air of owning the whole place. "You have gotten into things quite quickly, I see. No one can tell you more about Hawaii than Mapuana."

Sutton would have liked to pursue the conversation further, since it might shed light on some of the missing parts of the Captain's story—particularly the location of the "treasure island." The fact that Captain Brown may have operated as a pirate in the Paumotus might prove of considerable significance.

However, Hoffman showed no signs of departing; and finally Sutton and Mapuana Davis arose and walked inside. The party had begun to disintegrate and Dr. Luce indicated by yawning once or twice that he also would like to leave. Sutton made his adieus to the hostess and Angus MacGregor, a bristling Scotsman who seemed to combine the geniality of a good host with the conservatism of a sharp trader. Sutton managed to find Mapuana Davis, talking with a small group on the veranda. He felt an unusual sort of excitement when he approached her again.

She turned immediately toward him and smiled.

"Thank you, Mrs. Davis." He took her hand, and the hint of pressure against his palm assured him of her continued friendliness. "You were kind to talk with me . . . and I was most interested in what you said."

She moved a step or two away from the other group.

"Ask your Captain about the men from my old *tutu*'s island," she said, in a low voice. "Much of the island was destroyed by a great storm, but he will remember the men who came from there . . . and were killed on his ship."

Sutton nodded. "Thank you very much. I certainly will." He hesitated. "I hope I may have the pleasure of seeing you again—before we sail?"

Mapuana Davis smiled.

"I hope so, too," she said. She looked at him gravely a moment.

"There is one thing I wanted to tell you, Captain Sutton. My people are good to strangers and they will help you. But it is wrong to try to trick them . . . and that is what so many people have done." She held his hand as she spoke, and Sutton had the impression that she was trying to convey a message. "There is a love in the hearts of my people that is not like the others—the Chinese, who trade in our islands, or the white men who came and took them away from us." There was no trace of bitterness in her voice. "If you visit any of these islands, you will find people who are like your own family . . . they will always be good to you, and you should be good to them. This is not a lecture, Captain—it is just some advice."

She smiled again and pressed his hand.

"I hope we shall see you—before you leave."

Sutton nodded. He wondered whether he had been given advice, or some kind of a warning. He decided he would ask Captain Brown, at the first opportunity, about the men of Paumotu who were taken on his ship, and later died.

[3]

If there had been any element of secrecy as to the purposes and plans of the voyagers on the schooner *Herman* prior to the MacGregor reception, it was dissipated the following day. The three Honolulu papers—the *Evening Bulletin,* the *Star* and the *Pacific Commercial Advertiser*—carried extensive stories which Sutton recognized as undoubtedly the product of Captain Brown's garrulous performance at the party.

The *Evening Bulletin,* on the day of the arrival of the *Herman,* had described it as a "spick and span little schooner" which had paused in Honolulu "on a voyage around the world." Captain Brown was referred to as a "veteran mariner" who had been in bad health and was taking a few of his friends on "a small jaunt around the world to see if a sniff of salt air would give him back his health."

On Friday morning, August 15—the day after the party and two days before they were to sail—the *Commercial Advertiser* carried a story about "the strange little schooner tied up at Fishmarket Wharf bound for the South Seas on a voyage of mystery." Captain Brown was described as a "white-haired old man who has sailed all around the world, has been in naval fights, mutinies and all sorts of daredevil work at sea." The story concluded, significantly: "On the memory of this strange old sea captain, an eastern syndicate is staking thousands of dollars. The fifteen men on the schooner are expected to reap rewards of millions of dollars' worth of treasures supposed to have been first buried on Cocos Island and later buried on a South Sea Island." The writer then described the treasure in detail: "300,000 pounds of silver and gold, 733 bars of pure gold, four inches by three inches and two inches thick . . . bejewelled swords and precious stones"—which happened to be the precise description of the treasure Sir Edward Davis, the English buccaneer, buried on Cocos Island in 1684!

Sutton groaned when he read the accounts. The *Evening Bulletin,* after describing Captain Brown as having had "some of the wildest experiences of sea life . . . for years he has kept a secret about buried treasure in the South Seas," went on to quote certain "waterfront sources" as having said, "No one except Captain Brown knows where the craft is going—not even them noblemen in the cabins."

The references to "them noblemen" was based on an earlier account which noted that "two of the party—although sailing under American names—are in reality British noblemen."

Sutton was not sure who the "noblemen" were; Hoffman probably was one, and he presumed Frank Sharratt might be the other. However, he had no question as to the source of the story: the Captain's loquacious ramblings on the night of the MacGregor party were in every line.

The real problems began to develop on Saturday morning. A man from the Wilder Steamship Company, Captain Campbell, appeared with a process server and asked for Captain Brown. The Captain and Sutton had gone down to the custom house to clear the ship and only Dr. Luce was aboard. In a few minutes they returned.

"Look at this!" the Captain shouted to the doctor. "They want a hundred dollars' penalty—because I did not declare cargo on arrival. We have no cargo!"

Dr. Luce led the Captain and Sutton back under the awning and introduced Captain Campbell and the process server.

"We are libeling your ship, Captain Brown," the man said. "You owe the Wilder Steamship Company $281.21 for supplies, and until this bill is paid, you can't clear the port." He handed him the summons, which was returnable August 27. This was August 16.

Captain Brown stared at the man from Wilder's, his jaw working up and down, unable to utter a sound. Finally he said: "Those bills have been paid! Damn it—I gave all the bills to Hoffman yesterday for full payment!"

"Where is Hoffman?" Sutton asked. No one knew where he was. Willie Benton, the second mate—the only member of the crew aboard at the time—said he heard Mr. Hoffman had gone to Pearl Harbor to visit some friends.

Sutton motioned to the Captain and they walked to the forward end of the vessel.

"How much did the billing amount to?" Sutton asked.

The Captain figured mentally a moment and then said: "Eight hundred dollars—or thereabouts. Hoffman was to have paid off all the bills yesterday."

When they returned to the afterdeck, the process server and Captain Campbell had left. But another man was on his way up the gangplank. He asked for the master and identified himself as a Deputy United States Marshal. He went up to the mainmast and tacked a small white paper on it.

"This ship is under libel," he said. "You cannot clear port." He pulled over a deck chair and sat down. "I am under orders to stay here until libel is lifted." His manner was pleasant, but firm.

Sutton looked at the doctor and the Captain and finally said, "We'll have to find Hoffman—quickly." He turned to the deputy marshal. "We'll make you comfortable in one of the cabins. I assume you will want to remain aboard until this matter is settled."

The deputy marshal grinned and nodded.

"No *pilikia,*" he said. "Just doing my job, that's all."

Later Sutton wrote home: "The whole trouble arises from the fact that Hoffman assured us he had ample funds and credit to pay for all needed repairs. We find that he has only a hundred dollars or so in cash and not enough credit to raise carfare. We are up against it until we write to 'Frisco and get some money. The Captain, in my opinion, is in no way to blame . . ."

This was on Monday, August 18. The earliest date at which a reply could be received by steamer from San Francisco was on the S.S. *Korea,* due on September 4.

Captain Brown, meanwhile, was stunned by the unexpected situation and for a time speechless. From time to time he walked over and stared at the libel notice as if it were a quarantine. By the end of the day he had recovered some of his aplomb, however. He summoned reporters from the *Evening Bulletin* and the *Commercial Advertiser* and delivered a rather lengthy testimonial as to his own financial resources, pointing out that he had ample funds and the bills had been paid, and anyway the *Herman* had not planned to depart Honolulu until the following Wednesday because one of the passengers had a sore tooth and a dental appointment.

Both papers carried the Captain's statement on Monday; but they also noted that the creditors of the *Herman* had filed a libel against the ship and that it would remain in port until the bills were paid. One of the accounts reported that Captain Brown threatened to bring a suit for damages against the Wilder Steamship Company for "defamation of character." The *Commercial Advertiser* hinted that there was some "mystery" surrounding the fact that the *Herman* had sought clearance for Sydney, Australia, whereas it was known that it was headed for Tahiti on a treasure-hunting expedition. One account even suggested the *Herman* was under investigation for smuggling Chinese into Hawaii.

By the time all of Captain Brown's statements had been assembled, the *Herman,* lying snugly against the Fishmarket Wharf, had achieved so much notoriety, with the welter of conflicting rumors and statements, that it became the cynosure of a continuous gathering of Honolulans at the wharf—a public phenomenon that paradoxically seemed to please the Captain. He was on deck almost constantly, striding from end to end, making unnecessary examinations of gear and rigging, much as if they were getting ready for departure.

Sutton managed to locate Hoffman late Saturday afternoon. He had returned to Honolulu and was staying with his brother, Southard Hoffman, in order to be ready for the scheduled departure the following day. He seemed unconcerned over the problem of paying the bills.

"Probably an oversight," he told Sutton. "I thought I had paid them. We'll straighten this out Monday. We can't leave until next week in any event."

On Monday the bills were totaled up and they amounted to $850 for repairs to the *Herman* and incidental supplies. None of the bills seemed to have been paid. Hoffman airily brushed this aside.

"I'll settle them today," he told Sutton and Chetwood. "We have unlimited credit, of course."

As things developed, they had no credit. Frank Sharratt, who had also come down to the ship Saturday preparatory to sailing the following day, was considerably agitated over the possibility that they might draw on Donzel Stoney for credit.

"You can't move on this until you hear from the committee," he told Sutton. Sutton, looking at him rather coldly, said, "Why in hell don't you shut up, Sharratt? You haven't lifted a hand toward the success of this enterprise so far and you aren't helping now."

Sharratt's round, plump face seemed to freeze. He rose abruptly from the table in the main salon, where they were gathered in conference, and went up on deck.

"Why did you say that, George?" Chetwood asked mildly. "We've got enough troubles without stirring discord among ourselves."

Sutton leaned back and looked first at Chetwood and then the doctor. "We've got to face a problem which we haven't yet faced," he said. "Neither Hoffman nor Sharratt has contributed one damn bit to the success of this expedition, and in Hoffman's case, he's contributing to its failure. We're going to have to lay over here until the money is raised—at least a thousand dollars. I think we should use that time to dispose of the Hoffman question—and maybe Sharratt, too. Do we want them to continue on this voyage?"

Chetwood shrugged. "How can we stop them? Hoffman represents Mooser, as you know. Frank is one of the investors, and I guess he represents Don Stoney."

Sutton's voice was brittle. "We represent the success of this venture," he said. "I've got more personal cash invested than anyone, and I represent forty-five percent of the contributors. You, John, represent the committee. Unless the three of us act together, this expedition is going to founder before it starts. Waving guns at each other and threatening to shoot it out isn't the answer."

Chetwood nodded. It was agreed they would write to Stoney, in San Francisco, with all three—Sutton, Chetwood and Dr. Luce—signing the letter to indicate a uniformity of views. They needed not only cash to pay bills, but the authority to put Hoffman off the ship.

It would be September 4, however—the day of the scheduled arrival of the steamer *Korea*—before they could expect an answer. This was almost three weeks away, and it was beginning to be apparent that a lot could happen in three weeks.

It did. Among other things, members of the crew began to desert. The two sailors who disappeared the first day ashore never reported again; and since it would cost money to conduct a search through police channels, this was dropped. The Japanese cook was replaced by a Chinese who turned out to be a laundryman! The Japanese steward, Jimmy Akahito, remained faithful. He seemed to have a personal attachment to Captain Brown and was friendly to everyone. However, Willie Benton announced he was leaving. He pointed out that the *Herman* was virtually impounded and he saw little hope of drawing regular wages.

"A bloke can't go on forever, you know," he told the Captain. "Oi've got to 'ave vittles meself, an' the chow that Chinee cook puts out ain't fit to fill the gut of a bloomin' pig."

Mr. Benton's place, oddly enough, was taken over by a Mr. Benson, who was well known in Honolulu and had sailed in the Society Islands and knew the area of the "low islands" quite well. He seemed to have taken quite a fancy to Captain Brown and signed the sailing contract on the personal guarantee of the Captain that he would be paid.

Sutton had hoped that during the interim, while they were immobilized in Honolulu, he might have another opportunity to see Mapuana Davis, but he was not certain how to go about contacting her. He had thought of asking Hoffman's help, but finally decided against this. His motives were quite honorable—he was more or less sure that his main concern was learning more about the Paumotu Islands. But Hoffman would probably misinterpret his interest and spread gossip among the other passengers.

Trying to reach her by telephone posed some problems. Sutton had no personal friends in Honolulu whose aid he could very well solicit, and the rather unfavorable press the *Herman* party had received as a result of the ship being libeled would add to whatever embarrassment he might feel in trying to locate Mapuana Davis.

Finally fate interceded for him. He met her on Fort Street.

"Captain Sutton!" she exclaimed, extending her hand. Sutton thought she looked even more beautiful by daylight than in the dim light of the terrace at the MacGregor home. She wore a street dress, brightly colored, setting off the warm texture of her brown skin. "How nice to see you! I heard you had been delayed. . . . I've been away in Hilo to visit friends and just got back on the *Kinau* this morning. It's delightful to see you again."

Sutton nodded, a bit glumly. "Yes—we were delayed," he said. "Your brother-in-law's friend had something to do with that, as you may know. He forgot to pay bills we had run up on the *Herman*. We've had to send for more money."

"Oh, goodness!" She laughed in the trilling way that Sutton had found so captivating. "I read some of the newspaper stories in Hilo, and it seemed to me the Captain had lots of money to pay for everything." She leaned closer and said in a low voice, "Here he comes now—my brother-in-law's friend!"

Sutton looked around. Hoffman's annoying presence, wherever Mrs. Davis was concerned, seemed to border on the supernatural. Hoffman waved as he walked up.

"Hello, Sutton—glad I ran across you. Glad to see you, too, Mapuana." His expression was halfway between a smile and a leer. Sutton growled some response in his throat. "I've got some things I wanted to see you about, Sutton," Hoffman went on with customary imperviousness.

Sutton looked at Mrs. Davis. He would have liked to have arranged some means of getting in touch with her again, but this seemed out of the question at the moment, with Hoffman standing by. He smiled, rather helplessly, as he shook hands.

"Goodbye, Mrs. Davis. . . . I hope I will have the opportunity of seeing you again."

"I hope so, too, Captain. Perhaps you'll be up at Angus' house—before you leave?"

Sutton bowed, and turned to join Hoffman. They walked toward the wharf while Hoffman explained that arrangements had been completed by Frank Sharratt to obtain an advance of a thousand dollars from Tom Hobron, a local resident and the owner of the Hobron Drug Co., connected with Sharratt by some relationship which was not clear to Sutton. They would have to await the arrival of funds from San Francisco, of course, to repay Hobron; but this advance would enable them to clear the libel against the ship and prepare for departure.

Sutton decided it was time to face the Hoffman problem directly. "Look here, Hoffman," he said, "we've got some other matters to solve. Your handling of the funds has been questionable. For one thing—we've had no accounting from you as to where the money went that should have been available for payment of those bills."

Hoffman arrested his stride and stared at Sutton. "Are you suggesting there was anything improper, Sutton?" His voice had a hard edge; and Sutton was also experiencing a rising temperature. He tried to control his voice.

"I'm suggesting that we should receive an explanation," he said.

"My report will be made to Louis Mooser and he will report to the committee," Hoffman said, almost as if he were rebuking Sutton for impertinence. "There is no necessity of making additional reports to you or anyone else."

"Damn it, it's our money—and our expedition!" Sutton turned to face Hoffman and their voices rose to the point that passers-by glanced at them with some interest.

"Come—we can't discuss this here," Hoffman said, quickening his pace. "There is no reason for your attitude, Sutton. I've already made a fairly complete report to Mooser by letter."

They were walking down the waterfront road toward the *Herman,* whose tall masts and trim white hull had become almost a fixture on Fishmarket Wharf. Sutton could see that some of the crew were on deck, and he did not want to pursue his discussion with Hoffman aboard ship. He slowed his pace.

"Did you advise Mooser of the row we had aboard the ship—when you threatened the Captain with a pistol?" he asked. Hoffman glanced sharply at him.

"He threatened me—don't forget that!"

"Captain Brown is master, Hoffman. You challenged his authority and in any admiralty court, that is mutiny. You wouldn't have a leg to stand on if the Captain preferred charges against you."

Hoffman stopped in his tracks and glared for a moment at Sutton. "Are you threatening me, Sutton?" he asked.

"I'm telling you what Dr. Luce and Chetwood and I have discussed and agreed upon. Your present attitude toward the Captain is a threat to all of us—and to the expedition. I, for one, do not intend to continue with the voyage under these conditions."

"You are at liberty to leave—any time you wish, Sutton." Hoffman's voice was smooth, but hard; and it seemed to Sutton he was making no headway at all in pursuing this matter.

He and Hoffman reached the ship without talking further. Hoffman wanted to pick up some things in his cabin and he soon left. Sutton found Dr. Luce and Captain Brown below in the master's quarters. The Captain was striding restlessly about the room, at times uttering unintelligible grunts. The doctor had been standing, looking through the after port, which faced the harbor, when Sutton came into the room.

Sutton told them Sharratt had apparently arranged to obtain sufficient funds from local sources to pay the bills and lift the libel from the ship. Captain Brown straightened up; his eyes had a feverish look and Sutton wondered if he was coming down with one of his recurrent attacks of "the fevers."

"Good!" He slapped his big hands together. "We'll have a farewell party aboard the night before we sail! Eh? How's that?"

Sutton grunted. He was not in favor of any more "parties," but decided to say nothing about this suggestion.

"Our first job is to see that the bills are paid." He turned to the Captain. "We all regret this, Captain. It has been no fault of yours, and I've said so in my letters to San Francisco and to Walradt. But I think we should try now to keep things as quiet as possible, don't you?" He hesitated, then said, "If it meets with your approval, Captain, I'm going to suggest that Hoffman leave the expedition here in Honolulu. He's not necessary and in my own opinion he is a disturbing element."

Sutton was not at all sure at this point who was disturbed the most by Hoffman: the Captain, or himself. But he was fairly sure of one thing—if Hoffman remained aboard the *Herman,* somebody would be shot before many days at sea.

[4]

Mr. Benson, the new second mate, stood amidships, naked to the waist, hurling invectives at the Hawaiian sailors who had been signed on to replace the deserters from the crew of the *Herman.* He was a stocky man, heavy-set across the shoulders and chest, with short, powerful arms.

"Lay to, you Kanaka bastards!" he shouted; and the three Hawaiian sailors grinned good-naturedly. Sutton, watching the scene ts the *Herman* was made ready for sea, marveled at this curious relationship between the *haole* mate and the Hawaiian sailors. He sensed that if he—a *haole* in background as well as skin—had used the same words, one of the sailors might have clubbed him with his fist. But Mr. Benson, his face and body sunburned almost to the dark hue of the Hawaiians themselves, seemed to be one of them.

One of the Hawaiian sailors, who had been taken on from the crew of another schooner, the *Rosamond,* to replace two of the deserters from the *Herman,* stopped work and looked at the mate, his heavy-lipped mouth parted in a broad grin. "Get goin' y'self, white meat," he called out. "You make lotsa noise, no *hapai."*

The rest laughed and continued industriously cleaning the decks and bilge gutters, swabbing the launch until it was gleaming white, and washing down the deckhouse. Captain Brown stood by the wheelhouse watching the scene with apparent approval on his beaming face.

His self-confidence had been restored immeasurably by the arrival of funds from San Francisco. This was Friday, September 12, and sailing was scheduled for Sunday. All bills had been paid off from the money advanced by Tom Hobron and the funds that came in on the *Korea* were used to repay Hobron. He had volunteered to contribute five hundred of the thousand dollars lent to the *Herman* party as an investor in the treasure-hunting venture, and was consequently now one of the group. The expedition—financially, at least—was flourishing.

Sutton had returned to the schooner after a short trip into town to lay in personal supplies—shaving soap and such items—and he had hoped to find the Captain alone in order to settle finally the question whether Hoffman would continue on the voyage. No reply had been received from the joint letter to Donzel Stoney, but Sutton did not intend to let that prevent a decision. He had determined not to continue on the voyage if Hoffman remained aboard.

As he watched Mr. Benson prodding the three Hawaiian sailors to greater efforts, he began to realize what Mapuana Davis meant when she talked with him on the night of the MacGregor party. The Polynesians seemed to be naturally friendly people, good-natured and tolerant; but there was a deep sense of self-respect in these people that he was beginning to understand. They were an old race with a culture out of the deep reaches of the Pacific, which no anthropologist or ethnologist had been able to trace with any success. They were a primitive people, but not savages; and he understood the underlying plea for understanding that Mapuana Davis had made on the patio at the MacGregor home.

"Ho, there!" Captain Brown called down to him from the afterdeck. "Come aboard, Cap'n! Ye can well see what progress we're making. We'll have this old scow shipshape and ready for sea with this crew aboard!"

Sutton continued to be amazed at the old man's chameleon changes of mood. One moment he was arrogant and domineering; the next hearty and jovial; the next sullen and despondent. He was quickly affected by the attitude of those around him toward his own person, and his rather enlarged concept of his own importance.

Sutton had a serious problem on his mind, and he was not sure how he should brace the Captain with it. He was now certain, from checking over accounts and notes with Chetwood and Dr. Luce, that Hoffman had actually misapproapriated funds of the expedition. At least five hundred dollars had been turned over to Hoffman by Stoney in San

Francisco; and he appeared to have less than a hundred left, in spite of the fact that all bills had been paid from the money advanced by Tom Hobron.

When they were seated on the afterdeck, Sutton asked Captain Brown: "What is your feeling about Hoffman, Captain? The doctor and Chetwood and I agree that he should be removed from the ship—for various reasons. We realize that your own authority as master must not be interfered with. There is more reason than that, however—" Sutton hesitated and then added: "I have some reason to believe he is interfering with the crew members."

Captain Brown waved a huge paw in a deprecatory gesture. "I've handled gentlemen like him before—and I can handle 'em again. No man crosses Cap'n James Brown, an' you can lay to that! As for the crew—" He jumped up and shouted some unintelligible order to Mr. Benson, as if to demonstrate his supreme authority, and then resumed his seat. He wore his dark coat, in spite of the heat; it seemed to be a badge of authority or prestige. Sutton had noticed that the only time he removed his coat in any public appearance—even on deck in sight of the people on the wharf—was after the U. S. Marshal's libel notice had been posted on the mast.

"Let me tell you something," Captain Brown went on, putting a long forefinger on Sutton's knee. "That fellow will never see the island—ye can lay to that! We'll put him ashore someplace where it'll take him three years to get back!"

He roared at his own humor and slapped Sutton on the back.

"Dr. Luce and John Chetwood and I have reached an agreement on this," Sutton continued. "We will return to San Francisco if Hoffman stays aboard—and meet you later in Samoa or Tahiti. But we must see to it that we have the authority to put him off the ship if it becomes necessary."

Captain Brown nodded, stroking his whiskers.

"Sounds like a good plan," he said, his eyes shifting from Sutton to the work on the foredeck. He rose abruptly from his seat, as if this had settled the whole matter. "We're having the farewell party aboard tomorrow night, Cap'n—or maybe Monday. I'm asking all my good friends to come down to the ship. How's that?"

Sutton was not sure how it would be. It sounded as if the Captain might be inviting most of the town, and he shuddered to think of what consequences might develop. The Captain had demonstrated some unusual characteristics in his choice of social acquaintances, begin-

The letter to Captain Brown awarding him a refund on the fine imposed on the *Herman*.

No. 748

Office of the Collector of Customs,

Port of Honolulu, Hawaii,

September 18,1902

Captain James Brown,

Master of the Am.Schr."Herman",

Honolulu, Hawaii,

Sir:-

Referring to your letter of August 14th last, addressed to the Honorable Secretary of the Treasury, in which you enter protest against the penalty of $100.oo imposed by me, incurred through a violation of Section 4355 Revised Statutes, Fine Case No.334, I have the honor to transmit, herewith, for your information, a copy of Department letter dated August 30th last, No.31257-N, in which the Honorable Secretary mitigates the amount of the penalty imposed upon you to $5.oo.

I will thank you to call at this office at your earliest convenience and sign a receipt for the $95.oo, the amount to be refunded to you.

Very respectfully,

E R Stackable

Collector

This map, advertising the Hobron Drug Company, appears in Captain Sutton's journal and shows in ink the *Herman's* route from San Francisco to Honolulu.

ning with the ebullient Mrs. Samson in San Francisco. On several occasions, Sutton had come aboard with Chetwood or Dr. Luce and found the Captain entertaining a rather strange assortment of guests—from middle-aged ladies with fifteen-year-old daughters, whom he invited to "tea" on the afterdeck, to odd characters who seemed to have been swept up from waterfront bistros and cheap lodging houses. The old man was invariably garrulous, holding his guests at constant attention by the force of his voice, if not the intrinsic interest of what he was saying.

Sutton could readily envision what would probably take place at a "farewell party." However, there was not much he could offer in the way of objection, without insulting the Captain; so he merely remarked mildly: "I thought sailing was scheduled for Sunday. Anything happened to prevent that?"

The Captain assured him nothing had happened. All bills were paid, the libel was lifted and they were ready to sail. Even the customs office, in response to a letter Captain Brown had written to Washington, was about to reduce the hundred-dollar penalty for failing to declare cargo to a mere five dollars.

The Captain was at the height of one of his more euphoric moods, and he wanted to demonstrate to his "good friends" in Honolulu his appreciation of their steadfast confidence in him during his time of trials.

"I'll even invite them reporter fellows," he told Sutton, in a moment of exuberance. "Let 'em see what kind of fellow I am, and they won't repeat them damned lies! Eh? How's that?"

He also pointed out that the delay already occasioned by the lack of funds in Honolulu had made a few additional days of delay unimportant; they would have to lay over in any event during the midwinter months in one of the islands or at Sydney, to wait out the bad weather.

Sutton again raised the matter of Hoffman, but the Captain was quite settled in his mind. "Nothing to it—I'll handle that gentleman, an' you can lay to that!"

The variation of the Captain's moods was one of the more disturbing factors to Sutton in the whole complex of disturbances that beset the expedition. The old man would rise to a peak of enthusiasm and performance one day—and no one could doubt his seamanship; but the next day he might sink into despondency, usually accompanied by an announcement that he had an attack of "the fevers." Or, failing either of these moods, he would become irascible and angry over petty troubles and minor inconveniences, usually upbraiding patient old Dr. Luce.

Sutton had begun to regard the old man almost as a problem child; and as water fills empty spaces, the element of responsibility was rapidly pouring into his area of concern. Both Dr. Luce and Chetwood seemed to have shifted all this to Sutton.

As the time for departure approached, the Captain had gone into a feverish series of changes in the crew. He had hired a third cook, settling on a Japanese, Hasino, who had little familiarity with occidental culinary practices, but was better than the Chinese laundryman who preceded him. The only fixed members of the crew seemed to be Mr. Benson, who had replaced Willie Benton as second mate, and Willie Peterson, the bosun who had been taken on under exceptional circumstances in San Francisco. Mr. Hendrickson was temporarily off the crew list after a violent exchange with the Captain over some minor matter. His successor was presumptuous enough to smoke on the afterdeck and the Captain upbraided him so abusively that he quit. The Captain then made a hurried trip uptown to the lodging house where Mr. Hendrickson had gone and persuaded him to return to the ship.

The crew, as it stood on the eve of departure, consisted of Mr. Hendrickson again as first mate and Mr. Benson as second mate; the faithful Japanese steward, Jimmy; Willie Peterson, the bosun; three Hawaiians and the durable red-haired sailor, Pete.

Sutton, unable to make any headway on the Hoffman situation, went uptown to check at the post office for mail from the Mainland, leaving the Captain to his final tasks of "tightening up" the ship. He found Chetwood already there reading a letter which had come in on the morning steamer from San Francisco. It was from Donzel Stoney.

> We can see no reason for asking Ogden Hoffman to leave the ship [the letter said]. Louis Mooser has received reports from Hoffman, strongly indicating certain lack of capabilities on the part of Captain Brown. We must accept these deficiencies; he is a man over seventy, yet his presence is vital to the expedition. Nevertheless you three should be able to straighten things out. Mooser insists that Hoffman must continue on the voyage, regardless of any circumstances. The Committee is united in support of this view.

Sutton read the letter twice, with a sickening feeling. Stoney's attitude was surprising, and disappointing, particularly in view of his earlier letter, which Sutton had interpreted as a direct implication of Hoffman in the matter of a commission on the sale of the *Herman.*

"This means we have to go back to San Francisco to straighten this out," he told Chetwood. "I will not sail on that ship with Hoffman." He briefly recounted his discussion with Captain Brown. "He insists he can handle Hoffman and I think he can. He handled matters on the *Sea Foam* and he had a lot more than Hoffman to deal with."

"Yes—but he was a lot younger then," Chetwood commented, grinning wrily. "You know, George, if you hadn't stepped between them the other night . . . one of them could have been shot."

Sutton nodded. "It's a chance we've got to take. The Captain isn't inclined to bring this to a showdown now—and he would have to act drastically to get Hoffman off the ship. The only alternative is to charge Hoffman directly with misappropriation of funds, and I'm afraid we've already committed ourselves so far that this would be regarded as a malicious charge, and might even reflect on us."

Sutton had a clear recollection of his first meeting with Captain Brown, back in Auburn; and he could readily envision the Captain—fifty years thrown off his aging frame, his hair blowing in the wind as he stood above the break of the poop on the old sailing ship, moored in a lagoon in some remote tropical island, drawing pistol after pistol from the waistband of his trousers and firing shot after shot into the milling cluster of angry seamen below.

"I think it's Hoffman who's taking the real chance," he said, as an afterthought.

Later that day Sutton and Chetwood presented the matter to Dr. Luce, who had been at Queen's Hospital for several days due to mild heart trouble. It was agreed that they would reserve accommodations on the *S.S. Alameda,* sailing for San Francisco on September 24.

Captain Brown's "farewell party" was held on Monday, and as anticipated, it delayed sailing until the following Sunday, September 21. The schooner had been decked with bunting and a group of Hawaiian singers and ukulele players provided music for the affair. Hoffman and Sharratt did not attend; but Chetwood, the doctor and Sutton were there. Captain Brown even led the singing, roaring out sea chanteys with the same stentorian voice that he used in bawling orders to the sailors on the foredeck.

Representatives of all three Honolulu newspapers attended, presumably in the hope of being able to report on whatever brawls might occur. The farewell party ended without loss of blood or prestige, however, and the following morning the Captain announced that the *Herman* would sail on Sunday.

Saturday morning Hoffman arrived aboard the schooner. He seemed outwardly cheerful, but Sutton detected signs of trouble.

"Sorry I couldn't attend your party," he called out to Captain Brown, as he came briskly across the gangway. "I don't suppose it was official, was it?"

Sutton, standing near the Captain, said: "It was paid for out of the ship's funds, Hoffman—if that's what you're getting at."

Hoffman stared a moment at Sutton.

"I assumed I was custodian of the funds," he said, slowly.

Chetwood, glancing at Sutton, suddenly stepped between the two.

"George and I arranged with Tom Hobron for him to turn over his contribution of five hundred dollars, Ogden," he said. "I am holding the money. Very little was spent on the party—but the money is being retained as ship's funds."

"Damn it—you can't do that!" Hoffman said sharply. "You'll have everything messed up—and I've got to report on this to Mooser. This is a misappropriation of funds, and I'll not have it!"

Sutton gritted his teeth. He knew he was again on the point of losing control of himself, but he finally managed to say, in a tone that caused Hoffman to look sharply at him:

"Perhaps we'd better have an accounting of *all* funds, Hoffman—including the five hundred dollars you said you held for payment of bills . . . which were not paid!"

Hoffman stepped closer to Sutton.

"I'll hold you accountable for that remark, Sutton. If there's any implication—"

"It's a hell of a lot more than an implication," Sutton cut in angrily. "The money you held was the joint property of this expedition, Hoffman—and I, for one, am going to get to the bottom of it. Dr. Luce, John and I have already made reservations on the *Alameda* to return to the Mainland and present this matter to the committee."

Hoffman, for the moment, seemed to have become speechless with surprise. Sutton would have liked to have kept him off balance, but Dr. Luce broke in:

"Look, gentlemen—this isn't necessary, arguing like this . . . right out here. Everyone is listening." Members of the crew had edged closer, and it was evident there was very little privacy in the argument. Captain Brown suddenly roared out: "Get forward, ye damned swabs! Move lively!" He turned to Mr. Hendrickson. "It's your watch, Mr. Hendrickson. See to it the men are employed on work—not rubbering here on the afterdeck!"

Hoffman waited until the crew had retreated beyond earshot; then he turned toward Sutton, his angular, pale face drawn suddenly into harsh lines. His gray eyes shifted from Sutton to the Captain and then to Chetwood.

"If you three are working up any scheme—" he began; and then turned suddenly and strode off the ship. Sutton watched his back as Hoffman swung across the wharf. Finally, with a deep sigh, he turned to the Captain.

"I may as well tell you, Captain—we are investigating Hoffman's handling of the ship's funds. For the present, John"—he nodded toward Chetwood—"the doctor and I have agreed that the remaining money will be controlled by John. When we leave, he will turn over all remaining funds to you. You can sign a receipt and it will be up to you to keep an accounting of expenditures until we rejoin you in Apia or Papeete. Is that satisfactory?"

The Captain nodded. "Ye need have no worry about Mr. Hoffman," he said, quite calmly and, surprisingly, with no show of arrogance. "I'll handle this ship—and everyone aboard. We should make Apia in three weeks—that's where we'll be heading, an' the *Herman* has been cleared for that port. I'll await you in Samoa, an' there'll be no sailing to the island until you and Mr. Chetwood join me. You can lay to that."

Sutton did not see Hoffman aboard the *Herman* that night; but on Sunday morning, prior to sailing, Hoffman came aboard, spoke to no one and went below to his cabin. He was followed a few minutes later by Frank Sharratt, who waddled across the gangway, glanced around in obvious embarrassment at those near the afterdeck rail, and also went below without speaking to anyone. A few minutes later three Honolulu policemen arrived.

As Sutton found out later, Hoffman had gone to the U. S. Marshal's office on Saturday afternoon and sought to impound the *Herman,* on the grounds that he possessed Louis Mooser's authority of ownership and that Captain Brown, Sutton and the others had "threatened to take this vessel to sea, remove it from the jurisdiction of the United States, and sell it in a foreign port."

He added, "I'll be on the ship and there'll be shooting if anyone tries to take it out of the harbor!"

The marshal paid little attention to Hoffman's claim that the ship was about to be seized; he said it was no concern of his until something happened. But the remark about "shooting" caused him to notify Deputy Sheriff Chillingworth of Honolulu, who decided to send the three patrolmen down to Fishmarket Wharf.

A lieutenant of police soon joined them; and about an hour before sailing time the wharf was filled with curious onlookers, including several newspaper reporters and photographers. The report that a riot and gun-fighting was about to burst forth on the much-publicized *Herman* spread along the waterfront, and a crowd of perhaps a hundred or more gathered to watch the affair.

As reported in the Honolulu *Star* the following day (Monday, September 22):

"Mr. Hoffman is understood to have been the cause of the trouble. He has not, it is said, a penny of money in this venture . . . Captain Brown is reported to have declared that if Hoffman persisted in going with the boat, he would leave him on an island where it would take three years for him to get home . . . "

The story concluded: "The *Herman* is on a treasure expedition, but it is very doubtful that Hoffman will ever see the island where the wealth is hidden . . . Captain Brown does not feel kindly toward Hoffman and before the boat sailed there was a big row. There was no blood shed, however."

Sutton later discovered that Hoffman had come aboard the *Herman* the previous evening while he and Chetwood and Dr. Luce, who had only recently recovered from the attack of heart trouble, had gone uptown to arrange for accommodations at a local hotel until the departure of the *Alameda* on September 24. Hoffman had brought three or four bottles of *okolehao,* a Hawaiian form of distilled whiskey made from *ti* root, which had more than average potency. He had given two of these bottles to members of the crew and was drinking with them when Captain Brown came aboard. The Captain immediately demanded return of the liquor.

"Take them to your cabin, Mr. Hoffman—you can't bring these on the deck of any ship under my command."

Hoffman had apparently been about to challenge the Captain's authority but the old man must have presented a sufficiently formidable figure to cause Hoffman to hesitate. He took the bottles below to his cabin, and almost immediately afterward left the ship.

The Captain had not at first informed Sutton of this incident; but with the two men in the cabins below and policemen aboard the schooner, he gave Sutton and Chetwood a full account.

"The man's been tampering with my crew," he told them. "He's been talking with Mr. Benson, who reported the matter to me. I'll put him in irons, Cap'n, if this sort of thing continues."

The Hawaiian police lieutenant went below and called out to Hoffman through the door: "Mr. Hoffman! Come to the door—I've something to tell you, from Deputy Sheriff Chillingworth."

Hoffman opened the door cautiously. Sharratt was also in the cabin. Both held pistols in their hands. The police lieutenant shook his head.

"This is no way to act, Mr. Hoffman. You shoot gun in this harbor, an' you go to jail. You understand that?"

Sutton had come halfway down the after companionway, and Hoffman looked at him with an expression—as Sutton later told it—"of a man who wants to kill someone." The situation remained at an impasse for several seconds. Finally the police lieutenant returned to the deck and told Captain Brown: "I can put him in jail if you tell me, Captain. But you must make charges. Mr. Hoffman has not made trouble yet, an' I am only here to stop trouble."

The Captain nodded. "I'll take care of any trouble that happens—when we are at sea. That is my duty, and I can handle things." He turned to Sutton. "The tug is coming up, Cap'n—you'd better go ashore now with Mr. Chetwood and the doctor. You need have no worry." He clapped Sutton on the shoulder and smiled jovially, as if this were quite a normal farewell.

Sutton, taking a last look at the Captain, followed the doctor and Chetwood across the gangway. Once again he had the same impression of this old man as he had visualized before, as he must have looked fifty years ago on the quarterdeck of the *Sea Foam* . . . a powerful young man with blazing blue eyes, hair flying wildly, shirt open to the waist, a young man hardly into his twenties facing a gang of hard-bitten, angry sailors who had fought with him as pirates . . . coldly firing shot after shot into the crowd.

He had the definite feeling that Captain Brown was right . . . he could "handle things." Sutton wondered, momentarily, if he would ever see Hoffman alive again.

The South Pacific: Pursuit of the Herman

[1]

After the *Herman* had straightened out its towline, following the tug *Fearless* toward the narrow opening at the south end of the breakwater, Sutton, Chetwood and the doctor started walking slowly uptown. They passed the block-long Alexander Young Hotel, then under construction and soon to become the pride of downtown Honolulu, rivaling the gracious Moana Hotel on the beach. Their own hotel was a small frame building on Alakea Street, just beyond the old Royal Hawaiian Hotel, and as they walked past the spreading gardens of banyans and monkeypods and thick clusters of strange ferns and palm trees, Sutton made a quick decision in his own mind.

Just before they arrived at their hotel, he excused himself. "I've a couple of chores I want to get done. I'll see you at the hotel in a couple of hours."

Chetwood glanced at him in some surprise; Sutton had noted the slim lawyer's annoyance, almost bordering on resentment, whenever Sutton attempted to leave on any personal excursion of his own. Dr. Luce merely nodded, and Sutton turned back toward Hotel Street and the central downtown section.

He found a telephone at a small drugstore and telephoned Angus MacGregor's home. The voice at the other end sounded familiar, with its muted, musical note. It was Mapuana Davis.

Sutton felt his pulse beating faster—a phenomenon which distinctly annoyed him. He thought: This is ridiculus. I'm acting like a schoolboy!

She informed him that she had seen the *Herman* passing down the channel from her vantage point on the veranda of the MacGregor house, somewhat above the city. She had hoped that perhaps she might hear from him again before he left the following Wednesday on the *Alameda*.

Sutton, even as he rather formally acquiesced in this sentiment, had a sudden and surprising thought. What of Mapuana's husband? Who—and where—was he? The question had not previously occurred to him, but now it assumed large proportions.

He suggested, a bit awkwardly, that perhaps he might hire a carriage and ride up to the MacGregor home—if this were all right with her, of course—and she could accompany him on a short ride around the city pointing out places of interest. It might be his last opportunity to see the place.

Mapuana agreed readily to this suggestion. She said he might call early in the afternoon (it was now almost one o'clock) and she would be ready for the drive. Sutton, mopping his forehead, left the store and looked around for a carriage stand. He was still wondering vaguely about Mr. Davis—of whom he had thus far forgotten to inquire—when he found a carriage near the Royal Hawaiian Hotel.

Mapuana was waiting for him on the steps of the veranda as his carriage drove up the sweeping entrance road which curved off the Pacific Heights road. The carriage stopped under a white wooden portico of square columns massed along the outer eaves with hanging ferns and surrounded with tall, dark green plants. It seemed to Sutton that wherever there was room, some kind of luxuriant tropical plant had been hung, so that the outer side of the porte-cochere presented a solid green wall of plant life.

She was attired in a flowing type of "Mother Hubbard" dress, or gown, known as a *holokuu,* which had been introduced into the Islands by missionaries in earlier years when the going feminine fashion consisted of a swath of cloth wrapped around the hips and nothing much else. For the first time Sutton was able to gauge Mapuana Davis' age a bit more definitely; she was probably thirty, give or take a year or two. Sutton was not certain that the age of Polynesian women could be calibrated with the same mental measuring devices that would be applicable to American women.

She came down the steps and extended her hand and said in her soft voice, "Why don't you stay here and have the carriage return for you in an hour or so? I'm sure the gardens would be as interesting as the city—and you can see most of the town from the veranda."

Sutton did not even know what the local customs might require in the way of a chaperon and he was still completely in the dark as to the identity and location of Mr. Davis. For the first time he experienced a vague feeling of guilt . . . there was his own family, of course, back in New Rochelle. He wondered if Mapuana Davis knew about them.

Apparently Mapuana did know something about them. After leading Sutton to the end of the veranda, they descended a small stone stairway into the gardens which lay behind the house. There she asked, "How are Mrs. Sutton and your children—in New Rochelle, isn't it?"

Sutton nodded, a bit startled. He supposed Ogden Hoffman had supplied the information. This, he reflected bitterly, was merely another mark to be chalked up against Hoffman's obtrusive conduct.

"Fine—I suppose," he said. "Letters don't come very frequently on a trip such as this. I expect I'll have a letter when I get back to San Francisco."

She smiled—and Sutton was moved to ask, "Is this your home—yours and Mr. Davis' . . ."

She glanced at him, her dark eyes lively with amusement. "My husband died several years ago, Mr. Sutton . . . in an accident."

Sutton frowned. "I'm terribly sorry—I didn't know, of course."

"Of course not—how would you? Unless my brother-in-law told you, or Mr. Hoffman. It happened when I was quite young, just after we were married. I have been living with my sister and Angus since then."

Sutton nodded soberly. This was possibly another ramification of the *calabash* relationships in the Islands which he only vaguely understood. He wondered, in passing, where Mrs. MacGregor might be at the time. Mapuana, who seemed to be psychic, said, "My sister asked me to give you her greetings. She had an errand downtown, but she hoped she would be back to say goodbye before you leave."

This brief dialogue seemed to Sutton to have disposed of the amenities. He was not certain, due to his unfamiliarity with Polynesian customs, what his next conversational gambit ought to be. It was quite evident that, except for a couple of Chinese servants he had observed flitting like wraiths within the recesses of the house, there was no one else at home.

Mapuana broke the silence. She had led him to a small seat under an arbor of overhanging plants, spread like heavy green lacework above them; and now she put her hand on his. Sutton was surprised that there was no trace of deliberate familiarity in the action; it was merely a gesture of friendliness.

"I should like to know about your home and your people—in New Rochelle," she said, in the low, musical voice that seemed to reflect her gentle warmth. "In the Islands we have a saying that we know people better when we also know the places where they live. It is the feeling that people belong someplace, and that place is part of them. Do you understand?"

Sutton nodded. He told her a little bit about his home—a fairly large house in New Rochelle, which was only about twenty miles from New York. He could think of little to say about his family; it suddenly occurred to him that there was very little to say about anything in New Rochelle that would be interesting to a woman from the Islands. But Mapuana probed with questions, and he soon found himself telling her about his life back home—his wife and children, and the social activities in a city like New Rochelle. Mapuana frequently broke into rippling laughter at some of his remarks, now fairly objective in view of the five thousand miles of land and water that separated him from home.

"I've never been on the Mainland—even in San Francisco," she volunteered. "I think I would probably be quite frightened—don't you think so?"

Sutton assured her she need have no fears. Things were not as beautiful as in Honolulu, but there was general peace and decorum in most places. At least, he thought, there would be no "ghosts" to worry about!

"Yes, I suppose so," she agreed, nodding her dark head slightly. "But it is the difference in the people that would frighten me. You . . . you are not so different, Captain Sutton. You have more of the feeling of kindness that my people have. It is difficult for your people to understand us. You cannot know what it is like to live always on an island, with the sea around you. Our life is part of the sea . . . not the land. Do you understand this?"

Sutton thought he did. Mapuana went on to tell him of the life of people of the Islands—the long voyages her forebears made, across the trackless ocean for thousands of miles. "We are not afraid of the sea—but the land sometimes frightens us. My grandmother had to leave one island because a new volcano was coming up, but they moved to another island only a few miles away."

She paused and then said, "My people do not really understand hatred—as your people do. Perhaps that is our misfortune and it may be why my people are gradually disappearing. You must understand that, Captain Sutton, if you go down into the Islands. Some of your people are cruel and mean, but others, like Angus—and like you—are good, and can understand this. This man Hoffman—he doesn't understand it. I know that. I am very sorry that he is going with you."

"He won't," Sutton said, a bit grimly. "Not if I can help it."

Sutton thought to ask her about the typhoons. Were they as dangerous and devastating as he had been led to believe? She nodded.

"There are terrible winds in the islands. I have seen some of them that have not been so terrible—but others that my *tutu* told me about would come quickly across the sea and sometimes destroy whole villages, and even entire islands."

"Entire islands?" Sutton asked.

She nodded again. "In the Paumotu Islands ten years ago there was a very bad storm that blew for several days and the people of the villages had to tie themselves to the coconut trees to keep from being blown away. Some were even blown off the trees into the ocean. I did not see this, of course, but friends from Tahiti told me about it. Many hundreds of people were killed or drowned in the storm."

An odd thought crossed Sutton's mind. What if the island where Captain Brown's treasure was buried had been blown away? He recalled the curious reaction of the Captain when the subject of typhoons was brought up, during their first meeting back in Auburn. Was it possible Captain Brown also felt this foreboding?

Mapuana Davis arose from the seat finally and led Sutton down to the edge of the terrace where they had sat on the stone bench the night of the MacGregor party. She waved, with a graceful sweep of her hand, toward the long fringe of surf that could be seen clearly crashing over the reef, even at that distance. It extended in rows of huge combers, far out to the west and the north; and beyond these were the glistening blue lagoons of Pearl Harbor and beyond that the vast expanse of the dark blue ocean.

"I have known the sea ever since I can remember," she said. "When I was a small girl in Samoa, my brother—who is dead now—took me on long rides around the islands. The canoes were slender and longer than those in Hawaii, made entirely of trunks of large heavy trees. We lived on Manua, which now belongs to this country." She stopped speaking, and to Sutton it seemed that her dark eyes glowed with a kind of inner fire, a subdued light, which seemed to combine memories and sadness.

"Even the typhoons did not bring trouble such as we had in later years. Many diseases which we had never known were brought to us by sailors. Many of the people who came—like your Captain Cook—were kind and the people loved them and gave them everything they needed. But others were different . . ." She paused again. "The spirits of our people were not as strong as those of your people, Captain Sutton. They were strong when we went to sea. They led us in many directions, far from land, and our people always found their way back, even from as far away as Hawaii. But when the spirits of your people came, ours were weak, and that is why our race is dying out."

"By spirits—do you mean the spirits of people who have died?" Sutton asked.

"Yes . . . but this is not strange, is it? I am Christian, and I believe in the souls of people. What is so strange about souls or spirits that come back to help us?"

Sutton's thought flashed back again to the rather unusual question Captain Brown asked him in San Francisco: "Do you believe in ghosts?" This was followed, as Sutton recalled, by the rather ominous warning that Sutton would come to believe in them—before the voyage of the *Herman* ended! The "ghosts of a hundred dead men," according to the Captain, were watching over the treasure!

"It—it's a rather startling viewpoint," was all he could say; and Mapuana laughed.

"I hope you will come back to us, Captain Sutton—perhaps on your way home. But there is one thing you will find to be true. You will never forget Hawaii—or the Islands! Even if you live many years without returning, there will be a memory in your heart. But really . . . everyone comes back!" She took his hand, and held it a moment, without any affectation. It seemed to Sutton that everything she did was quite natural. "You will remember the sound of the wind through the coconut palms, rustling the leaves . . . and the green lagoons that turn dark when the sun goes down. This is something that will be with you always, and you will learn to make it a part of you . . . like a place high on the cliff, where a child learns to go when he wants to sit alone and look at the sea and the sky . . ."

She smiled and pressed his hand.

"These islands will always be like the dreams of the little *keiki*—the children, or even dreams of old people who like to remember when they were children."

Sutton was aware of the sound of a carriage driving up the coral roadway. It was evidently his carriage, returning to take him back to the hotel.

He glanced at the woman beside him as he arose from the bench. In spite of what he had heard of the rapid maturity of Polynesian women, it seemed to him that Mapuana had retained to an unusual degree the lively charm of youth, with a kind of ageless womanliness.

"I suppose I'd better be getting back to the hotel," he remarked, and she laughed in the rippling manner he enjoyed so much.

"You sound like a boy going back to school," she said.

Sutton nodded, glumly. "That's about what it is," he said. "I've got to go back to San Francisco and get some things settled. I'm afraid they won't settle easily."

"You *haoles* are all very much alike," she observed. "You borrow trouble that may never happen—and you make yourself quite miserable thinking about things in advance. Why shouldn't you think things will happen for the best? Our people always leave their trouble to the *menehunes* and they usually take care of them for us."

"What are—menehoonies?" He pronounced the word the way she said it.

"They are the little people. If you are good to them, they will help you—but if you are mean, they will plague you. That is what you might call the Polynesian conscience."

They had turned and started back toward the porte-cochere, where the carriage would be waiting. Sutton was doing his best to prolong the walk.

"Your 'little people' are like our elves," he said. "There are good elves and bad elves, you know."

Mapuana laughed.

"In our case, we have only good *menehunes.* It is the people who are good and bad. We also have a saying—*pau pilikia.* That means no more trouble. Why don't you say that, and perhaps your elves will help you."

Sutton grinned. He felt quite pleasant, with the fresh, scented wind blowing down from the Nuuanu *Pali* and the green hills around him and the city bathed in sunlight below them. It seemed rather senseless to be leaving such a place.

As Sutton walked slowly back across the terrace to the front of the house, it seemed to him that this was like something dimly remembered, a link with a forgotten past. And the woman who walked beside him seemed to possess in some inscrutable way the secret of that link, through a kind of alchemy of thought that he did not quite understand.

He realized that he had not gotten to the root of the question that had been uppermost in his mind; and before climbing into the carriage seat, he said to her, "You spoke of knowing who Captain Brown was—

that your grandmother's people knew of him. Do you really have a reason for believing that?"

She nodded gravely, looking at him. Sutton was a fairly handsome man, with curling brown hair, neatly parted in the middle, and a well-kept mustache, curling slightly at the ends. He was not insensitive to the feeling that there was some mutual attraction between Mapuana Davis and himself, but he tried not to be aware of this.

"The stories your Captain told—here at my sister's home the other night—were very much like the stories my *tutu* told me. He was on a big ship that took away young men from the islands—to fight with other ships. That was what my *tutu* told me. Your Captain was not lying, Captain Sutton—he was only bragging, as old men often do. Have you asked him about this?"

Sutton shook his head. "No, but I will. I think it's quite important."

"Yes, it is . . . because for many months the big ship was at an island west of the place where my *tutu* lived. I do not know what it is called now, but then it was called the 'Island of Smoke' because there was a small volcano there. It was not a large island and the volcano was apparently very old and dead."

Sutton nodded. It was not a great deal of information; yet if what Mapuana Davis said was based on fact, and Captain Brown had been on the "great ship," as she said, then it was some indication of the location of the area where the *Sea Foam* had been fifty years ago, perhaps using the island as a base for piratical trips to intercept Australian specie ships.

He said goodbye, shaking her hand. It seemed to him, as he looked into her eyes, that he was seeing for the first time in perfect clarity the inborn wisdom of a people who were so primitive they did not understand feelings of hatred.

Sutton stood at the rail of the *Alameda* as it slowly pulled away from the wharf at the foot of Fort Street, listening to the soft strains of the Royal Hawaiian Band as it broke into the first bars of *Aloha Oe*. Chetwood, at his side, was exhibiting an expression of solemn regret at their departure. His mouth had lost, for the moment, its characteristic puckered grin. Dr. Luce, on the other side of Sutton, watched the scene with his usual placid kindliness, waving now and then at strangers on the dock below, who waved at the departing passengers, shouting "Aloha! Come back to see us!"

Sutton felt that he alone had a real reason for sadness at their departure. He would have liked to have seen Mapuana Davis again; yet he felt any further visit would be presumptuous, and might even smack of incipient unfaithfulness toward his own family ties, now dimly remembered, back in New Rochelle.

More than anything else, however, he was concerned with decisions that must come up in San Francisco. He had determined in his own mind that he would not rejoin the expedition unless Hoffman left the ship; and yet he had a stake in the venture that could not be readily tossed away. When he left New Rochelle, he had embarked on a course from which there could be no retreat.

It had not been an easy decision at that time, and he was well aware that other members of his family could not quite understand why a man of his normal habits and unspectacular conduct should suddenly set forth on an argosy five thousand miles into the Pacific, looking for pirates' gold!

He turned to Chetwood and said, "John, let's agree on one thing. We aren't going to settle for a licking in this thing. We're going to get it straightened out—and we're coming back!"

Chetwood looked at Sutton's face, as if to probe the reason for the remark, and nodded seriously. "I'll agree with that, George. We won't lie down. What worries me most is what happened to Don Stoney? After his first letter—and then our letter! Why should he have accepted Hoffman's position—when he certainly knew what Hoffman's actions had been in San Francisco?"

Dr. Luce, who had leaned over to listen to Chetwood, also nodded.

"We may be walking into a mare's-nest," he remarked, soberly. "You know there's one fellow we may have been overlooking in all this."

"Who is that?" Sutton asked.

"Louis Mooser. I have a hunch he and Hoffman might have planned this bit of intrigue—more than we suspect. It would be a good way to get rid of some members of this expedition—particularly you and John. It would also leave the field open to get rid of Captain Brown, too. Have you thought of that?"

Sutton nodded. "I've thought of it—and I think perhaps the Captain has, too. But I've an idea he can handle Hoffman—as he says."

Dr. Luce nodded assent; and then he said, with a slightly twisted smile, "There's one thing I forgot to tell you two. The other half of the can of strychnine is now missing from my medicine cabinet, along with the arsenic and 'Rough on Rats' that I brought along to get rid of rats." The doctor paused, and added, "Whoever's doing this is getting pretty well stocked up for a long campaign of poisoning."

[2]

The *Alameda* steamed through the Golden Gate shortly after dawn on September 30, having passed the Farallons at daybreak. Sutton was on deck to watch the approach to the city, rising in terraces toward the covering blanket of fog. He was possessed by a peculiar assortment of emotions: anxiety at the approaching meeting with the committee; some excitement at his return to San Francisco and the country of his own family—even if they were some three thousand miles farther on; a trace of guilt at not feeling too much excitement at returning—since he might be on his way across the Pacific again in a few days; and a sensation which he could not quite define, having to do with the land he had just left. The latter emotion was somewhat ameliorated by the expectation that he might be back again soon, at least momentarily, in Honolulu . . . and perhaps there might be longer visits later on.

Had Sutton possessed powers of precognition, he would have realized that he would see Honolulu twice again during the next three months, *en passant,* as it were.

There was no one at the dock to meet them, since they had not given definite notice of their return, so they made their way to the Grand Hotel. Chetwood telephoned Donzel Stoney and they learned that a meeting of the committee had been called for the following evening.

The next morning Sutton received a brief letter at the hotel from H. B. Montague, one of the principal sponsors and chairman of the committee:

"Will you call to see me at the office tomorrow AM about 8:45 or 9 before going to Stoney's. I'm expecting to be called out of town about 10 and I want to have a word with you before I go. . . ." It was dated September 30.

Sutton showed Chetwood the note at breakfast and they agreed to go together to Stoney's office, which was on Montgomery Street, stopping at the Mills Building on the way to see Montague.

Montague was an elderly man, a lawyer with a solid, dignified appearance. Sutton had met him several times before leaving San Francisco, and was impressed with his good sense and quiet friendliness.

After listening to Chetwood's brief summary of events—particularly on the matter of Hoffman's handling of funds, his quarrels with Captain Brown and some indication that Hoffman had tried to tamper with the loyalties of members of the crew, he nodded gravely.

"You will find a divided camp here," he said. "Mooser is the chief dissenter. He feels—or at least says he does—that Hoffman acted within his rights, and that the Captain was incompetent, reckless and extravagant."

He looked at Sutton for an instant, and then said, "He seems to feel that you and Dr. Luce were mainly responsible for the agitation. He said"—a fleeting smile crossed Montague's face—"that Hoffman had driven you off the ship at pistol point to prevent bloodshed."

Sutton smiled grimly. "I can well understand Hoffman's antipathy toward me—and perhaps John. We told him we might prefer charges against him. But why Dr. Luce?"

Montague shrugged. "I know George very well. He is one of the kindest men alive. Anyway"—he arose, and shook hands—"you'll have some solid support at the meeting. Sorry I'll have to miss it. Don Stoney is in the middle, of course . . . but perhaps it will be better that way. Shafter Howard is hunting Hoffman's scalp."

Stoney was glad to welcome Sutton and Chetwood. He explained quickly that while their return had not been anticipated, it would provide some firsthand information as to the troubles that apparently beset the expedition in Honolulu.

"Your last letter was a bit unexpected, Don," Chetwood told him. "In view of your previous letter—in which you must have had Hoffman in mind—it was hard for George and myself to understand your sudden burst of confidence in Ogden."

Stoney sighed. He wore a perpetually worried expression; and when he was not engaged in dominating a group—as he usually did—this gave him a look of harassed uncertainty.

"Mooser thinks everyone is responsible except Hoffman," he finally said. "He had to approve my letter, since it represented the feeling of the committee. We hoped you three might straighten things out—between Ogden and the Captain." He looked over his glasses at Sutton. "You must know, George, that Ogden is not any particular favorite of mine."

Sutton's usually mild expression became firm. "There's more to this than I thought at first," he said, looking directly at Stoney. "I want to get at the bottom of it just as much as the committee does. I've got quite a sum of money invested in this—more than I could really afford. If Mooser has any plans for getting me out of it, he's going to find I'm hard to get out."

Stoney shrugged and sighed again. It was agreed that they would present the full account of all that happened at the meeting, regardless of what the consequences might be. "It's too damn late for politeness," Sutton reminded Stoney as they left. "The *Herman* is already on its way to the South Seas and I've told the Captain I would meet him at Apia or Sydney—within six weeks. There is one thing the committee and Mooser can bet on. Captain Brown will not sail for the island with Hoffman aboard that ship—even if he has to kill him!"

The meeting turned out to be all that was expected: a general Donnybrook, with Mooser and Shafter Howard, one of the principal sponsors, opening with salvos at each other that threatened to break up the gathering at the outset. As Sutton described the affair, in a letter to Walradt:

> Hoffman had written a long letter to Mooser trying to explain his actions and the reasons for the trouble, and after Mooser read it, John Chetwood and I told our story. Then Shafter Howard insisted that as Hoffman was Mooser's agent, Mooser should pay any additional expenses resulting from his conduct. Mooser has taken Hoffman's letter at its face value, and now the whole camp is split. . . .

Several days later—on October 14—Sutton wrote again to Walradt:

> We have had quite a few meetings and a cat-and-mouse game here, harmonizing the various interests and getting all parties together. Mooser has given the most trouble. Some of us wanted to handle him without gloves at the start, but Don Stoney took a more conciliating view, and as a result it began to look as if Mooser would dictate the whole course.
>
> The real trouble arose at the first meeting when Shafter Howard shot it into Mooser, claiming Hoffman was his agent and responsible for the trouble, and he [Mooser] was therefore responsible to the rest of us. This I believe is good law and a justifiable statement, but it was not good politics. Up to that point, Mooser had almost conceded that Hoffman was to blame, but to save himself from the responsibility he had to defend Hoffman. I kept pretty much out of it until I realized Mooser was trying to shift the responsibility to John Chetwood and the doctor and myself. . . .

At this point Sutton had turned to Mooser and said:

"If you want to take over the expedition, Mr. Mooser—you go ahead.

Pay me back what I put into it and I'll get out. I don't think you and Hoffman are going to find the island very easily—without the Captain!"

Mooser, a bulldog sort of man, looked at Sutton for a moment. "Are you trying to threaten me, Sutton?"

Don Stoney broke in: "Look, gentlemen—we will get nowhere this way! Sutton is right . . . without Captain Brown, the entire expedition may as well be called off, and we will all have to take our losses. It is my understanding that the Captain expects some definite action by this committee, and wrangling over responsibility for what has happened isn't going to give him that action."

Mooser's expression had undergone a curious transformation. It seemed to Sutton that Mooser suddenly lost his air of domineering belligerence and the owner of the *Herman* now exhibited signs of uncertainty and perhaps of panic.

Sutton decided it was the moment to plunge in.

"You asked me if I was trying to threaten you, Mr. Mooser," he said, quietly. "Obviously, I'm not. But there are certain things that lead me to think your representative, Ogden Hoffman—and perhaps you, yourself—would like to take over this expedition. I've pointed out one way you can do it—and that's to buy us out. The other way is to try to take over the ship—and that, as you must know, is mutiny, or piracy, and perhaps both!"

There was complete silence in the room. Mooser's face became white and then highly flushed.

"I'm not making any accusations now," Sutton went on, still speaking deliberately. "But if you have any plan in mind—you'd better be damn sure it's a good plan!"

Mooser was a rather large, wedge-shaped man with a round, bullet-shaped head. He hunched forward in his chair, staring at Sutton as if by sheer force of looking at him he would be able to read what was in Sutton's mind. Then he grunted and gave a quick shrug which might have been halfway between anger and disdain and muttered that the only "plan" he had was to make the expedition a success.

The others had listened quietly; no one said anything for a moment. Then Stoney proposed a solution which the others who composed the committee—Montague, Mooser, Jim Moffitt and Frank Whitcomb—agreed upon: First, Stoney was to be authorized to proceed with Sutton to Apia or Sydney, stopping at Honolulu en route to investigate the matters related by Sutton and Chetwood. Second, upon Stoney's agreement, a letter was to be dictated by Sutton and signed by the committee members, authorizing removal of Hoffman from the *Herman* if this was considered by Stoney to be in the best interests of the expedition.

Everyone except Mooser agreed; and he offered no overt objection.

Sutton and Chetwood remained a short while after the others had left—Mooser in obviously disgruntled disagreement, but apparently with no particular basis for dissent; and the others in equally obvious relief that a solution had been reached.

Sutton, his face still set in rather grim lines, said to Stoney, "I wasn't talking through my hat, Don. It may seem a bit fanciful, but I believe there is a real probability that Mooser intended to disrupt this expedition from the start, getting rid of John and myself—and the doctor—so that Hoffman could take over. Everything points to it—and I think the Captain has suspected this all along. I think he trusts John and myself, and of course the doctor—even though he has quarreled with him. But when you consider each point, one linked to the other, it begins to make sense. And remember"—he looked sharply, first at Stoney and then at Chetwood—"just remember that it was Hoffman who wanted the information the Captain intended to give to me to be passed on to the rest. Just suppose, for instance, that Captain Brown had delivered the information on the location of the island to me—and it fell into Hoffman's hands? There would be damn little to stand in the way of getting rid of all of us, including the Captain. A hundred million dollars is not to be sneezed at!"

The following day Sutton wrote again to Walradt:

> Last night I was ready to kick over the traces and leave immediately for New York. Everybody but Mooser, however, had concluded that if I did not go back and meet the Captain, the jig was up and the expedition would be ended. Yet they were afraid to antagonize Mooser for fear he would pull some stunt that would also end it . . . Finally I agreed that if the Committee would sign a letter, which I would dictate, removing Hoffman from the ship, I would go back.
>
> Don Stoney leaves with me tomorrow, and final action will be subject to his decision after investigating the affair. I have no doubt he will find everything as John Chetwood and I stated.

The committee agreed to raise an additional forty-five hundred dollars through subscriptions of the sponsors and promoters; and on October 16 Sutton and Stoney left on the *S.S. Sierra,* bound for Honolulu, Samoa and Australia.

Sutton left with mixed feelings, not a small part of which was the realization that he had been within a week's traveling time of being at home with his family . . . and now he was turning westward again, across the Pacific! As he later told Walradt, had he known that he would make three trips across the Pacific, and require almost three months to catch up with the *Herman,* he probably would have decided to go home to New Rochelle.

[3]

On October 29—two weeks after leaving San Francisco—the *Sierra* stood off Pago Pago harbor, on the island of Tutuila in Samoa. Sutton and Stoney were at the rail, looking despondently at the little town nestled against the sloping hills. The chief steward had just come by and announced: "No one will go ashore, gentlemen. Order of the Health Service. We have sickness aboard."

Stoney turned to Sutton, with a wry smile, and said, "It's measles, The ship's doctor told me this morning. It's worse than smallpox down here." He explained that the disease itself was no worse than anything else, but it struck among the natives with such sudden effect, and with a high fever, that they would immediately run for the water—which was usually fatal. For this reason, no contact between those aboard ship and those ashore could be made, and the *Sierra* would continue on to Sydney.

Sutton nodded. The news did not improve his mood. His thoughts were still tethered, in a sense, to Honolulu. During the day and a half they had spent there while the steamer was laying over to discharge and take on cargo, he had tried unsuccessfully to reach Mapuana Davis by phone. A strange voice, obviously the Chinese servant, had said: "Missee Davee no stop. She all-a-same stop Hilo. Solly!"

Sutton was "solly," too, but there was not much he could do about it. During the few hours ashore he helped Stoney round up information from Tom Hobron, Southard Hoffman—Ogden's brother—and others. Stoney's reports, which he relayed in a letter to the committee, written at sea on October 24, confirmed the account given by Sutton and Chetwood. Among other things he was able to refute some of the comments about Dr. Luce. "The first point I wish to bring out is that some of you have an erroneous impression of Dr. Luce's position," Stoney wrote. "No one has heard a word of complaint against the doctor."

The letter detailed an interview with one of the sailors who had deserted—presumably "John Smith" or Johnson, the Swede—expressing the view that "the Captain's dislike of Hoffman will never leave him." Stoney also reported that the second mate (Willie Benton) was "exceedingly bitter toward Hoffman" and had told Tom Hobron that "at the first sign of serious trouble between Hoffman and the Captain, he would shoot Hoffman."

The day before the *Sierra* reached Pago Pago, one of the stewards had pointed out to Sutton a gray shadow far down to the southward, appearing to lie above the clouds. "That's Manua—the eastern part of the Samoan group." This, Sutton remembered, was the island where Mapuana was born and had lived as a girl.

Stoney and Sutton were able to inveigle the harbor officials into confirming that the *Herman* had been sighted about ten days ago, off Upolulu, some forty miles northeast of Apia, and was reported to have left later for Sydney. The first report was confirmed in the log of the *Herman* much later. The entry of October 20 said: "Strong southeast breeze, heavy squalls and rainy weather. 10 A.M. aft topsail and flying jib furled. 11:30 A.M. sighted land 'Upolulu,' eastpoint, bore southwest by south, 40 miles distant."

The report that the *Herman* had sailed for Sydney, however, was somewhat in error; the schooner was still lying at Apia, some sixty miles west of Pago Pago, when the *Sierra* passed through. The Captain and Hoffman at the moment were each trying to get a legal stranglehold on the other for possession of the *Herman* through the rather indeterminate entanglements of the complex judicial relations of the New Zealand resident commissioner and the American Consul.

The *Sierra* docked in Sydney on November 7, but it was not until a week later that Sutton and Stoney were able to discover the whereabouts of the *Herman*. This was in a rather roundabout way. A "Mr. Fisher" of the American Consul's office called them at the Hotel Australia, and read the following cablegram from Auckland, New Zealand, unsigned, but evidently from Brown:

> SCHOONER HELD APIA BY AMERICAN CONSUL. COME AT ONCE. HOFFMAN SHARRATT WAITING. FIND DELIVER THIS MESSAGE TO DONZEL STONEY PASSENGER ON SIERRA FROM SAN FRANCISCO LAST TRIP. STONEY WILL PAY CABLEGRAM EXPENSE AND SEARCH IN SYDNEY.

The message had arrived at Auckland—by steamer from Apia, since there was no cable connection with the Islands. Stoney and Sutton decided—as Stoney later wrote to Montague in San Francisco—that they "belonged in Apia." They made further inquiries of the master of a steamer from Apia, which had just arrived in Sydney, and found out the *Herman* was impounded in Apia. On November 7 the two travelers left for Pago Pago, where they expected to get passage on an inter-island vessel for Apia. They missed the connection by about six thousand miles and nearly four weeks.

As their steamer—it was again the *Sierra*—plowed around the western point of Tutuila and headed toward the single large wharf which comprised the port of Pago Pago, word spread among the passengers that there was again a case of measles aboard! This time it was little "Pick" Stoney, Donzel Stoney's daughter, who had made the trip with Mrs. Stoney to Australia. The ship could not discharge passengers, so it continued on to Honolulu.

After a few hours in Honolulu, there would be a connection with the *Ventura,* a sister ship of the *Sierra,* en route to Samoa and Australia; and Sutton decided to make another effort to talk with Mapuana Davis. He managed to slip away for a short time uptown and telephoned the MacGregor home. This time Mapuana was there.

Sutton—whose feelings by this time were so scarred with frustrations that he could view the matter with some semblance of objective humor—recited his tale of travels and travails. Mapuana broke into a peal of laughter—a sound that might have set Sutton's heart thumping under other circumstances.

"I did manage to see your island—from a distance," he told her.

"You saw Manua?" Mapuana seemed delighted. "Tell me—what did it look like?"

"From about fifty miles away? It looked like a cloud of smoke on the ocean."

Mapuana laughed again.

"You must come back with your pockets full of gold, and then perhaps you will take us all on a visit to Manua . . . will you not? With Mrs. Sutton and the children?"

Sutton muttered something about east being east, said goodbye hurriedly, and dashed for the ship. He decided it was time to root out any emotional entanglements connected with Honolulu; he doubted that he would be back soon—at least not until they caught up with the *Herman!*

They almost missed their boat a third time. There was another case of measles aboard the *Ventura* but Sutton and Stoney persuaded the health officer that they were immune—and they had traveled 15,590 nautical miles to reach Pago Pago! They were permitted to land.

This was December 11. The following day they took a small inter-island steamer for Apia. Captain Brown was aboard the schooner when they arrived, as were Tommy Benson, the second mate, and the ubiquitous Willie Peterson, who appeared to be a permanent fixture on the *Herman*. Mr. Hendrickson was uptown; the others had deserted. The Japanese cook, Hasino, and the steward, Jimmy Akahito, were in Apia and would probably rejoin the ship when it sailed. Hoffman and Sharratt had moved to a hotel in town.

Captain Brown, his expression alternating between joviality, repressed rage and occasional bursts of blazing anger when Hoffman's name was mentioned, recounted his experiences during the two and a half months since Sutton had watched the *Herman* pass out through the breakwater entrance to Honolulu harbor.

Shortly after the schooner was tied up in Apia harbor, according to the Captain, Hoffman had presented a letter to him carrying a power of attorney from Louis Mooser, permitting Hoffman to take over or to sell the *Herman,* if necessary.

The Captain drew the back of his hand across his bewhiskered mouth, as if he would physically stifle the things he would like to have said. Then he continued, in a growling voice: "As you gentlemen know, I had the same kind of paper. I demanded his papers. As master of this vessel, I could not have a man aboard who holds papers authorizing him to take possession of the ship. He refused to give them to me."

Sutton looked at Stoney.

"Louis Mooser again." Stoney nodded.

Things went from bad to worse. Hoffman and Sharratt moved off the ship, taking rooms in town; and on November 5 the Captain was served with a notice from George Heimrod, the American consul general, stating that "with the evidence in my possession relating to certain documents belonging to Mr. Ogden Hoffman," the schooner *Herman* was impounded indefinitely, pending advice from San Francisco.

Captain Brown tried to sell provisions for money, but was restrained again by a consular order; and he finally ordered Hoffman and Sharratt to keep off the boat, threatening to shoot them if either came aboard. He was then charged with criminally threatening passengers, and apparently all hell was about to break loose when Sutton and Stoney arrived.

In Stoney's report to Montague, from Pago Pago on December 19, he wrote:

"That afternoon [the day of his arrival with Sutton in Apia] the Captain drove from the Custom House to the American Consul, picking us up at the hotel and telling us he wanted to get away at once. He had paid his bills and was anxious to leave that afternoon. We cleared the American Consul's office, upon my showing that I possessed full authority from the Committee, including Mooser; but a little later we were served with an order from the German Consul, which Hoffman got, preventing our leaving."

Stoney, now thoroughly angered, went over to Hoffman's hotel, and as he reported: "I jumped Hoffman at once and told him he was bucking against the whole expedition. He said he did not care—if he did not get his rights, he would have the Captain arrested and keep the vessel at Apia for another six months."

Stoney conferred with Sutton; and at this point Sutton made no effort to conceal his suspicion.

"Hoffman is trying to break up this expedition. He may even have an idea he already knows the position of the island, although I doubt that he does."

Stoney nodded; and it was agreed that they would immediately pay Hoffman's hotel bill and deposit sufficient money with the American consul, as required by law, to return Hoffman and Sharratt to San Francisco.

The *Herman* sailed from Apia on December 16, putting into Pago Pago the following day. As Sutton later wrote to Walradt: "The Captain was really enraged when he found we were leaving without Hoffman and Frank Sharratt on board. I actually think he wanted the satisfaction of dumping them overboard in mid-ocean." The Captain had said he wanted to take them to Pago Pago "in irons."

The next day the little schooner sailed for Sydney, where repairs would be made and the expedition would await the passing of the typhoon season—although the word "typhoon" was not mentioned in Captain Brown's presence.

The run down to Sydney lasted twenty-one days, with Christmas and New Year's spent at sea. The *Herman* sighted the Australian coast late in the afternoon of January 10. On the following day she came around North Head under a spanking southeast wind, entered Jackson Harbor—Sydney's long, winding ship channel—and was taken in tow to Watson's Bay where she lay over for immigration inspection until nightfall. Then she was towed on to Neutral Bay, across from the docks on Wooloomoloo. The trip was without incident, except for two things:

"The Repose"

The sailing of the *Alameda*.

Both the above pictures were taken at the Sydney harbor and show Donzel Stoney, Mrs. Stoney and their daughter Pick.

Two views of the *Herman* at anchor in Neutral Bay in Sydney.

Sutton was washed overboard in a blustering southwest gale and was barely hauled aboard by two of the sailors; and the Captain's mercurial temperament underwent a series of spectacular changes. In place of the repressed rage he had exhibited at Apia, he now assumed a domineering air of command, quarreling at times with Sutton and more frequently taking out his wrath on members of the crew. The latter had shipped out of Pago Pago—except for Mr. Hendrickson, Tommy Benson, Willie Peterson and the two Japanese—consisting of three Samoans and a sailor named Robert Unea who hailed from Hilo, Hawaii.

Stoney described the Captain's temperamental outbursts in a letter to Walradt:

> The old man is a remarkable combination of quick temper and good will; but his temper gets the better of the argument, and he usually takes it out on the sailors, and sometimes on the cook or mate. His squabbles were all based on small matters, but were extremely annoying. He is a great deal of a blowhard, and for the purposes of the expedition we have had to humor him. He is so possessed of his own importance it annoys him to see anyone enjoying himself. . . . He even objected because George and I played cribbage on the boat.

The day the *Herman* and its expeditionary forces sailed into Jackson Harbor, another member of the expedition arrived to join them—Dr. Luce. He had come on the *S.S. Sonoma* in response to a message Stoney had sent from Sydney in November, which was relayed through London to Vancouver, and thence to San Francisco. Stoney had said: "SEND CHETWOOD AND DR. LUCE WHEN CONDITIONS FAVORABLE IN APIA."

Dr. Luce said he had arrived in Pago Pago after the *Herman* had sailed and therefore continued on to Sydney. Chetwood was due to arrive on the next steamer. Stoney left for San Francisco on January 19 and Chetwood came in on the thirtieth.

Meanwhile Captain Brown announced, with some satisfaction, that he had accomplished another major stroke of good leadership: he had obtained quarters for the group so they would not have to live aboard the *Herman* while the schooner was being fitted out. Both Sutton and Dr. Luce were quite anxious to obtain some kind of lodging ashore; the boat was no place for comfort. But the Captain's announcement—and his manner of announcing it—aroused some misgivings.

It appeared he had met the husband of a red-haired lady named Ruby Short while he was in Apia. Mrs. Short was the keeper of a lodging house in the suburban hamlet of Mossman, near Neutral Bay. She was—in the Captain's words—"a gorgeous woman," somewhere in her mid-forties; and among other things she had a daughter, about seventeen. The daughter—whose name was Lilli—proved to be dark, slender and sloe-eyed, with an assortment of ancestries that seemed to include not only Polynesian and French, but probably, from the cast of her eyes, some Chinese. Mr. Short, who was "a ruddy Englishman" according to the Captain, may also have contributed to the mixture.

The Paumotus: Treasures of Capricorn

[1]

The *Herman* was hauled out on stocks at Neutral Bay, where it was to remain until about March 1, when it would be made ready for sailing. At this time the hurricane season along the tropical belt would normally be over—or as nearly over as it ever was. The sudden fierce typhoons that often swept along the "horse latitudes," disturbing the baffling calms with unexpected and insane fury, were not predictable in any season. Nevertheless, the worst of the storms would probably have blown out by late March or early April; and the plan was to set forth in the first week of March.

However, mid-March found the *Herman* still lying at the shipyard in Neutral Bay, with a libel notice again tacked to its mainmast. Captain Brown alternated between rage and indignation. The funds of the expedition had been dissipated—no one knew exactly how—and he was beset with bill collectors. Lack of money seemed to be regarded by the Captain as a personal affront to his dignity and position.

Sutton and Chetwood noticed a sudden change in the old man's demeanor. At first he had demanded the attendance of his associates almost every minute of the day and well into the night. Sutton was the principal recipient of his dubious favors; he insisted that Sutton take him out to the shipyard and back in the launch each day, and his presence was required each evening at "The Repose," which was the idyllic name Mrs. Short had chosen for her lodging house.

Chetwood and the doctor were highly amused at these command performances; but one day Dr. Luce remarked upon the change in the

Captain's attitude. "The old boy seems to have found companionship somewhere else," he told Sutton. "I notice he dosen't have you in attendance all the time."

Sutton smiled ruefully, and shook his head. "I guess I've been jilted. I don't think I'm going to break up over it, however. How would you like to be called out of your room while you're writing a letter home —to play a game of whist? And he can't even play. He cheats all the time and wants to do my bidding as well as his own."

Chetwood's expression showed more concern, however. He looked at Sutton and then the doctor with a worried frown; and finally he remarked: "There may be something more significant than your broken romance, George. Have you noticed the old man seems preoccupied lately? Maybe we're *all* being jilted."

Chetwood had brought a letter from the Captain's wife—with whom he had corresponded a great deal during the three months he was back in San Francisco—and delivered it to the Captain. In a separate note to Chetwood she had written: "I am deeply grateful to you and Captain Sutton for your kindness to my husband and for your forbearance. You must try to understand him. He is determined to recover the treasure."

This had been a matter of encouragement to Sutton and the doctor when Chetwood showed it to them; and apparently the letter to Captain Brown had bolstered his morale, at least momentarily. He told Sutton shortly afterward: "I am putting together the paper, with information about the island. I will put this in your hands—to use in case of an emergency."

After that, nothing further was said. Sutton had been certain, from remarks the Captain had made from time to time, that his wife also held the secret of the island's location—perhaps confided to her in one of the old man's rare moments of trust. "She spoke to me with such assurance that day in Auburn," he told Chetwood. "She believes in it as strongly as he does."

The Captain had become sullen and resentful over the failure of the committee to provide funds—which had been promised by March 20; but more than that, he began to be reticent. He seldom spoke to any of his three associates, even during the evenings at "The Repose." Usually he would establish himself in a large chair in the sitting room and hold forth on his own adventures and exploits at sea, embellishing them with almost inexhaustible imagination. During these times Sutton and Chetwood would try to leave, as unobtrusively as possible; but the doctor often stayed on, having nothing better to do.

Dr. Luce noticed that the red-haired lady of the house was always in attendance at these performances, usually sitting beside her daughter, Lilli, both listening with rapt attention. He observed that Mrs. Short would incline her head this way and that, as the Captain's narrative would rise and fall with the intensity of his experiences, and the daughter would move her head in rhythmic unison with her mother's. This amused the doctor for a time; then he began to observe the scene with greater attention.

He told Sutton and Chetwood that it looked almost like a marionette performance. "It looked as if she had supernatural strings attached to the girl's head."

Chetwood nodded grimly. "They are strings, all right—but I don't think they're supernatural. By God"—he slapped his leg—"that's it! It's the girl! That red-haired Jezebel is using the girl for bait—and the senile old idiot is falling for it!" He turned to Sutton. "That's probably why you're no longer in demand, George."

Sutton laughed, and Dr. Luce smiled in his dry way.

"I can stand it," Sutton said.

Chetwood was quite serious.

"That old madam isn't doing this just to amuse herself—or train her daughter professionally. She's got something up her sleeve!"

Shortly afterward—during one of the Captain's spells of friendliness—Sutton asked when the *Herman* was due to sail.

"The libel should be lifted—as soon as funds arrive from the States. We ought to set a definite date of departure, hadn't we?"

The old man arose from the big chair, where he had been sitting in his parlor—he was the only one of the four who had that additional accommodation at "The Repose"—and stared for a moment at Sutton, his whiskers bristling.

"By God—" His face was almost apoplectic. "You want an answer, Cap'n Sutton? Well, by God, you'll get it!" He paced around the room, while Sutton and Chetwood, who was with them, stared in astonishment. Finally the Captain turned and pointed a long, quivering finger at Sutton's chest.

"I cabled today—again! For five thousand! That what I want—five thousand dollars! Damn me, if I continue to stand idle while those—those—" He was inarticulate for a moment. "That damn Hoffman and

Mooser are behind this, mark ye! I have the right to sell the *Herman*—an' unless I get five thousand dollars this week, you can lay your course on that, Cap'n Sutton!"

Sutton had arisen also from his chair; but then, to avoid the appearance of an outright argument, he sat down again.

"You can't do that, Captain Brown," he said, trying to pacify the old man with the mildness of his voice. "Donzel Stoney has assured us the money will be here within a day or so—to settle all claims. But the most they could raise was fifteen hundred. That will pay our bills, and leave several hundred to go on—if we need it in Tahiti."

This was March 20, and a cable via London from Stoney had been received several days earlier, stating that fifteen hundred dollars would be cabled on that date. Previously the Captain had asked for three thousand dollars but Stoney had replied: "CANNOT RAISE MORE THAN $1500 NOW. PLEASE INDICATE PURPOSE IF MORE NEEDED. OTHERWISE TRIP MUST END."

"I've cabled today," the Captain repeated, in a somewhat moderated tone, but still exhibiting the familiar signs of anger. "I cannot have my judgment questioned—or my position jeopardized. They must place five thousand in my hands—now! Or the expedition will end right here, an' I will sell the boat for my bills." He stood over Sutton, and for an instant it looked as if the old man would strike him. "Do ye understand me?" he roared.

Sutton again arose from his chair, and this time he remained standing. He looked directly at the Captain, and his voice was controlled but firm.

"We've done everything possible, Captain, in this emergency. We know it has been trying—to all of us. I think they know our situation—Don Stoney knows it, anyway. They'll do everything reasonable to support us. You have no right to sell the boat, or even talk about it."

"Rights, have I?" The Captain continued to shake his finger. "I'll show you what rights a sea captain has! I've got the papers—Mooser signed 'em—"

He stopped, as if he suddenly realized he had said too much. Then he turned abruptly and walked into his bedroom. Chetwood looked at Sutton, and they both left the room.

Mrs. Short had a "party" that night—a reception, she explained, "in honor of the Captain." How much honor was involved was difficult to determine; but when Sutton and Chetwood returned that evening (the doctor had gone up to his room) the sitting room was populated with one of the strangest assortments of people—mostly women and mostly of very dark coloration—that Sutton had ever seen.

He had agreed with Chetwood that they ought to remain at the party for a few moments, in order not to stir up any further indignation or resentment on the part of the Captain. There was a large bowl of a curious, pink-colored punch in which Sutton detected the unmistakable taste of Bulimba rum, and everyone was helping himself or herself at will. Most of the women were advancing upon middle age, or had passed it; so that Lilli's youth stood out, almost as a stark reminder of approaching old age of the others. The Captain was all over the place, and particularly all over Lilli. She hardly dared leave his side; when she moved even a few feet away he would stride across the room and repossess her with something that was a cross between a fatherly embrace and the hug of a grizzly bear. Mrs. Short hovered on the edge of things, her eye constantly on Lilli and the old man; and when Lilli would seem to draw away from the Captain, Mrs. Short would shake her head slightly. She appeared to be keeping them in rapport with waves of her head, like a psychic puppeteer.

Mrs. Short was attired in a billowy dress, cut rather low at the neck, that looked as if it had been taken from costumes left over from an impoverished carnival troupe. In fact the whole assembly of guests resembled, in a bizarre way, the leavings of a band of gypsies. Lilli was dressed more conventionally than the others, in a closely fitting, flowered dress that performed all the functions of decency, and a few others besides.

A few men were present, short, swarthy, slightly furtive in their manner, as if they were not certain why they were there. It seemed to Sutton the atmosphere of the party was secretive and almost conspiratorial, as if something was afoot. They talked in whispers and stopped talking when Sutton and Chetwood passed. As Sutton found out, most of them were from Auckland—"old friends" of Ruby Short, who seemed to have occupied some position in the world of entertainment in her palmier days. The women were all dark-skinned, and Sutton supposed there was a Maori mixture in most of them, together with traces of practically every other ethnic group that had lived in or passed across the Pacific in the past century and a half.

Sutton and Chetwood were somewhat bored, and were about to leave and go upstairs when a particularly active, if somewhat antique, lady caught hold of Sutton's arm and half dragged him out on the veranda. After one or two burbling exclamations about the light and the stars, the lady said, "You'll be on the Captain's new boat, of course."

Sutton stared at her. "What new boat?"

She squeezed his arm, confidentially. "You know—of course." She turned beady eyes upon him. "The new boat he's getting after he sells the one he now has. We're all going to Tahiti with him!"

Sutton, surprised as he was at this unexpected information, could not help envisioning the variously dressed women of the party, draped about the decks, companionways and other parts of a small craft such as the *Herman*. He nodded, and then almost forcibly ejected himself from her grasp, leaving the astonished woman to make her own explanation of his departure.

Inside the large room again, he motioned to Chetwood to follow him. They left—without incurring the Captain's displeasure, since he was giving his full attention to Lilli—and went upstairs. Sutton told Chetwood what he had heard.

Chetwood's face was grave. "I haven't spoken much to the Captain recently," he said. "But do you realize what this means? The old pirate practically told us before—and this confirms it. He's planning to sell the *Herman*—and he has papers signed by Louis Mooser which give him the authority to do it!"

Sutton nodded. "It would be a clever trick—to sell the ship, leave us stranded, and take off with this riff-raff for the island!"

The following day a cable was dispatched to San Francisco:

CAPTAIN PROVED DISHONEST. TO MOOSER: WITHDRAW AUTHORITY GIVEN BROWN. TELEGRAPH QUICKLY NECESSARY AUTHORITY SUTTON OR MYSELF TO USE IN ADMIRALTY COURT.

This was April 15. Two days later Mooser's answer was received:

BROWNS AUTHORITY WITHDRAWN. PROCURE BILL OF SALE RE HERMAN FOR SUTTON OR YOURSELF. DO YOUR BEST.

That afternoon Chetwood obtained a restraining order, and went aboard the *Herman* with Sutton. Tommy Benson was aboard. "I'm glad you've come, Captain Sutton," he said. "The Captain has given me orders to put your luggage off the ship."

An hour later Captain Brown came aboard. He had been served with a copy of the court order, which he waved angrily at Sutton and Chetwood.

"Ye damned landlubbers—ye can't do this!" he roared. For an instant Sutton thought the old man was having a stroke. He gripped the rail

The Treasure Hunters.

CAPTAIN JAMES BROWN OF THE HERMAN.

There came here in January last Captain James Brown, a veteran Yankee skipper, and his trim little schooner Herman, now lying in Neutral Bay, as shown in our photograph. Captain Brown is a tall, sinewy, blue-eyed, grey-bearded, hard-bitten seaman, a man who seems to have had a most remarkable career, and looks capable of continuing it vigorously for many a year yet. A San Francisco syndicate sent him out here with the Herman to recover a small matter of £5,000,000 worth of Chilian treasure which Captain Brown alone is supposed to know the hiding place of, but the Captain fell out with the syndicate, and when its representatives came here to go to the Islands with the Herman they were not allowed on board, so they moved the Courts to prevent the Captain selling the schooner to Burns, Philp, and Co. (he says that not being coppered she is not suitable for work among coral reefs), and also to prevent his taking certain moneys out of the Union Bank, and an injunction has been granted pending hearing.

Captain Brown called in last week to announce his intended departure by the Ventura on Monday for San Francisco. There he says he will form another syndicate to get the treasure.

According to the captain's story he went to sea at 11 from San Francisco, making his way to New York, where he got into the West Indian trade. To give his own words to an interviewer last week, he said :—

"I was born in 1832, in California, my parents being Mexicans, and I went to sea when very young. That's all I need say about myself just here. But in regard to the treasure, I must tell you that in 1822 there was trouble between the Spaniards and the Peruvians, and as it was feared that the Spanish gunboats would bombard the city of Callao the authorities transferred the whole of the national funds to an American schooner called the Black Witch, Captain Smith, which hailed from Salem, Massachusetts."

"What was the value of the treasure, do you think ?" he was asked.

"Well, it was said to be worth some 50,000,000dol. It consisted of a great quantity of jewellery, church service plate, and barrels of silver dollars. Captain Smith sailed from Callao with this valuable freight and went to Cocos Island, which was then little known. He took the treasure ashore and 'cached' it. Then trouble arose amongst the Black Witch's crew, and heavy weather was also experienced. The upshot was that Captain Smith and another man were the only persons to return to the mainland. The Captain made his way home to Salem, and related his experiences to his son."

"And how did you become connected with the matter ?"

"Well, that's what I'm going to tell you. In the latter part of 1849 I was mate of a New York ship lying at Kingston, Jamaica, West Indies, which in those days was the most approved rendezvous for pirates in those parts. I made the acquaintance of Captain Smith's son, who was master of a fine big schooner which he was fitting out ostensibly for pearl-fishing.'

"Why ostensibly ?"

"As a blind to the Customs-house officers. He was realy going for the Cocos treasure. At that time of course I was only a youngster and fit for anything, and he had little difficulty in inducing me to join him, which I did ; he sailing as master and I as mate. Well, to cut a long story short, we arrived at Cocos Island, and had no trouble in finding the treasure, which we quickly transferred to the schooner. Then we set sail for a certain island in the Tahitian Group. There we excavated a cave and planted the treasure, together with some more which we had added to it. Well, after that I came away in a small yacht."

"And what about the master and crew of the schooner ?"

"They died and the schooner was burned."

"Why was she burned ?"

"Well (with a significant shrug of the shoulders), the captain knew, but he's dead."

"And where did you go to ?"

"I came across to Australia and landed at Guichen Bay, near the mouth of the Murray. I brought with me £1,000,000 of the treasure, but as a blind I first went on to the gold diggings. Subsequently I took up a cattle and sheep ranche at Mount Gambier, and later on I went to England. I remained in London about 10 years as a shipbroker. Then I went to America, and I have since then been carrying on business as a 'wrecker' and shipbroker in Providence City, Rhode Island. Later on this syndicate was formed by Dr. Lewis, and the schooner Herman was brought in San Francisco for the purpose of this expedition."

"And why didn't you go direct to the treasure island instead of coming from San Francisco to Sydney ?"

"Because we could not get down to the islands in time to escape the 'hurricane season.' But I am ready to start now if this legal trouble was only over."

This story appeared in the *Sydney Mail* on May 6, 1903.

with one hand and waved the summons with the other. His eyes rolled wildly from one side to another; and then, with what seemed a superhuman effort at self-control, he stood rigid for a moment, except for the trembling of the paper in his hand. Finally he said, in a calmer voice, "Gentlemen, I have had to arrange for the sale of this boat—to Burns-Phillips Company, here in Sydney. There was nothing else I could do. We have no money."

Sutton, who had been able to calm the old man in the most trying conditions, said in a low, mild voice, "We understand, Captain—but we've had to take over authority . . . to protect us all, and those who put up money for us. If you sell the boat, the entire expedition will go under. You would be liable—and your wife knows that—"

"My wife! She knows this—you have written?"

For an instant there was such a stricken expression on the old man's face that Sutton said quickly: "We have not informed her of anything, Captain. John Chetwood wrote her in San Francisco, as you know. But she understands that you have an agreement with us. She knows that, Captain. She would bear the brunt of any failure on your part—which you would have to face if you ever returned to the United States."

Sutton's calmness seemed to restore some order to the Captain's thinking. He stood at the rail, breathing heavily. His great frame seemed almost to shrink physically. He remained at the rail, drawing in great lungfuls of air and expelling them with a rumbling sigh, as if the act of breathing would get the whole thing out of his system.

Finally he turned away, without a further word, still clutching the court order, and shambled slowly toward the after companionway and disappeared below.

[2]

Sutton and Chetwood held an emergency meeting with Dr. Luce at the Australia Hotel to decide on a course of action. The wire from San Francisco had given them clear authority to take over the *Herman,* removing the Captain as master. This, however, was only part of the problem. Their ultimate objective was to recover the "church treasure" of Peru and, as far as anyone knew, Captain Brown was the only man alive who knew where it was.

Sutton expressed the problem quite succinctly.

"We've got to kick the Captain off the ship and then kick him back on again," he said. "Otherwise we have only a salvage operation—to sell the ship for what we can get for her, and go home."

Chetwood and the doctor agreed, a bit glumly.

"You'll have to take over as master," Chetwood said to Sutton. "You're the only one qualified, and from past experience, you're probably the only man the Captain would listen to in matters of seamanship."

"I'm not sure he'll listen to anyone," Sutton said. "But we've got to make some kind of move that will satisfy him. John, you know the common law in matters of this sort. Can the Captain desert us—simply leave us?"

"Not in a foreign port," Chetwood said. "I haven't looked up Australian law—we'd have to get a local barrister. But I think we could get a court order that would force him either to leave with us or go to jail. Our first step is to get the matter into the courts, without unduly riling the old boy."

This step was accomplished quietly, with the help of the American Consul, a Mr. Orlando Baker, to whom they presented their credentials and the wire from Louis Mooser. Captain Brown was then approached as tactfully as possible, under the circumstances. Chetwood and Dr. Luce spoke to him first, explaining that Sutton had been named master for the good of the expedition, but that Captain Brown's rights under their agreement would be fully protected with respect to the treasure itself.

Captain Brown, although shaken by these unexpected events, was in no sense defeated. The old man had come through many bitter fights and he was not inclined to back down from this one.

However, as Chetwood astutely pointed out, he was no longer a young man in his early twenties, or even a grizzled veteran of the freebooting business in his fifties; he was an old man, past seventy. And beyond everything else, he was possessed with an iron determination to "recover" the vast wealth which he now felt belonged to him, by moral and physical right.

"This is our best hope," Chetwood told Sutton and the doctor. "We must arrange things so that his pride is not defeated too much—although any small scratch seems to cut the old man to the bone. But if we are to continue, the Captain must go along with us. And I don't think he's really made up his mind what to do. Probably this is the reason, George," he said to Sutton, "why he never turned that paper over to you, as he promised."

Sutton nodded. "If worse comes to worst, I think we could get the information from Mrs. Brown, providing she was sure we would protect the Captain's interest. But that would take time, and it's risky. Don Stoney would have to go east—I don't think Arthur Walradt could handle it. No"—he shook his head—"we've got to handle him out here."

Handling the Captain was a marginal business. He came into court "under protest," and charged conspiracy on the part of his associates to "take over my command." Chetwood and a Sydney solicitor, J. Stewart Thom, presented a long and detailed bill of particulars in which the entire purpose of the expedition had to be disclosed. By the end of April, Captain Brown had been legally stripped of his authority, and Sutton was sworn in by the American consul, Orlando Baker, as master of the *Herman*. And almost everyone in Sydney knew about it.

Meanwhile work proceeded rapidly on the schooner to get her ready to sail. With the libel lifted by payment of the bills, and Chetwood maintaining close control over all expenditures, the little ship was rapidly fitted out for the voyage. Tommy Benson, who had been discharged by Captain Brown the afternoon the restraining order was served on him—the Captain's final act of defiance—had been rehired. Mr. Hendrickson remained as first mate and the two Japanese—Jimmy Akahito and Hasino—were back again.

Sutton and Chetwood had some reservations about both Jimmy and the cook. As Sutton pointed out to the doctor, "We still haven't located that can of strychnine and the missing rat poison. Jimmy and the cook probably had nothing to do with it, but we don't know for sure."

The ship was searched for the missing poison, and no trace of it was found; so it was classified as an unsolved mystery—and an additional reason to be on guard.

"The Captain didn't feed it to Hoffman—and that's what I thought he wanted it for, if he took it," Dr. Luce pointed out. "If the old man has it, he doesn't keep it on the ship. I've looked everywhere."

By this time all of Sydney had read newspaper stories about the *Herman* and the search for the lost "church treasure" of Peru. Even the judge who held the hearing, the Honorable H. P. Owen, noted as an *ex parte* utterance of the court that "it seems a pity that anything should prevent such an outstanding expedition from being carried out to its conclusion—whatever it may be!"

The Captain at first was adamant in his refusal to continue on the trip under the humiliating loss of command. His burden of humiliation was increased when Mrs. Short, the erstwhile dowager empress of his lodging house, demanded some thirty-six pounds for back rent at "The Repose," and peremptorily cut off the Captain's diplomatic relations with her sloe-eyed daughter.

Sutton, the only one of the group adept enough to salve the Captain's feelings, held a conference with him in the Hotel Australia.

The Captain was once again in the depths of despondency. Not only was he faced with eviction from his rooms at "The Repose," but he would be left derelict on the beach at Sydney, and perhaps be put in jail. Sutton, without pressing the point too far, let this sink in.

"We will undertake to pay your bills—including solicitors' fees," Sutton told him. "We are under instructions from the committee to pay them directly, if you agree to continue. Otherwise, the court order absolves us from all further responsibility."

The Captain nodded glumly; the "degradation and humiliation," as he expressed it, were almost more than he could bear. Sutton felt genuinely sorry for the old man; but he also realized that unless the Captain agreed to come along under these conditions, the expedition would be ended and they would have to return to San Francisco emptyhanded. So he did not relax his own firmness.

The Captain finally agreed to terms, with one provision: they must never reveal to Mrs. Brown his "degradation and humiliation." Sutton agreed to this; and the Captain was signed on as a "supercargo"—to "protect his seaman's rights." This also protected the expedition against his last-minute desertion.

During the last days before departure—which was to be on May 20—the Captain suddenly experienced an inexplicable reversal of attitude. In fact, his old joviality seemed to have returned. He came aboard the *Herman,* offered a few suggestions in the outfitting of the ship, and settled himself in his quarters. This puzzled Sutton, and he mentioned it to Chetwood and the doctor. "He acts as if he had a new lease on life." Chetwood screwed his mouth into a smile.

"As far as I can see—he has. At least it's a different lease."

As a final bit of insurance against a last-minute defection on the part of the Captain, Sutton obtained from the American consul an order requiring the Captain to be aboard the ship when it sailed or be sent to jail as a deserter.

On Wednesday, May 20, the *Herman* weighed anchor in Neutral Bay, took a towline from the tug *Shamrock,* and with Captain Brown sitting regally on the afterdeck, threaded through the winding passages of Jackson Harbor and out toward the sea. Shortly before noon the

CONSULAR SERVICE, U. S. A.

George William Sutton, having taken the oath required by law of the United States, is hereby appointed by the power invested in me (Consular Regulation Section 216.) by the Government of the United States, Master of the schooner Herman, Official Register 96031. K.G.V.S. and authorized to assume control April 24th 1903 at noon. Witness my hand and Official seal this 24th day of April 1903

Orlando H Baker,
U S Consul,
at Sydney
N.S.W
Australia

The letter appointing Sutton the "master of the schooner *Herman*."

CONSULAR SERVICE, U. S. A.

Consulate General of the United States at
Apia, Samoa, November 5th, 1902.

James Brown,
Captain of the American Schooner " Herman ".
Apia Harbor.

Sir:--

With the evidence in my possession relating to certain documents belonging to Mr. Ogden Hoffman, which he asserts show his authority to represent Mr. L. H. Mooser of San Francisco, Cal., the equitable owner of the vessel, I, George Heimrod, Consul General at Apia, hold this vessel until such a time as advice is received from the United States, determining Mr. Ogden Hoffman's position relative to the vessel.

I have the honor to be, Sir,

Very respectfully,

Geo. Heimrod

Consul General, U. S. A.

The holding letter from the Consul General at Apia.

schooner dropped the towline off South Head, broke out sail and nosed to seaward under a brisk southwest wind.

One incident puzzled and disturbed Sutton to some extent. As he stood at the forward rail to watch the *Shamrock* take in its line, a small cruiser steamed out of the harbor in the wake of the *Herman* and circled the little schooner. Sutton thought at first it might be some last-minute creditor anxious to slap another libel on the ship or a summons on the Captain; but the little cruiser circled around, tooting its whistle, and headed back into the harbor.

Sutton could not be certain, but he was virtually sure he saw a red-haired lady at the rail of the cruiser, waving a white handkerchief. She looked remarkably like Mrs. Ruby Short. Captain Brown must have thought so, too, because as the little boat gave a farewell blast of its whistle, he arose from his chair and waved back.

Sutton glanced at the Captain as he went aft to set the watch, but no explanatory comment was forthcoming. The Captain continued to stare ahead with profound indifference.

Aboard the *Herman* at this time, in addition to the Captain, Sutton, Chetwood and the doctor, were Mr. Hendrickson and Tommy Benson; and there was also the reliable Willie Peterson, who came aboard a few days before sailing and asked to sign on. Since he was a competent seaman and knew the *Herman,* Sutton took him in the crew.

Two other seamen, Jack Jensen and Jimmy Wilson, had been taken on by Mr. Hendrickson in Sydney; and a third sailor—Willie Fisher—came aboard the morning of departure, and was taken on to fill out the crew. Sutton wondered how Fisher had known the *Herman* was short-handed—he thought possibly Willie Peterson, the bosun, had told him—but there was not much choice. Fisher was a thin-faced, undersized man with sparse whiskers and unsteady blue eyes, and his principal recommendation was that he had sailed among the Society Islands and the Low Archipelago.

The two Japanese—Jimmy the steward, and Hasino the cook—were also aboard. The latter had tided himself over during the months in Sydney working at Mrs. Short's boardinghouse.

Also aboard was a remarkable arsenal of weapons: three Lee-Enfield repeating rifles replacing the Winchesters, which had been sold for cash in Sydney; seven pistols—two each for Sutton, Chetwood and the doctor, and a spare left over from Captain Brown's complement of arms. There had been another pistol—one of the two allocated to the Captain when they left San Francisco—but Chetwood, who was charged with checking the weapons locker, was unable to trace it. There was also a heavy-gauge shotgun owned by Dr. Luce, capable of blasting a load of shot that could almost clear the deck; and a stand of cutlasses and knives to be used—as Sutton put it—for "deck action." Except for one pistol each in the possession of Sutton, Chetwood and the doctor, the rest of the armament was to be locked in the weapons chest.

The *Herman* was scarcely under way, making her easting under a buffeting southwest gale, when Captain Brown's natural arrogance began to reassert itself. He had been given his old master's cabin, as a concession to his wounded dignity; and he quickly assumed a dictatorial air with members of the crew and Jimmy, the steward.

Sutton did not observe this at first. The activity of getting under way on what they hoped would be the decisive leg of their expedition, together with the new responsibility of command, occupied most of the time during the first hours after departure. Dr. Luce was the first to bring the Captain's attitude to Sutton's notice.

Sitting in Sutton's cabin after the evening watch was set, the doctor remarked, with unusual acerbity: "I don't mind making concessions to the old man's dignity—as you call it, George—but I'm damned if I'm going to take the same kind of abuse I suffered on the way to Honolulu!"

The use of profanity of any sort was rather unusual in the doctor's speech, and Sutton looked at him with a worried frown.

"I looked in on him this evening to see how he was," Dr. Luce went on. "He was lying on his bed and seemed to be brooding. He told me to get the hell out of his cabin and not disturb him again. I'm almost sure he has something on his mind." Dr. Luce's expression and tone of voice betrayed some uncertainty, as well as annoyance.

"We've done everything we could to make him feel that he's still part of the expedition—short of turning over the command to him," Chetwood said, looking at Sutton with a slight grin. "I don't think George is quite ready for that."

Sutton shook his head and said to the doctor, "I'll talk to him and see what's the matter." Inwardly he was more concerned than he would have liked to admit; the Captain seemed to have accepted his new lot, in a grudging way, but Sutton had enough experience with the old man to know that he was not the kind who gave up easily. The recollection of the red-haired lady, who might have been Mrs. Short, waving from the little cruiser as they sailed out of Sydney, still stuck in Sutton's mind.

By the time the *Herman* had run down the 32nd parallel to a point midway between Norfolk Island and Three Kings, at the northern point of New Zealand, the ship had covered almost a thousand miles in less than a week. Sutton proved a different kind of master from the Captain; he confined his attention to watching the operations of the crew, giving such commands as he felt were necessary in moderate tones to Mr. Hendrickson, who relayed them to the crew.

The first mate was a reserved, conscientious man, skilled at the art of sailing; and in Tommy Benson he had an able second officer. Benson was more outspoken than the first mate, and would curse the sailors roundly from time to time; but he seemed to provoke no ill will. He was a big man, not as to height, but across the beam. His arms were as thick as tree trunks, and all muscle, which possibly contributed toward the crew's acceptance of his bursts of profane orders. "Haul the Goddamn mainsheet in you damn swabs—haul in, or I'll lay you on the deck!" he would bellow; and the sailors would lay to without complaint. Mr. Hendrickson would usually stand back with a kind of reserved amusement in his expression, saying nothing; and in general the ship ran very well.

The weather was foul for the first five days; and on the night of the twenty-sixth, Sutton had all hands on deck, struggling to reef the main- and foresail and lash down the outhaul earing on the foresail, which had been wrenched loose by a quick shift in the gale-force wind. The massive waves, rushing down upon the windward quarter, smashed across the poop and ripped off the skylight over the main cabin, pouring down into the passengers' quarters.

Captain Brown came bounding up on deck, his hair flying wildly as he struggled to hold up a pair of flapping pants which he had hastily pulled on, and began bellowing commands. Sutton, who was at the wheelhouse, made his way across the tumbling deck, holding the rail, and shouted at the old man: "Get the hell below—or you'll be locked in your cabin! The men are handling things—and I want no interference! Do you understand that?"

Captain Brown muttered quite audibly about "damn fools . . . landlubbers . . . can't hold a helm in a running sea . . ." Nevertheless he made his way below. The next day he remained in sullen silence under the awning which had been spread over the afterdeck while the skylight was being repaired, refusing to speak to anyone.

The *Herman* reached the Kermadec ridge—a series of low islands stretching southward from the Tongas—on the seventh day, crossed the

180th meridian on May 28, and Sutton then laid a course for a point due south of Tubuai, the largest of the Austral group, where he planned to turn northward.

Somewhere in the immense triangle of water stretching northwest to the Paumotus and eastward to the "low islands," the fabled treasures of the Peruvian churches must lie. Thus far, Captain Brown had given no indication of where the position was, although he had agreed "on his Masonic oath" while in Sydney to lead them to the island.

As the *Herman* bore down on the turning point, the tension aboard the schooner increased noticeably. Even Captain Brown would stir himself from his customary repose on his chair on the afterdeck, where he sat hour after hour in morose silence or glaring at Sutton as he passed along the deck; and in his slow shambling way would move forward to midships. Standing there, his hairy paw clutching the mainstay rigging, he would gaze out at the misty horizon, first to windward and then to leeward, as if he expected "his island" to rear itself from the surface of the sea. For hours he would clamber back and forth behind the stern of the launch, lashed down between main- and foremast; but whatever hope or solace he gleaned from these efforts he kept to himself.

Even Tommy Benson, his powerful torso rolling with the heave of the deck, would find time to go forward now and then and stare at the horizon. It was evident to Sutton that members of the crew knew quite a bit about the expedition, the general purpose of which had been openly disclosed in the Sydney papers during the legal altercation with Captain Brown. He spoke to Chetwood about this.

"It's time we got something definite from the old man," he said. "The crew seems to be expecting something. I notice he talks a lot with Willie Peterson. I spoke to Mr. Hendrickson about that. It's got to stop."

Chetwood's smile was faintly bitter. He had begun to feel the strain, also.

"Doc and I were talking about it," he said. "The old man used to talk with him—when he was sick and needed pills. But now he doesn't say anything. The doctor thinks the Captain is sore at him."

"Or he's got something up his sleeve. I don't like this sort of thing, John. The old man has tried to cheat us before, and he'd do it again. He talks a lot with Tommy Benson, too."

Chetwood nodded. "I know. Benson told the doctor things he said."

Sutton decided to speak to Benson, but an incident occurred which

THE TRAVELLER HEARD FROM.

SEWER COMMISSIONER G. W. SUTTON WRITES US.

He Tells Where He Has Been.—Also That He Thought His Head as Sewer Commissioner Had Dropped Into Mayor Clarke's Official Basket Long Ago.

THE "AUSTRALIA" HOTEL COMPANY, LIMITED.
45 Castlereach Street,
Sydney, 13th Jan., 1903.

To the Editor of THE PRESS.
New Rochelle, N. Y.

Sir:—

From advices recently received, it seems there is some spec[illegible] in New Rochelle regarding my [illegible]onged absence, which I take this means of setting at rest.

Considering that I was a city official at the time of my departure, such speculation will no doubt seem not unnatural. The fact is, that when I left in June last on the enterprise in which I am at present engaged I had no idea I would be away more than a few months at most, and consequently (beyond stating that I was about to leave town on a more or less extended business trip,) did not think it necessary to go further into details even to my close friends. My trip has, however, been prolonged far beyond anticipation, and even yet promises to be of some further duration so that under the circumstances, a few words of explanation may be deemed not out of place. When I say that letter and local papers from home under date of August 15-25, have but just reached me, you will readily perceive that what would be considered stale news in New Rochelle is real live news to me out here. This is occasioned, not on account of the length of time it takes mails to get here, although they only arrive once in three weeks, but by the fact that my movements have been very uncertain and rapid, and that all my mail is addressed care the American Consul here, and by him forwarded to me from place to place, sometimes thousands of miles apart and at times reaches me several months late. A glance at the following will readily expain this, and show that letters sometimes travel back and forth several times before reaching me.

Left San Francisco July 20, arriving Honolulu August 8;

Left Honolulu Sep. 24, arriving San Francisco Sep. 30;

Left San Francisco Oct. 16, arriving Pago Pago, Samoa, Oct. 29;

Left Pago Pago, Samoa, Oct. 30, arriving Auckland, N. Z., Nov. 3;

Left Auckland, N. Z., Nov. 4, arriving Sydney, Aust., Nov. 7;

Left Sydney, Aust., Nov. 17, arriving Honolulu Dec. 2;

Left Honolulu Dec. 4, arriving Pago Pago, Samoa, Dec. 11;

Left Pago Pago, Samoa, Dec. 12, arriving Apia, Samoa, Dec. 13;

Left Apia, Samoa, Dec. 16, arriving Pago Pago, Dec. 17;

Left Pago Pago, Samoa, Dec. 20, arriving Sydney, N. S. W., Aust., Jan. 11.

I am no[illegible] in Sydney and expect to remain here several weeks, although there is no certainty about this and may be called to the Fiji Islands or t[illegible] Tahite, or some other port in the South Seas on almost a moment's notice. This you will see accounts for my lack of early information regarding affairs in New Rochelle. This settlement w[illegible]l, I trust, settle the question of my pr[illegible]nt whereabouts and future move[illegible]s satisfactorily, and prevent furth[illegible] uncertainty on that score. As to the nature of the enterprise in which I am at present engaged and which keeps me continually on the move some ten thousand miles from home, that is a matter which can of course interest only my immediate family, who are constantly advised of my intended journeys as soon as I know them myself. I will say, however, that I am heartily weary of "wandering on foreign shores" and most anxious to return to my family and friends, but must perforce finish the business in which I am now engaged, however distasteful and inconvenient such a prolonged absence must necessarily be [illegible] self and family.

As far as any neglect of my duties to the public as Chairman of the Board of Sewer Commissioners is concerned, I will only say that my "official head" has been at the disposal of the administration for months past, and I was under the impression until very recently that I had long since ceased to be a member of the Board and had thus no official connection with City Government, and consequently gave this aspect of the matter no further thought.

In conclusion, allow me to express to you and to all friends in New Rochelle, my very best wishes, and hoping that I may ag[illegible] see you all in the near fu[illegible]e, I [illegible]main,

Sincerely yours,
GEO. [illegible] S[illegible]TT

This letter was reprinted in *The Press,* of New Rochelle, New York. It would seem that Sutton wrote it in response to criticism from the New Rochelle administration.

changed the entire complexion of the Captain's relations aboard ship. Prior to leaving Sydney, a concession had been made for the Captain in the way of supplying beer. Captain Brown was virtually a teetotaler, but he had a fondness for rum, which he said give him "peace of mind," and beer, which was good for "the fevers." A considerable store of beer was laid in, and the Captain given access to it.

One evening Sutton came on deck to set the watch, and found Benson abaft the wheelhouse, in the act of throwing one of the Captain's bottles into the sea.

"Where did you get that?" Sutton asked.

Benson grinned fatuously, and reached up with one powerful hand to grasp the companionway stanchion. He hauled himself to his feet, slipping slightly on the wet deck.

"Cap'n Brown gave it to me. Said he had lots o' beer, an' if I liked it, I could have all I wanted. Well—" Benson drew his stocky body to full height and hauled in on his belt. "I like beer."

"Mr. Benson, you know the rule of this ship. There is to be no drinking on deck, or among the crew. Do you understand that?"

"Aye, sir." Benson tipped his hat and went forward, stumbling a bit. Sutton went below to Dr. Luce's cabin, and told him what happened.

"I'm ordering Mr. Hendrickson to jettison the Captain's beer," he said.

Dr. Luce looked at Chetwood, who had come into the cabin, and nodded.

"Benson's all right," he said. "I'm not worried about him . . . but the Captain has been talking with him a lot. He tells me pretty much whatever the old man tells him. He didn't mention the beer, of course. . . . But I'm still not satisfied the old man doesn't have some scheme up his sleeve. I passed him the other afternoon when he was up forward, talking to Willie Peterson. Peterson's his man, you know."

"I know," Sutton said, grimly. "I'm not worried about Benson, either. But I've noticed the Captain and Peterson. I don't want to confine the Captain to his quarters, but damn it, I will, if he interferes with this crew! We're going to have enough trouble keeping things under control on the way home—if we find the treasure—without having an incipient mutiny on our hands."

"There's another thing," Chetwood broke in. "We still haven't had any word from the Captain as to the location of this island. He thinks we're going to Tahiti first—and I have an idea he isn't going to tell us anything until we get there."

"We aren't going there," Sutton said. "Our arrival in Papeete—with all that notoriety we got during the hearing in Sydney—would simply alert the French Government and everyone else. We'd have a convoy following us wherever we went." He stopped to scratch his head. The problems of treasure hunting, which had been considered more or less academically up to this time, were growing thicker. It began to look as if the mere locating of the treasure would be the least of their worries; getting it off the island and taking any considerable part back to San Francisco would present the real problem.

The following morning Dr. Luce reported that the Captain was again ill with "the fevers."

"It's more or less of a cold and sore throat," he said. "But when I told him we had pitched his beer overside, I thought he was going to have a stroke. He stood up and gargled at me a bit, and then sat down on his bunk and wouldn't talk."

The thought had been growing in Chetwood's mind that Captain Brown was going to impose some more conditions before taking them to the island. He told Sutton and Dr. Luce he had watched the old man, brooding in his cabin and on deck; and he was sure he had worked up some new scheme.

"He's too damn suspicious not to," Chetwood said. "He wants to postpone giving us any information until we arrive at Papeete. He doesn't know, of course, that we aren't going there."

Sutton told them about the red-haired lady on the cruiser, waving to the Captain as they left Sydney.

"I've got a hunch that was more than a farewell. I think the Captain has some scheme up his sleeve. He was pretty well smitten with that young girl."

Chetwood snorted, but Sutton went on: "Don't underestimate that old boy. He may be senile, but he's killed people before—to get what he wants. We still don't know whether he's got that strychnine aboard . . . and I don't know enough about the Oriental mind to be able to tell whether the cook is in cahoots with him or not."

It was finally left in suspension: they would continue toward the Low Archipelago and when they were within striking distance of the Captain's treasure island—which Sutton had already calculated as being somewhere between the Australs and the Paumotu group—they would hold a conference with the Captain and determine what they would have to do to assure his cooperation.

"It's a hell of a way to go treasure hunting," Sutton said, with a humorless smile. "But I can't see that there's any other way we can go about it."

[3]

On the afternoon of the seventeenth day out of Sydney—June 5—the *Herman* made easting down the 32nd parallel, passing north of an area known as "Maria Theresa's Reefs." She had sailed approximately three thousand miles from the Australian coast, and was a thousand miles south of Tahiti. This was the "turning point" where Sutton hoped to veer northward in the direction he believed the Captain's island lay; but heavy northwest gales, which had battered the ship all the way from the Kermadec ridge, had shifted eastward and were abeam of the course. If the *Herman* turned northward, she would plow into headwinds all the way up to the islands.

The trim white schooner was somewhat scuffed and dirty from the buffeting seas and winds through which she had wallowed almost from the hour of leaving the Sydney Heads. The constant battle had taken its toll of both ship and crew, and tempers were getting testy. Even Mr. Hendrickson, calm and reliable as always, showed the effect in the brusqueness of his manner. Watching the trim of the main- and foresails, he shook his head slightly, and turned to Sutton.

"If we wear ship now, sir, it will put us into easterly seas that come off the trades. She may well snap a stick. We need more easting."

Sutton nodded. He was beginning to feel the rising tension; and he was also a bit uncertain. Within a few days they would be among the "low islands" and somewhere in these scattered fragments of coral and volcanic rock lay the Captain's island. But where? The old man, sitting in his deck chair and gazing grimly at the wide spaces of water, had given no hint. Now and then he would arise from his chair and cross the afterdeck, or go forward to the mainstays, presumably to get a better view of the empty sea. Standing there, his baggy pants blowing and white hair streaming back from his weathered face, he looked like a part of the ship (he still wore his dark coat as a trademark of dignity—even for a "supercargo"); but he gave no evidence that he was still part of the treasure-hunting party.

Dr. Luce and Chetwood also felt the tension. The doctor had become almost taciturn; and Chetwood, while he felt a strong bond for Sutton and his determination to "see it through," had expressed some discouragement.

"When is the old man going to tell us where the island is?" he asked Sutton. "He promised—on his Masonic oath"—he shot a grim look at Dr. Luce—"that he would give us the location as soon as we were in the area. Well, we're getting there."

Sutton shrugged.

"He doesn't talk to anyone—except Peterson," he said. "He's even quit confiding in Benson."

Hasino, the cook—who, it turned out, was something of an artist—had come up on deck with a board and a pan of water-color paints, and settled himself on a stool below the break of the poop. Captain Brown, sitting above him, did not favor him with as much as a glance.

Sutton had taken to observing the crew more carefully. They now seemed to toil wordlessly under the hot sun, the usual seaman's banter gone from their routine. As the weather became warmer, most of them took off their sweaters or shirts. Willie Fisher, the ragged little Australian who had been taken on at the last minute, crouched in the lee of the launch amidships, mending lanyards and winding cord on the foreboom. He had turned out to be a skillful but lazy sailor. He now wore a red handkerchief around his head as a concession to the broiling sun, which gave him the appearance of a wizened pirate.

Jensen and Wilson seemed to be steady, reliable men, judging from their conduct. Willie Peterson was still an enigma. He was usually at the wheel and Sutton noticed that from time to time he walked over to exchange a word with the Captain. Now that they were approaching the critical part of the voyage, everything had become significant. An air of conflicting conspiracies seemed to pervade the ship and its people.

On the tenth of June Mr. Hendrickson gave orders to "wear ship." The heavy booms were swung over, creaking in their yokes as they took up new stresses after having worked on a port tack for three full weeks. The sails bellied out on the port side of the ship, which was gray and dirty from days of foul weather. As the bow rose, mounting each successive swell of water, it scooped up spray and foam which washed down the scuppers. The afterdeck became hot and sticky, in spite of the breeze—which now came from the southeast—and Sutton ordered a span of awning abaft the wheelhouse, under the boom.

They were on a northeasterly course, which would carry them east of Tahiti. The Captain seemed to be aware of this, and he frequently arose from his chair and walked over to stare at the binnacle, and now and then mutter a word to Peterson at the wheel. Sutton remembered that they were now heading into the islands where Mapuana Davis' grandmother had lived.

On June 13 they sighted the first sail since leaving the Australian coast; and it seemed to have a remarkable effect on Captain Brown. At Jimmy Wilson's cry of "Sail, ho!" he almost jumped from his chair, and gazed at the white speck, far to the west. Then he turned abruptly and went below. Sutton wondered if the sight of the sail had resurrected memories . . . perhaps a reminder of things that haunted him, the "ghosts" of the dead men of the *Sea Foam* to which he had referred so mysteriously in San Francisco.

He gave no specific indication, however, that these recollections had prodded him into disclosing the location of his island. The next word Sutton had was from Jimmy Akahito, the steward. Captain Brown was "sick" and had asked that his dinner be brought to his cabin.

Sutton was rapidly losing patience.

"We're getting into the area where his island is supposed to be—and the damn fool gets sick!" he told Dr. Luce and Chetwood, disgustedly.

It was the doctor's turn to shrug.

"He won't even let me look at him—to see how sick he is."

Sutton made a quick decision; he went below and rapped at the Captain's door. The old man opened it, his expression a curious combination of sullen anger and a kind of desperation, which showed in his eyes.

"I'm likely to die," he said, hoarsely. "Damn ye—what do ye want now?"

"I want to come in," Sutton said, and pushed his way through the door. The cabin, with closed ports and little ventilation, had the musty smell of an old man's room. Sutton thought almost unconsciously of the old Captain's "ghosts" and vaguely wondered if any were closeted with him in this evil-smelling room.

"Captain Brown—you are to be disrated as 'supercargo.' You have failed to respond to orders. You distributed liquor to members of the crew, which was specifically forbidden. You are to be moved from this cabin."

Captain Brown, surprised by the unexpected offensive, worked his jaw up and down a bit, and finally managed to say: "I—I'm damned . . . damned if I will!"

"You will," Sutton said. He had previously asked Chetwood to move his belongings from the cabin which Hoffman had occupied—and which Chetwood had taken over. He intended to move Captain Brown into that cabin which was farthest forward, taking over the master's cabin himself and installing Chetwood in his own cabin. The plan was not designed for increased comfort, but to jar the Captain into some realization of his position aboard ship.

"You will be moved—and if you refuse, I will order you put in irons and held up forward. I'm not anxious to cause you trouble, Captain, but you have consistently refused to cooperate. We're reaching the end of our voyage, as far as our objective is concerned. . . . You must be aware of that, Captain."

Captain Brown managed to get in an inarticulate growl, but said nothing intelligible. Sutton's voice was still calm, but he spoke more sharply.

"We're all pretty damn tired of your attitude—and unless we have a definite understanding that you will cooperate, you will be put ashore at the nearest port where there's an American consul, and turned over to the authorities."

Sutton paused long enough to let these points sink in; and suddenly the Captain leaned forward, his bewhiskered face clasped in his huge hairy hands, and to Sutton's utter amazement, he began to weep. Sutton stared at him, not knowing exactly what to do; for a moment he thought the old man must have completely cracked up.

Captain Brown looked up, his eyes blurred with tears and his jaw still working.

"I'm a sick man . . . sick man," he finally said. Tears were running down his nose and dripping on his whiskers. He closed his hamlike fist and pounded it on his knee. "You are throwing me to the dogs . . . a sick man!"

Sutton went to the door and called to Dr. Luce, who had been standing at the foot of the companionway. The doctor came in, his kindly face creased in a worried frown. Sutton explained the situation. The Captain looked at the doctor a moment and then said, "If you tell me to go, Doctor—I will."

Dr. Luce nodded. "I think you'd better go," he said gravely. "Captain Sutton is in command of this ship and you'd better do as he says."

Captain Brown nodded, rubbing his eyes with the back of his hand.

"Ask the steward to put some clean sheets on the bed," he finally said. "I'd like to stay here until he does that . . . I'm sick."

Sutton said, "You can have any reasonable time you want, Captain.

UNITED STATES CONSULATE.

SYDNEY. NEW SOUTH WALES.

MAY 19th. 1903.

I, GEORGE WILLIAM SUTTON, Master of the ship "HETMAN", and sole owner in trust, knowing the uncertainty of health and life, in case of any causality rendering me incompetent to command and direct the ship as Master do hereby name and appoint as my successor in command, GEORGE JOHNSON LUCE, now ship's Surgeon, and in case, he may from any cause become incapable of commanding, JOHN CHETWOOD, now the ship's Purser, shall become master.

Witness my hand and seal this

19th. day of May 1903.

Geo W. Sutton

I, ORLANDO H. BAKER, U. S. Consul at Sydney, have witnessed the signature of George William Sutton to the above instrument, and do hereby ratify and confirm the order of succession of Masters as above mentioned, on the conditions above stated.

WITNESS my hand and Official Seal this nineteenth day of May, in the year of Our Lord One thousand nine hundred and three.

Orlando H. Baker

U. S. CONSUL.

A Copy of the above document was filed at the U. S. Consulate at Sydney, N. S. W., May 19th. 1903.

If Dr. Luce believes you are sick, you will get all the medical help we can give you. But you have got to accommodate yourself to orders on this ship. . . . We followed your orders when you were commander."

"The hell you did!" the Captain muttered, and lay back and closed his eyes.

Sutton and the doctor left and Sutton issued orders to Jimmy to prepare the forward cabin with clean sheets and move the Captain's dunnage to the new cabin.

"Damned if I know what effect this will have," Sutton later told Chetwood and the doctor. "But he's got to understand that this voyage isn't being carried out for his pleasure, and maybe this is the way to get it over to him."

The following day, as the *Herman* sailed northward, heeled over on a starboard tack, the lookout at the forward mast cried out, "Land, ho!" They could see a low-lying island, apparently of the Austral (or Tubuai) group, some distance to the northwest, apparently of such scant height that the clouds had hardly formed over it. There was some debate as to whether they should sail closer; and Captain Brown, who had come on deck at the first shout of "land," stood for a long time, shading his eyes as he looked at it. Sutton wondered what strange thoughts might be passing through the old man's mind at this first visible evidence of the "low islands" of the South Pacific which he had not seen for almost fifty years.

However, the trade winds had suddenly blown up, and with the shift to a southeasterly breeze, the *Herman* was moving along briskly, heading in a northerly direction. Captain Brown meanwhile had returned to his chair on the afterdeck. When Sutton came over to ask him how he felt, he seemed suddenly to have become quite affable.

"Better, Cap'n, better," he said. "These damn fevers come an' go . . . never can tell what to expect." He looked up at Sutton, squinting his pale blue eyes. "Tell you what, Cap'n. . . . You get me ashore so I can rest up a bit, an' then we'll go right for the island. I know where it is, Cap'n—never you fear about that!"

Sutton was unable to resolve in his own mind whether this shift of direction, which was as unpredictable in the Captain as it was in the winds of the seas, was due to an actual desire to join forces for their common goal; or whether it was merely another chameleon change of the old man's mercurial temperament, or perhaps a new ploy in some devious scheme he had worked up to outwit the expedition and take over on his own. At that very hour (although Sutton of course did not know it) the red-haired Mrs. Short was en route to Papeete, to join her husband, who had come over from Apia, intending to wait there, rather impatiently no doubt, with the seventeen-year-old Lilli, for the Captain's arrival in Tahiti!

For two days the *Herman* sailed northward on the steady southeast trades, and on June 16—the twenty-seventh day at sea—another island was sighted, identified as Maitea Island, southeast of Tahiti and one of the outposts of the Low Archipelago. This time the *Herman* passed near enough to land to see the sloping ridges, crested with coconut palms and a higher eminence, evidently of volcanic origin, that formed the backbone of the island.

The charts of the "low islands" were not too well defined in those days, and the *Sailing Directions* left a good deal to be desired. Sutton had no intention of risking his ship making an entrance into any of the uncharted lagoons that surrounded most of these lonely slabs of coral and volcanic rock. Some of the islands formed the center of a larger underwater mass of treacherous coral reefs and shoals, and others extended in a half-moon shape with breaks in the reef making the only passage from the open sea. Even after entering the lagoons, a ship might be caught in a backwash of tide and smashed against the reef itself; or it could become snagged on the "niggerheads" which lay below the surface and could rip the hull of a ship like a knife driven through a crust.

The "low islands" for the most part do not have the sharp pinnacles of volcanic formations that characterize the Society Islands, where peaks such as Oro-hina, on the larger island of Tahiti, rise several thousand feet into the sky. Many of the islands of the Low Archipelago are without fresh water, and consequently uninhabited; and a few have been virtually denuded of trees and other vegetation (and also of inhabitants) by the devastating typhoons that sweep across the area, literally blowing away all signs of life and sometimes the island itself.

The natives on the populated islands have little fear of the lagoons, knowing the shoals and breaks in the reef, and can thread through the shoals swiftly and without danger; but any vessel the size of the *Herman* would have little chance of getting safely to the beach. The Paumotus (or Tuamotu Islands, as they are called today) are sprinkled with such treacherous approaches.

The first island of any size large enough for the men aboard the *Herman* to observe possible landing beaches was Makatea (Aurora Island). Sutton ordered the vessel hove to offshore while he took the launch, with Tommy Benson, Chetwood and the doctor, and made a reconnaissance. The island was several miles in circumference, with a circular ridge of volcanic rock forming a wall perhaps three hundred feet high around a central lagoon. Chetwood and the doctor carried rifles, and started along the beach in opposite directions, intending to shoot any small game they found. Sutton meanwhile searched for water to replenish the tanks of the *Herman,* but since it would have been necessary to scale limestone cliffs to reach the inner lake, and since their water supply was not critically low, this mission was abandoned.

Dr. Luce reported finding the remains of some previous human habitation—perhaps an abandoned native village—on the southern side of the island, where a deep lagoon protected the entrance; but he did not stay long enough to make any more substantial investigation—an omission that would later assume rather startling significance.

They returned to the schooner and found Captain Brown at the rail, staring steadfastly at the island. Sutton approached him, and the Captain said:

"What island is this, Cap'n?"

"Makatea," Sutton said. "At least that's what's marked on the chart."

Captain Brown nodded, and stroked his whiskers. Sutton hesitated an instant, and then, when the Captain seemed to have no further comment, he went forward to attend to lashing down the launch which was being hoisted on the davits.

"We'll try to find anchorage at Tikihau—that's about thirty miles north of here," he told Mr. Hendrickson. "If not, we'll go on to Matahiva. That's the largest of the islands around here, and from what the *Sailing Directions* say, we can find good anchorage inside the lagoon and replenish our water."

Sutton walked back along the deck to where Captain Brown was standing at the rail, rolling with the motion of the ship, which was very slight in the southeast swell. He was still staring at the island.

"Do you recognize anything about the place, Captain?" Sutton finally asked. "We seem to be in the area you spoke about—where you said the *Sea Foam* was—"

"I said nothing!" The old man turned angrily, his beard lifted straight ahead of him as the breeze caught him from the back. He looked extraordinarily fierce at the moment, his eyes again blazing bitterly. "You made me come with you, Cap'n—but you can't make me say a damned thing!"

He turned away; and then, as if he had immediately reconsidered his words, he turned back to Sutton and asked, "Did you find any oysters in the lagoon, Cap'n?"

Sutton shook his head.

"No—we didn't look around much. When we cleared the reef we headed for the beach. The oysters would be pretty deep, wouldn't they?"

The Captain shook his head, stroking his beard.

"Not too deep. . . . They were there, Cap'n. I remember it very well. We lay outside—just like this—an' took the longboat in. There were oysters—an' pearls, too! Ye can lay to that, Cap'n!"

Sutton stood for some moments at the rail, trying to fathom the strange currents of the old man's thoughts. It seemed to him Captain Brown alternated between moments of outright fantasy and lucidity. The difficulty was in separating the two. As the Captain looked off across the lagoon, at the darkening shores where the sun slanted over the rim of cliffs, he began to realize fully that the first—and perhaps most important—task they had was to find some way to penetrate that old and encrusted mind, covered with barnacles of memories, and corroded with the almost insane seepings of suspicion.

"We're going to move on—to Tikihau," he finally said. "You're going to have to help us, Captain Brown. It's to your interest as well as ours."

It was Sutton's intention at this point to bring things to an issue with Captain Brown. They had reached an area where he was sure they were within striking distance of the Captain's "treasure island"—if there was such a place; and he had no intention of postponing the showdown any longer.

Sutton's entry in his journal, upon leaving Makatea, said: "Have no special destination. Simply killing time to give Brown a chance to come around."

The *Herman* made a slow passage to Tikihau, due to light winds during the night, and arrived off the island early the following morning. The schooner hove to on the southwest side of Tikihau, a circular atoll surrounding a large lagoon. Sutton and Dr. Luce took Mr. Benson and two sailors in the "jolly boat" and went ashore through an entrance to an outer lagoon that was indicated in the *Sailing Directions* as having a "fast tide." Benson had told Sutton he had sailed into the lagoon, and the entrance was quite safe; but Sutton found that in spite of the depth of the channel, the tide was ebbing at six to seven knots.

After several attempts, which nearly wrecked the jolly boat, the landing party made the run into the lagoon. However, Sutton decided to lay offshore during the night and see if the tide changed in the morning.

14 5 65 S | 148 18 W

WINDS	LEEWAY	Temp. Air	Temp. Water	BAROM.	REMARKS Thursday 18th June day of 1903
E N E					This day begins with fresh breeze and clear weather at 2 h p m found the entrance to lagoon Capt and Doctor with 3 men went a shore to inspect and sound the entrance returned at 4 p m found the current to strong running out to attempt entring the lagoon hove too for the night Midnight do wind and weather at 8 h a m the same Capt Doctor and three men went a shore again and boarded a cutter which was in the entrance and partly on the Reef they advised the Capt not try to enter as the current was setting the same direction always made sail and proceeded towards Matahiva Island Pumps lights and lookout with care attended 30 Days out

Lat.	Departure	Lat. by D. R.	Lat. by Ob.	Variation	Diff. of Lon.	Lon. In.	Lon. by Ob.

Page from the log of the *Herman*.

...e Island towards Matahiva Island

WINDS	LEEWAY	Temp. Air	Temp. Water	BAROM.	REMARKS day of 1903 Friday 19th June	
N E						A. M.
					this day begins with fresh breezes and clear weather	
					at 4 h P m got round to Western side of Matahiva Island sent the Boat on shore to	
East					find the Boat Entrance that the Directory claims to be on the Western side but culd find no entrance there	
					hove the ship too for the night	P. M.
					at day light made sail and proceeded to beat back to south side where we	

thought that we had seen an Entrance to the lagoon
at noon arrived on the southern side of the Island where we thought the entrance was but could find non through the reef proceeded to the West side again 31 Days out

Lat.	Departure	Lat. by D. R.	Lat. by Ob.	Variation	Diff. of Lon.	Lon. In.	Lon. by Ob.

It did not. They decided to abandon the effort, and pointed for Matahiva, some thirty miles to the north. On rounding the island, it was found that the force of winds on the northeastern side of the atoll backed up the water in the lagoon so that it might take days or even weeks for it to spill out through the lagoon on the southwestern side!

Sutton observed that Tikihau also had considerable interest for Captain Brown. He stood at the rail, staring at its contours—which rose in some places thirty feet or more above the rim of surf which encircled the island; and in other places was only a few feet above the sea. The island was entirely of coral, with no evidence of a volcanic upthrust; and along the lower levels of the "backbone" of the island the opposite side of the lagoon looked like a distant shore.

That day Sutton wrote in his journal: "Brown is commencing to talk freely to the doctor, who has been nursing him most carefully."

The *Herman* arrived off Matahiva, largest and most beautiful of the outer Paumotu Islands, late the same day; and after skirting the southern shore hove to off the lagoon at the western end. The boat was sent ashore to probe for an entrance to the lagoon which the *Sailing Directions* indicated on the west end. Chetwood, in his diary, described the inner lagoon as "deep and teeming with life, and of transparent clearness, having for a border a strip of sand, extremely fine and smooth. . . . The shoreline, shrinking into little bays or projected in low, green capes, was visible from every point."

The following day Sutton and Dr. Luce went ashore and found that the island had every appearance of having been deserted by its former inhabitants, possibly due to the fierce typhoons that were known to have raged across the Paumotus in 1893. They talked for a long time and Sutton finally said to the doctor:

"We've got to have a showdown, George. We can't roam around these islands forever. He's been talking more freely to you—why don't we put it up to him now, and if he still refuses we'll go on to Penrhyn?"

That night Sutton and Chetwood went down into the Captain's cabin. Dr. Luce was already there, giving the old man some medicine. Sutton sat down.

"Captain Brown, I want directions from you now that will take us to the island. We are in the area—I'm sure of that, from what you have told us. You've seen three of these islands, and now it's time you told us where your island is."

The Captain had propped himself up in bed. His old face was weary, and from the feverish look in his eyes there was no doubt he had been sick. He looked at Sutton for a moment, then shook his head.

"Not until you put me back in command of this ship," he said. "I told you I'd lead you to the place, an' I will—but I'll do it myself, in my way!"

Sutton reminded him of his agreement when they sailed from Sydney, and offered to restore the old man to his position as "supercargo."

"You ain't got a decent crew aboard this ship, Cap'n," the old man finally said. "Any one of 'em would cut your throat—an' you may lay to that. You couldn't trust 'em . . . not a damned soul, Cap'n."

Sutton was doing his best to keep his temper; but it was evident to both Chetwood and Dr. Luce that Sutton's nerves were at the breaking point. Chetwood finally broke in: "You made an agreement, Captain Brown—and if you fail to keep it, I for one will see that you face the full penalty for breaking it. I will have you arrested the day you set foot on United States soil again—if you ever do!"

Captain Brown looked at Chetwood with some astonishment; it was the first time the lawyer had actually spoken harshly to him. Then he looked over at the doctor, who had moved to a seat across the cabin.

"Don't ask me to support your position, Captain." Dr. Luce's voice was mild, but his gray eyes were quite stern. "You swore a Masonic oath to me—and you're breaking it."

The Captain looked at the faces of the three men. It struck Sutton at the moment that there was something wild and almost insane in the way he looked at people, and he wondered if the Captain actually had become insane.

"I never gave no oath," the Captain finally muttered, in a grumbling voice.

"You did," the doctor pursued, more sternly. "You took a sacred Masonic oath in Sydney that if we paid your bills and got you cleared out of that port, you would carry out your agreement." The doctor arose from his chair, apparently outraged at the enormity of the Captain's behavior. Captain Brown cringed for an instant, almost as if he had been struck in the face.

Sutton began to feel sorry for the old man. He seemed suddenly to have become like a child, beset with small scoldings. But he was aware that they must either bring him to terms now, or give up the expedition. There was no possible hope of finding the island without the Captain's help.

"That . . . that's not an oath, Doctor. You know I made no promise!"

"You did, Captain!" Dr. Luce stood over him, with an expression of

From Diary of Dr. Geo. J. Luce. for June. 1903.

June. 14. All went to the cabin and George asked the Captain what direction to sail for the Island. Brown said he would not go to the Island with this crew; that he would not go to the Island unless George would sail into Tanite, discharge the crew and put him in full command. Agood deal of talk but nothing gained. At noon George refused to let him eat at our table or to send his dinner until all were through.

June. 15th George ordered the Captain out of his cabin. After some trouble he was put in Hoffman's old room. Sutton has promised to put him in the forecastle an make him work his passage.

June. 21st. The Captain promised me if we would sail to some island where he could go ashore for a few days he would tell us just where the Island was and would go to it. We headed for Penrdyn at once.

June. 26th. Anchored in Penrhyn Lagoon at 4.30 P. M.

This page was copied by Sutton from a diary that Dr. Luce apparently kept for the journey. This copy was kept by Sutton in his journal.

SEARCH ... TREASU...

EXPEDITION TO THE SOUTH SEAS.

April 21. 1903 Sydney

EQUITY COURT PROCEEDINGS.

The facts connected with an agreement for "sending out an expedition to search for treasure in the South Seas" were before Mr. Justice A. H. Simpson in a suit in the Equity Court yesterday.

The plaintiffs were George William Sutton, John Chetwood, and George J. Luey, and the defendant Captain James Brown, master of the American schooner Herman, which arrived in Sydney on January 11th last.

Mr. Maughan (instructed by Mr. J. Stuart Thom) appeared for the plaintiffs; and Mr. Loxton (instructed by Messrs. Laurence and Macdonald) for the defendant. The plaintiffs asked for an injunction restraining the captain from withdrawing or receiving any moneys standing to his credit with the Union Bank of Australia, and from selling the vessel.

From the affidavits read it appeared an agreement was entered into in San Francisco for the despatch of the expedition. Captain Brown was to be master of the schooner, which was originally owned by an American gentleman, and was to conduct it to the locality of the treasure. The captain was to receive 25 per cent. of the treasure, the promoters 20 per cent., and the subscribers of the capital 55 per cent. It was arranged that in accordance with American law Brown should be registered as the owner of the vessel. He held the vessel in trust.

The vessel reached Sydney in January last, the captain being apparently engaged in fitting h... for the expedition, the objective of wh... ...s some islands under French control. ... ...aintiffs had come out, intending to accompany ...e expedition to the islands, but in April a dispute occurred between them and the defendant in consequence of which the defendant expressed his intention of selling the vessel. Brown had cabled to America for 3000 dollars, and a considerable part of this was forwarded by the syndicate. Plaintiffs complained that some money received by the plaintiff had not been used in accordance with the agreement.

The defendant's case was that he had an absolute right to sell or dispose of the vessel in order to secure a more suitable one for cruising among coral islands. He denied the suggestion that he intended selling the vessel, pocketing the proceeds, and going to London. The vessel not being copper-bottomed was not suitable for the purposes of such an expedition. He had not wrongly converted any money.

It was submitted, on behalf of the defendant, that the Court had no jurisdiction in the matter, all the parties being American subjects, the vessel being American, and the contract being one to be performed within a French possession, and not in any territory over which the Court had jurisdiction.

His Honor: The chances of finding the treasure do not seem to be very auspicious. (Laughter.) It does not seem to me to be a happy party, and the better course one would think would be to sell the ship, divide the money among the legal profession, and consign the episode to oblivion. (Renewed laughter.)

The case was not concluded when the Court rose.

A story from one of the Sydney newspapers in April, 1903.

A view of Matahiva Island.

Jovian wrath on his countenance. "Damn it, man—you know you did!"

The Captain seemed to flinch. It was the first time the doctor had sworn at him.

"I tended you when you had your illness, Captain," Dr. Luce went on, relentlessly. "I've taken care of you on this ship . . . you know that, don't you? You've broken every promise you ever made—"

The doctor stopped in the middle of the sentence, and stared at the Captain. Then suddenly he jumped forward and reached for the Captain's arm, which was partly under his pillow.

"Why, damn you—" Dr. Luce's face was red with anger. He pulled the old man's arm out from under the pillow. He had a pistol in his hand.

"Where did you get this?" he demanded; and Captain Brown, shaking his head from side to side, gave up the gun without a struggle. "How did you get this?" the doctor asked again. Sutton had taken the gun and examined it. It was loaded.

"I got to protect myself," he said. "If Cap'n Sutton wanted to shoot me—I was going to shoot first." His voice had become hoarse and inarticulate, and ended in a kind of strangled noise in his throat. Sutton realized that the old man was completely demoralized.

"I'll take you to the island," the Capain finally mumbled. "But first I got to get rid of the fevers. You take me ashore and let me rest up, an' we'll go right to the island. It ain't far from here . . . I promise you, Doctor." He looked at the doctor. "I told you I would . . . an' I mean to do it."

It was evident that there was nothing further to be gained by talking to the Captain. Whether the old man would keep his promise, or renege again, was something no one could foretell. But his mind was like putty at the moment; and Sutton also observed that he was crying again.

"We'll sail for Penrhyn Island," Sutton said, in a kinder voice. "We can promise you that—but nothing more, unless you keep your promise. If you don't you'll be turned over to the authorities at Penrhyn."

"Penrhyn! . . ." The Captain struggled almost to a sitting position, leaning on one elbow, and stared at Sutton. "Damn you, Cap'n Sutton—we were to go to Tahiti! You said that—"

Sutton suspected the reason for the Captain's violent outburst; but he shook his head firmly.

"We'll sail for Penrhyn in the morning. You can rest there, Captain. And then you can take us to the island, or we'll leave you in Penrhyn and head for home. This is the last time you'll have a chance to lie to us."

They went up on deck, and Sutton gave orders to Mr. Hendrickson to lay over during the night inside the lagoon; the next day they would weigh anchor for Penrhyn Island (now known as Tongareva) some six hundred miles north of Tahiti.

The *Herman* arrived at Penrhyn on Friday, June 26, at two o'clock in the afternoon, and dropped anchor in the lagoon at four o'clock. Sutton and Chetwood went ashore to pay their respects to the New Zealand Resident Agent, Captain M. J. Nagle.

Penryhn: Death of an Island

[1]

Captain Nagle, the Resident Agent, was a hearty, red-faced Englishman with a bristling mustache, curving downward over a square-cut jaw. He had the expansive geniality of a plantation host, coupled with the old-school character of a British army officer. This, together with his sense of humor, made for good discipline and good relations in the remote island outpost.

As the pilot boat pulled in, he arrived at the jetty with his entire family—his smiling, round-faced wife, evidently Polynesian; one son and five daughters, the oldest apparently in her early twenties. Sutton observed that she was quite attractive, with a small, delicate face and the classic symmetry that lends that air of grace and beauty to so many women of the South Seas.

The arrival of a schooner was not an ordinary occurrence at Penrhyn, and half the population of the Residency village—Oruna—was at the jetty, staring at the newcomers and offering a variety of greetings.

Sutton explained briefly that they were on a "cruise" in the South Seas. He saw no reason for dissembling if he were asked direct questions—since the purpose of the voyage of the *Herman* had been spelled out in detail in the Sydney papers and he had intended to answer questions honestly and briefly. However, Captain Nagle seemed to have no particular curiosity. He asked them to come up to the Residency, a small frame building with a wide veranda facing the lagoon.

Sutton said there were two others aboard—Dr. Luce and Captain Brown—whom he would like to bring ashore. First, he wanted to know if there were accommodations available in the village, or should they plan to remain on board the schooner.

"Ashore—by all means!" Captain Nagle threw up his hands. "We have so few visitors—and very few Americans. You are welcome—as our guests!"

A cheery, round-faced man came striding down the coral pathway leading from the Residency, and Captain Nagle called out: "Tommy, old fellow—come and meet our new arrivals!" He turned to Sutton. "This is Mr. Thomas Eustace, who runs one of the two trading stores at Tautua—our biggest village. About nine miles up the coast. You'll want to get supplies from him—and from MacDonald . . ." He leaned forward and winked significantly at Sutton. "Buy from both," he said, in a heavy whisper. "Old Mac is a Scotsman, and they check on each other's sales. There's a regular row when one gets more of a sale than the other."

Captain Nagle was roaring at his own joke as Tommy Eustace came down to join them; and soon Captain Sutton and Chetwood began to feel—almost for the first time since leaving Honolulu—that they were among friends.

Penrhyn Island, as Sutton had observed when the *Herman* was rounding the southern reef to reach the leeward side, was a large circular island, perhaps thirty miles in extent, almost completely surrounding an immense lagoon. It was actually a wide strand of coral reef and sand, crowned with clusters of coconut palms and pandanus, or "screw palms"; and like Matahiva, its inner recesses, along the shores of the lagoon, were filled with extravagant tropical vegetation. Low shrubs and stubby trees grew profusely out of a carpet of volcanic soil along the lagoon, with a few spreading trees and tall, stately palms, and a wealth of hanging "parasite plants" which made the interior appear even from a distance to be a dense jungle.

The only claim to international importance that Penrhyn possessed was the fact that Robert Louis Stevenson once visited the island, some twelve years before; but he had failed to tell about the place in any of his writings, and so little was known about it. Penrhyn was actually an outpost of the Cook Island group, some four hundred miles north of Raratonga, and at one time it had been inhabited by cannibals. The population had been decimated by Peruvian slave traders in the early nineteenth century; and the barbaric culinary habits of its earlier inhabitants were gradually eradicated by missionaries of the London Missionary Society, a few of whom were reported to have made the supreme sacrifice in attaining their objectives.

The island also had at least one local distinction. It had been in the path of the Great Typhoon of 1893—a point which assumed some significance during the visit of the *Herman*—but had not been badly damaged, since it was in the earlier course of the hurricane that wiped half of Flint Island off the sea and destroyed dozens of villages in the Paumotus.

Sutton sent the launch back for Dr. Luce and the Captain, but the latter at first declined to come ashore—even though the reason for putting in at Penrhyn was to provide rest for the old man. He told the doctor he was "too sick" to leave his cabin, but might come ashore the next day; and so the doctor left, with instructions to Mr. Hendrickson and Tommy Benson to "keep a sharp eye on the old man."

Except for Willie Peterson, who was the Captain's "man," and Willie Fisher, the rat-faced little Australian who was an unknown quantity, Sutton was fairly certain of the loyalties of the crew members—at least for the moment. He had taken Peterson in hand, shortly after the discovery of the pistol under the Captain's pillow, accusing him directly of providing the Captain with the gun. Peterson denied it so vehemently—and profanely—that Sutton was able to place charges of insubordination and the use of profanity toward an officer of the ship; and this threat was held in suspension over Peterson's head during the layover in Penrhyn.

Shortly after the arrival of the *Herman,* Captain Nagle announced that a "reception" would be held in honor of his distinguished visitors from the United States, selecting the Fourth of July as a sentimental time for the affair. Captain Brown finally had come ashore, meanwhile, since this was an event in which he obviously could not deny himself the pleasure of an appearance. He was dressed in full nautical attire, his dark coat buttoned and a cap with master's insignia crowning his extensive head of hair, which he had combed for the occasion.

A couple of days before the party, Chetwood made a discovery which, coupled with some of the events at the party, shed new light on the Captain's curiously intractable and erratic conduct; and to Sutton's way of thinking, it explained many of the unsolved phases of the mystery of Captain Brown's "treasure island."

Chetwood and the Captain had taken a long walk one day into the interior of the island—which was not more than a mile wide along most of the circumference. As they passed along a trail leading to the inner lagoon, the Captain stopped to look at a small volcanic crater, only a few feet deep—apparently the pit of a tiny eruption in ages past, filled with a heavy mass of shrubs and ferns which grow luxuriantly in the rich volcanic soil, with a small pool of water at the bottom.

"That's where you have to get most of the fresh water on these islands," the Captain remarked. "Sea water don't get into them—an' there ain't any other source of fresh water."

The rim of the crater was only a few feet above the ridge they were crossing, and the bottom must have been close to sea level. Chetwood noticed that the Captain, as he walked around the little crater, seemed to be quite familiar with this kind of formation.

Later Chetwood spoke about this to Sutton. "You know—I have an idea the Captain knows about these volcanic islands, but he doesn't seem to know much about coral atolls. That might help us to locate the island where he says the treasure is buried."

Sutton shook his head slightly. "He hasn't given us much to go on. From what he has said—and from what he told me at Auburn—he seemed to be describing a low coral island, without much height to the land. Not more than fifty feet or so, I gathered. And the treasure was buried in a cliff facing the lagoon. That doesn't sound like a volcanic formation. They usually go up to two or three hundred feet on the ridges."

Dr. Luce, who had been listening with interest, suddenly broke in: "You know—I think we may have missed something on that first island we stopped at. Makatea. You remember John and I walked along the beach in different directions, to get some shots if there were any small game. I told you I found the remains of an old village. . . . Well, I didn't look around very much, but as I remember, it wasn't like most of the native villages. There were some old rusted pieces of tin sheets. The place had been pretty much torn up by the wind, but it looked more like a white man's settlement. It was about a mile or more back of the lagoon, and out of sight of our ship—so it wouldn't have been seen by any ship coming into the lagoon. I wondered at the time why it was so far back."

Sutton frowned. "You think that might have been an island that the Captain knew about? You remember how he kept looking at the island . . . but he never went ashore."

"I don't know, frankly," the doctor said. "But there may be some connection between his knowing about volcanic formations—as John says he seems to—and this island. Of course, it doesn't jibe with your theory that it was a coral atoll."

Captain Nagle and his family, excluding his daughter Maeva. In the rear, at the left, is Tommy Eustace. The girl standing behind Mrs. Nagle is unidentified.

Maeva, Captain Nagle's oldest daughter.

The "party" on the Fourth of July turned out to be a pleasant, home-made affair. The two traders—Tommy Eustace and MacDonald—came over from Tautua, and the members of Captain Nagle's "official family" stationed at the Residency also joined. Captain Brown, who had experienced a resurgence of his waning ego as a result of coming ashore to "spruce up," as he called it, immediately established himself as the center of interest.

The affair began at mid-afternoon with a kind of feast, somewhat similar to a Hawaiian *luau;* and by evening everyone was in a state of gastronomic exhaustion. Captain Nagle supplied rum in various assortments, and quite liberally; and in addition there was a small quantity of *awa,* a native drink peculiar to these regions, which was sipped ceremonially out of coconut shells.

Captain Brown had taken a fancy to the second oldest of Captain Nagle's daughters, who went by the name of "Parie" and was about fifteen (the other two were under six, and consequently ineligible) and to the considerable amusement of Mrs. Nagle and the older daughter, he showered her with small trinklets, including a locket and chain.

Maeva, the older girl, smiled at Sutton and remarked: "What is it you say in America . . . no fool like an old fool, eh?"

Sutton, who was not insensible to Maeva's charms, had spent a good deal of the afternoon with her, listening to her amusing anecdotes about life on a remote island. She had attended school for two years in Auckland, and was more sophisticated than most of the other women on Penrhyn—a point which she made with grave modesty, to assure Sutton that she was no child.

Captain Brown, fortified to some extent by the various rum concoctions which their host had provided, settled himself on the veranda in a large, comfortable chair, and began expounding on his favorite subject, which had to do with his own exploits. At one point, in recounting one of his adventures—glancing from time to time at Parie to assure himself that she was properly absorbed by his tale—he told of running down a fast-sailing little vessel, only to find it was a French war frigate, well armed and apparently on a scouting mission.

"We turned on a shilling . . . gave our heel to her. She gave chase, but we could outrun anything in the Pacific—"

He glanced at Captain Nagle and noticed that the Resident Agent was staring at him rather intently.

"When was this, Captain . . . how long ago?"

"Oh . . . years ago." The Captain waved his broad hand, as if to sweep the years back and out of the way. "I've forgotten most of these times—but by Jove, we had some real times in those days, yes, by the Great Horn Spoon, we did!"

The Captain was silent a moment, possibly digesting unconsciously the import of Captain Nagle's curiosity; and MacDonald, the Scot trader, who was hard of hearing, leaned forward and asked: "How did you come through it, Captain?"

"Come through . . . eh? Come through what?"

A certain look of caution came over the Captain's face; perhaps he sensed that the Resident Agent's inquiry was close to home, or he may have been puzzled by MacDonald's question.

"The typhoon," MacDonald went on. "Ye said, mon, that ye'd come through a typhoon, didn't you? We know something about typhoons in this part of the world, don't we, Tommy?"

Tommy Eustace nodded, and took advantage of Captain Brown's momentary puzzlement to deal with the subject a bit further. "You never saw a typhoon, unless you saw that blow in '93! I was in the lagoon on Vostok Island, trying to get some shells for trading . . . when the bloody thing hit. Holy Mother—did she hit! We didn't get it as bad on Vostok—or on Penrhyn, from what I found out later—as they did on Flint Island. It blew the deck house off my lugger and landed it halfway across the island. The boat was on the beach, and half the rigging was blown away. But it wiped half of Flint Island off the sea—blew the lower part clean out of the water. That storm carried waves fifty feet high and they went right over the island."

Sutton happened to be watching the Captain's face. He sat with his mouth open. It was neither a grin nor a grimace; his whiskered jaw simply froze in that expression. It suddenly became quite clear to Sutton what had happened. Captain Brown was in the grip of a kind of internal fright—a terror that disclosed itself in stark nakedness whenever a typhoon was mentioned. It suddenly revealed the curious psychological complications in the old man's strange behavior.

The next day he told Chetwood, "It explained everything—the way the stubborn old fool has been acting ever since we reached the islands."

Tommy Eustace had gone on, completely unaware of the reaction his story was having on Captain Brown.

"Yes sir, you haven't seen a blow until you see one like that. Missed Papeete by a hundred miles, but she hit the Paumotus and drowned hundreds. Nobody knows how many were blown off the trees. They tie themselves to the palm trees, halfway up, so the waves won't catch them, or the tops of the trees won't be blown off and take them along. But when a fifty-foot wave hits one of those atolls, even the coconut trees don't stand up. Some of the bodies they found later had been lashed to the trees and battered to death with flying coconuts."

Sutton leaned forward and asked Eustace: "I've heard of islands being blown off—is that possible, Mr. Eustace?"

"You can be sure it's possible!" The trader, warming up to his subject, aimed a finger at Sutton. "Do you know what a fifty-foot wave can do, Captain Sutton? When there's a wind behind it that can send a spear of palm leaf through a two-inch board? It can blow an atoll so far you could never find the pieces."

His curiosity aroused, Chetwood broke in with a question:

"What about the volcanic islands? Do typhoons blow them away, too?"

Eustace shook his head.

"There's always a reef around these atolls," he said. "They break the big swells, so when they hit the beach they've gone across a lagoon, and don't do much to the beach. The sand and the plants that grow on the low islands keep building up to anywhere from ten to fifty feet—but not much more than that. The typhoons send the waves right over these atolls and wash them away. But the volcanic islands are usually higher and have a solid base, so they stand up under it."

At this point it became absolutely clear to Sutton what was on the Captain's mind; and he was certain he knew the answer to the frustrating attitudes of the old man that had baffled them before. Captain Brown was no longer sure he could locate the "treasure island"—because it might have been blown away!

Sutton brought this up with Chetwood and Dr. Luce the next day when they went out to the *Herman* to check supplies.

"You remember what you said, Doctor—about the signs of a deserted village on Makatea Island? It seems to me quite possible that Makatea could have been the base from which the *Sea Foam* operated—when it was raiding the Australian specie ships, as we believe it was."

Dr. Luce nodded, and Sutton went on: "If it was their base, it's quite possible that they buried the treasure—or some of it—on one of the coral atolls in that area, rather than on Makatea. That would make it safe in case they were chased back, or captured. After Brown and Schmid had gotten rid of the rest of the crew, they could go back to the atoll and recover the treasure. . . . And now the Captain is afraid that maybe the island isn't there any more."

Chetwood pursed his lips and nodded agreement.

"It looks like a good case, George. . . . But what do we do now?"

"We make the Captain go back with us—to Makatea. If he knows that we know what he is afraid of—that the island has been blown away—he may settle down and give us some idea where to look for it. After all, we don't *know* that it's blown away. But put yourself in the old man's place. . . . He's lived for years now on the absolute belief that he could go back and get that treasure. Suddenly he's afraid it may not be there—that the island may be gone! He's an old man, and that would be enough to drive a much younger man out of his mind."

"Yes . . . it's driving me out of my own mind," Chetwood said, his mouth twisted in a grimace.

Dr. Luce nodded, with a tired smile. "I'm not a young man," he said. "I think I know how the Captain feels. Perhaps we should change our methods of handling him."

"My God!" Sutton looked at the doctor. "We can't go much easier than we have."

Dr. Luce shook his head; his expression was a little grimmer. "I think what he needs is what any boy needs—a damned good whipping now and then!"

[2]

Another change seemed to have taken place in Captain Brown. It was not particularly evident on the surface—he still preserved an air of arrogant importance. But there was an emptiness to it. It was like an erosion from within, the seeping of water into the base of a cliff that weakens the inner structure, even before the outer wall collapses.

The Captain said very little to anyone during the days immediately after Captain Nagle's party. His principal interest seemed to be to supply little Parie with seashells. He shambled along the beach for miles, and returned to empty shells from his pockets before her, like a man pouring out treasures. The little girl had spent all fifteen years of her life paddling along the beach among these shells; yet the Captain presented them to her with an almost ceremonial manner. Each time the girl would gravely accept them and make a little curtsey of thanks.

Chetwood and Sutton, sitting on the veranda of the Residency, watched the performance with some humor; but there was little humor to be found in the total situation. As a matter of fact, there was something tragic in the sight of the old sailor, trudging along the beach in the late afternoon, stooping now and then to pick up a small shell, and then

Thomas Eustace. This picture was presented to George Sutton by Eustace.

Captain Nagle's house on Penrhyn Island.

slowly plodding onward through the sand, his head bent forward in concentration upon the senseless task he had set for himself.

"If the old boy cracks up now," Chetwood observed, "we might as well go home."

Sutton nodded. "I think we've got one more chance," he said. "I have an idea Makatea may hold the answer. If we can get him to agree to go there, maybe it will settle him down and he will guide us to the island . . . providing he still knows where it is."

Chetwood's mouth was flexed in his characteristic smile.

"You still have faith, haven't you, George? . . . I guess you've had it all along. So did I—at first. But lately I think my confidence has been weakening. But you've never given up. You still believe the treasure exists."

He looked at Sutton, almost as if he marveled at him.

Sutton nodded again. "I think so—more now than at first. . . . I'm not sure we'll find the treasure, of course. But I am sure the old Captain wasn't spinning a yarn. It was buried out there somewhere. I think the old man has more stamina than we may have realized. If he's been following a will-o'-the-wisp all these years, John, then it's the damnedest one anybody ever followed."

Chetwood shook his head.

"I haven't an ounce of faith left," he said.

This was July 7; and the *Herman* was scheduled to sail the following day. Dr. Luce, who had been staying with the Captain at MacDonald's place at Tautua, reported briefly on the old man's state of mind.

"He seems to be almost in a state of shock," he said. "He doesn't say much of anything. . . . Like a man trying to work his way up out of a dark hole. He blinks now and then, as if the light bothered him."

The Captain's attachment to little Parie Nagle did not seem to bother Captain Nagle or the girl's mother. She was a pleasant-faced Polynesian woman, with the deep understanding of human nature that seemed to be a natural trait of her people; and she smiled at the old man as he tried to please, in his own way, the fancies of the girl.

Chetwood, again surmising Sutton's thoughts, said, "How the mighty have fallen, eh? I thought we were taking a beating on this trip, but maybe he is. This has been a long trip for him, and he's got to go back and face his wife. She's a sweet old woman, but I think if the Captain is afraid of anyone, it's Mrs. Brown."

Sutton glanced sideways, and said grimly, "He's not the only one with a wife, John. I've got to go back to New Rochelle. I feel sorry for him, but I'm not going to let him wriggle off this hook if I can help it. He hasn't said definitely what he intends to do. Last night he asked if he could remain here, and I told him he could if he would give us the information about the island. We'd go and look for it, and if it was a wild-goose chase, he would have to pay the piper."

"I've cleared that with Captain Nagle," Chetwood said. "Under New Zealand law, we have to take him off. But he goes in irons if he refuses to obey the order to leave. Nagle is making out a paper to that effect."

Sutton had already talked with Captain Nagle and disclosed in general the purpose of their trip. The Resident Agent had known something of it, and upon the arrival of the *Herman* he had inquired of his own government representative, at Raratonga, what the status of the schooner might be.

"You're going into French territory," he told Sutton. "It isn't my business what you do there. If you find what you're looking for, stop by on the way back and we'll have a drink over it. We may have a representative of the British Admiralty here—to meet the Captain, you know!"

Sutton had grinned, good-naturedly.

"If we find what we're looking for, nobody will hear from us until we reach San Francisco. However . . ." He looked, with some sort of nostalgia, across the glittering ocean. "I'm beginning to like it in these parts. I might be back."

Mrs. Nagle, who had been listening, smiled at Sutton, and said in a gentle voice:

"You will come back, Captain Sutton. . . . Everyone does!"

Before the Captain returned that evening to Tautua, Sutton talked with him. "We'll be sailing at two o'clock to catch the tide," he said. "We'll have the boat in for you at the dock at noon."

Captain Brown suddenly shook his head. "You've got my cabin, Cap'n," he said in a grumbling tone. "I got to have that back. Those sailors have got to respect me. . . . They don't respect a man that's been Captain, and then moved down."

Sutton said, firmly but gently: "You have comfortable quarters and there will be no change made. This is your last chance, Captain—to come through with your end of the bargain. We'll go back to where we were—in the Paumotus. You will have to guide us to the island . . . your island. Or we will turn back to San Francisco."

After the Captain had left in the launch for Tautua, Sutton sat for a long time on the porch at the Residency—his last night in Penrhyn—

and watched the sun drop beyond the islands of fiery clouds that rimmed the western sea. The red glow cast across the sky was fading rapidly, but it was a sailor's omen that good weather would come tomorrow. Sutton found himself thinking of Mrs. Nagle's remark . . . "You will come back . . ."

The darkness crawled quickly across the sky, with stars beginning to pierce the eastern half of the black dome of night. Overhead were the dimly radiant points of *Pisces Australis* and down on the bulky end of the Milky Way the constellation of Capricorn. Stars of the southern sky were seldom known to mariners in the north.

Sutton watched the flare of torches along the beach as the native fishermen moved warily across the water, their naked bodies sometimes glinting in the light which reflected on the lagoon as they probed into the spots where fish lay, ready to dart up curiously toward the light and become impaled on the points of iron-tipped spears. Sutton could not help marveling at the difference between this scene and the life he had known back in New Rochelle . . . and the same random thoughts caused his mind to drift to the north, where the same tropical sky covered the dark mound of Oahu and Pacific Heights . . . Mapuana Davis had also reminded him that "everyone comes back."

While he was wondering whether this was true, Maeva came out on the veranda, so silently that he was not at first aware of her presence. He had talked a great deal with this lovely, dark-eyed girl, who seemed on the threshold of life . . . yet she was living on a remote island, where the only passing scene was the scattering of trading ships, and once a month the small steamer from Raratonga.

She sat down beside him, saying nothing for a short while. The faint light from a lamp inside the house cast a shading of light on the smooth outline of her face and caught the glint of her dark eyes.

"It is sad that you must go—so soon," she finally said, in a low voice that was not much louder than the soft sigh of the surf, beating against the reef on the far side of the lagoon. "We see so few people here . . . and then they go—pop! Like that!" She laughed and clapped her hands suddenly. Sutton felt the same delight he had felt at the rippling laughter of Mapuana Davis. He wondered at the lot of Polynesian girls—for people to come and go—pop! Like that!

Maeva could have been his daughter, he thought—and this reminded him of his daughter—back in New Rochelle. It seemed to be a long way from where he was at the moment.

"You will be gone, too, Maeva," he said, his voice also low. "That is—you will be gone for all of us, when we leave here. You have been very good to us." Abruptly Sutton recalled, with another inner twinge, that almost identical words had been spoken many months ago—in Honolulu. Mapuana had said: "My people are good to strangers . . . but it is wrong to try to trick them . . ."

Sutton wondered: would he try to "trick them"? The people of the Southern islands seemed to be "good," as Mapuana had said. And the strangers who came among them for the most part seemed to have had no real desire to help them . . . and they certainly did not hesitate to hurt them. Tomorrow, he thought, he would be sailing toward the Paumotu Islands—the islands where Mapuana's people lived many years ago. Probably some of her relatives had been blown away in the hurricane which Tommy Eustace had described so graphically. Sutton could imagine the terror of people, on a dark night, with the wind blowing with demoniac fury across the sea, lashing waves to incredible height, snatching people off coconut palms, where they had lashed themselves . . .

He must have grunted at the notion, because Maeva laughed, in her low, melodic way, and said, "You should get some rest tonight, Captain. . . . And do not feel worried—you have been quite good for us, too, since you came here."

Captain Brown made one more protest the next morning when the boat came for him and Dr. Luce. At Captain Nagle's request, Sutton and Chetwood appeared before the Resident Agent. He told them Captain Brown had protested that he was ill and could not sail; and at this point Sutton showed the Resident Agent a certificate signed by Dr. Luce, stating that he had examined the Captain and found him in good health.

In his journal on Wednesday, July 8, Sutton wrote:

> Everything is ready. The launch is back and Captain Brown is aboard. We will again resume our voyage at two o'clock. Where, God only knows! The old man sent for me before breakfast and wanted me to give him assurance in the presence of the Resident Agent that I would not put him in the forecastle. Then he wanted to be left behind at Penrhyn. I refused to give him any assurances, beyond telling him that if he obeyed my orders without question, I would protect him from any personal violence. The Resident Agent informed him that he would have to come aboard quietly, or by force. He concluded to come quietly.

Early the following day, Captain Brown asked Sutton for a "conference" in his cabin. The old man was sitting on his bed, staring at the porthole through which the long rippling water could be seen, rising and falling with each lurch of the ship.

"It's Flint Island," he said, pointing to the island on a chart which he had spread on his knees.

Sutton stared at the Captain, torn between disgust and pity. Finally he sat down. His voice was low, but he continued to keep it firm.

"You have called each of us a liar, Captain . . . And yet you tell me a lie like this! Do you know who is being deceived?" Brown looked up, his pale eyes gazing blankly at Sutton. "You are," Sutton went on, more gently. "And your wife . . . Mrs. Brown believed in you, more than any of us. Do you realize what this will mean to her, Captain—if you go back as a failure?"

The Captain nodded.

"If you are afraid the island is no longer there," Sutton continued, "you may be sure we have all thought of that." He thought he detected a stiffening of the muscles of Captain Brown's face, but the old man did not look up, continuing to stare at the floor. Sutton had the queer feeling that he was talking to a small boy who was being reprimanded and was afraid to look up.

"If we don't find the island—if it has disappeared, or been blown into the ocean—that's a chance we have to take. But we must look for it! Do you understand me, Captain—?"

Sutton arose, suddenly so angry at the old man that he almost grabbed his shoulder to shake him. Captain Brown must have sensed this anger, and he reacted in kind. He looked up, glaring at Sutton; and for an instant Sutton thought he would have to grapple with the old man. Dr. Luce came into the cabin, apparently hearing the loud voices, and Sutton turned to him.

"Doctor—I want you to listen to this." He turned to the Captain. "We will remain on a 130-degree heading for four days. That will take us past Papeete, in the neighborhood of the Paumotus. At that time, Captain, unless you give us the position of the island, we will turn back for San Francisco. If that happens, you will betray every man in this group —your wife—and yourself! You can shout and cry all you damn please—but that's my last word!"

He turned and walked out of the cabin. Dr. Luce followed him topside.

Sutton gave instructions to Mr. Hendrickson to lay the course. He looked at the doctor and shook his head helplessly.

"What can I do with the old fool?"

Dr. Luce snorted impatiently. "Do what anyone would do—put him in the forecastle as a deck hand and make him work his passage. He's no sicker than anyone else on this ship, George. . . . And I think you've proved humoring him won't do anything. I've nursed him until I'm sick of it—and I'm sick of this damn cruise!"

Sutton looked at the doctor, startled by the sudden anger in his voice and the unexpected sharpness of his words.

"Don't you agree with our plan?" he asked mildly.

"I don't agree with a damn thing—except that we should turn back to Tahiti, sell this boat and go home! There's no treasure—and if there was one, either the Captain doesn't know where it is, or it's been blown into the sea. John thinks the same thing."

The doctor turned on his heel and went back down the companionway. Sutton stood for some time, stroking his mustache—which he still kept trimmed and curled, in spite of the exigencies of the sea voyage. The night before he had been dreaming of life on a tropical island, with some mixture of Mapuana, and even Maeva, vaguely included in the dream . . . and now he was aboard the turbulent *Herman* again, quarreling with his friends and associates!

"Damn his dirty treasure," he muttered, and went forward to check the watch.

That night Sutton wrote in his journal:

> The doctor thinks I should put him [the Captain] in the forecastle at once and make him work his passage. John was also inclined to take this view, believing I had made a mistake in treating him decently. Later when I talked to the old man, he agreed to what I proposed. He said if he deceived me this time I could shoot him, or put him in irons and he would not complain. This of course is all nonsense; but I take the view that as we are going to Tahiti anyhow, it does not take us much out of our course or involve anything to treat him decently in the hope he will come through. This matter of treatment of the Captain is in fact the only issue between me and my two companions. They both claim it is only another case of fraud, although John is now inclined to favor my view that under this plan there is a bare possibility of succeeding, although it may be a remote one. I claim we owe it to the San Francisco people to catch at straws if necessary, to do anything in our power to give them and us a run for our money.

[3]

The *Herman* worked its way to the southeast, under gray overcast skies with dark scudding clouds blowing in lumpy masses constantly from the east and north; and on the morning of the fourth day the schooner lay at Lat. 14.48 S., Long. 149.11 W., less than a day's run from Matahiva.

"We'll make Matahiva by two or three o'clock and anchor inside the lagoon," Sutton told Chetwood and the doctor. "We've been running through some heavy seas and I'd like to get the ship in trim."

The air had been hot and heavy since leaving Penrhyn; and to an extent the atmosphere aboard ship was not dissimilar. The Captain had stayed well to himself, remaining in his cabin except for occasional excursions on deck, during which he communed with the seas and himself. Now and then Willie Peterson would stop to exchange a word or two; and once the little Australian, Fisher, stood by the Captain at the rail, and seemed to be talking with him.

Sutton was not a martinet; but he wanted as little fraternizing between the Captain and members of the crew as possible. He told Mr. Hendrickson to see that the men on watch were kept busy and did not chat with Captain Brown. Peterson had been surly and uncommunicative since the dressing down Sutton had given him in Penrhyn, and Fisher was an enigma.

Relations between Sutton and his two companions were hardly more sociable. Chetwood sat and talked with Sutton now and then on the afterdeck; but the doctor said little and it was evident he was thoroughly fed up with the expedition. Sutton was on the point of remarking, after one of Dr. Luce's more acid rejoinders, that since the doctor had invested little besides his time—and he was more or less in retirement—he had less to be concerned about than Sutton and Chetwood; however, he refrained, feeling that everyone's nerves were already stretched to the breaking point.

The hot, humid air did not help; and looking worriedly to the south, as they entered the lagoon and dropped anchor at Matahiva, Sutton wondered what dirty weather might be kicking up.

As the *Sailing Directions* noted, in rather vague and uncertain language, storms in the tropical belt of the Pacific usually are formed when hot air lies for some time over the water and begins to develop low and high spots. This causes the air to spin in circles with ever increasing speed, until the hot air begins to "feed" on the outer edges of cooler air, quickly extending to a vast whirlpool of raging wind, sometimes spreading thirty to forty miles across.

Sutton had read the book carefully and brought the matter up with Tommy Benson, who was standing the evening watch.

"Nobody is ever sure about the damn things," Benson said. "I've been in winds up to a hundred miles an hour and some of 'em go almost twice that, from what I've heard. We got blowed right through the lagoon in Tikihau one time—landed on the beach in a small lugger, an' I never saw the reef. But it went down as fast as it came up, or I guess we'd have sailed across the island."

The following morning the crew worked industriously, cleaning up the decks, which had been awash much of the way down from Penrhyn. Sutton watched the Captain for a time, as he sat on the afterdeck, his legs stretched out and his pale eyes staring—sightlessly, it seemed—across the dark mass of trees which formed the jungled inner ring of the island.

"We'll be at Makatea by nightfall and lie outside the lagoon," Sutton finally said to the Captain. "Tomorrow I'd like to have you come ashore, Captain Brown—I want you to look around and see if you recognize anything."

"Recognize . . . what?" The old man looked up. "I ain't never been on that island."

Sutton shrugged.

"Perhaps you'll remember something. Anyway, we've got to try everything we can, Captain Brown. It's to your interest as well as ours, you know."

The Captain suddenly drew his legs up, and hunched forward in his chair.

"You take me back to Tahiti, Cap'n! We'll find the island all right. You treated me right—when I told you that lie about Flint Island. Didn't you? Well, I got feelings, too, Cap'n . . . an' that damn doctor don't think so. He's to blame for this whole damn thing . . . Tried to get me to spill what I know, he did . . . when I was sick! We'll get rid of this crew, Cap'n, an' get a new crew. Blacks—that's what we'll get! They don't know anything an' they do what you tell 'em to, without watching all the time . . ."

Sutton shrugged. The old man's rambling was getting on his nerves, too; and he had now decided that if nothing definite developed when they reached Makatea—if the Captain remained obstinate and stubborn in his refusal to give any specific directions, he would agree with Chetwood and the doctor to head for Tahiti and home.

Shortly after noon the *Herman* was ready to depart. Sutton took the ship out of the lagoon under foresail and a single jib, tacked a bit to the west to pick up the easterly wind and jibed to the southwest, working gradually around toward the southeast. Sutton estimated they were about 220 miles east of Papeete, and he did not want to run closer for fear of being observed by one of the fishing luggers which plied among the islands. He was quite sure, from the Captain's previous remarks, that the treasure island itself must lie to the south, away from the usual tracks of sailing ships; but he felt that Makatea could very well have been the base from which the *Sea Foam* had operated. Once they got the Captain ashore, Sutton was convinced they would be able to discover whether the island was familiar to him.

Matahiva lay almost due west of Tikihau, and Makatea was south of the latter island; so Sutton planned to run the base leg of the triangle at about a 135° heading, making Makatea around nightfall. This would carry him some fifty miles west of the course the *Herman* had previously followed northward from Makatea, but it would avoid the need of beating into easterly winds.

There was a good beam wind during the first hour, coming from the northeast; but then it began to drift to the southward, forcing the *Herman* to pay off on a more southerly course. The air became hot and almost still at times; and at one point Sutton, looking overside at the curling wake thrown off by the schooner, was startled to observe that it seemed to have lost way entirely.

"Trim the jib and mainsail," he ordered to Mr. Hendrickson. "Let me know your heading and the direction of wind."

"Aye, sir," Mr. Hendrickson said. Tommy Benson, coming by the wheelhouse, where Willie Peterson stood at the wheel, with a deep scowl on his face, muttered to Sutton: "It's beginning to foul up, sir."

The sails, as Sutton looked upward, seemed actually to sag; and Sutton wondered if they should run up the staysail or the gaff foretopsail to give some extra canvas. He decided against this, however; the wind would have to pick up to do any good.

The schooner wallowed for at least an hour, it seemed, in long, glassy swells, and the sea itself had taken on a saffron hue. There was a coppery tint to the sun, shining dimly through the overcast; and Sutton noticed far to the south a layer of olive-colored clouds on the horizon. He called Tommy Benson over.

"What's that?" he asked, pointing to the clouds.

Benson shook his head. "It ain't good, Cap'n. Better reef the mainsail for a time . . . looks like we're in for a blow."

The *Herman* continued to wallow along on a light beam wind, and the swell seemed to have swung around behind the ship and was now coming out of the west.

"Perhaps we can make a run for Makatea," Sutton told Mr. Hendrickson. "The wind must be moving around off the starboard quarter."

Mr. Hendrickson shook his head. "I don't like it," he said. At that moment there was a shout from forward.

"Land, ho!" It was Jimmy Wilson, at the foremast. Sutton went forward, and could see well down on the horizon, off the port bow, a low-lying slab, glinting in spots from the faint gleam of the sun, which seemed to pierce the overcast where the island lay.

Captain Brown and the doctor had come on deck, disturbed by the wallowing roll of the schooner, and now Captain Brown came forward. He stood for a minute beside Sutton, staring intently across the water.

"Better keep her a bit to the west," Sutton called out to Mr. Hendrickson, who quickly relayed the order to Peterson at the wheel. "We may have a blow coming up and we'd better stand clear of the land."

The sea, meanwhile, had taken on a kind of churning appearance, as if some deep vibration under the surface were stirring it up, like a pot beginning to boil. The swells no longer seemed to rise and fall; and off to the south it seemed to Sutton that the surface of the sea was flat and white, like a plain of froth.

The *Herman* was now sailing to the west of the island, and Sutton decided to continue on about a 170-degree heading, holding well off the land so that the schooner could make a run for Makatea if the wind veered farther to the west, as it seemed to be doing. The island seemed to be only about three miles long, with no high points—apparently an atoll, which would be surrounded by the inevitable reef and an outer lagoon. Sutton had no desire to probe any entrances while the sea was coming up and a blow seemed in the offing.

He suddenly realized that there was a long, pulsating hum in the air, a kind of low rhythmic cadence; and at the same time a dead calm seemed to have settled on the sea. Almost at that instant, a sharp gust of wind struck the *Herman* from the southwest, heeling her over as it caught the expanse of the mainsail.

"Better get the sails shortened, sir," Tommy Benson shouted. "We're in for it."

Captain Brown had been standing beside Sutton; and now he grabbed him by the arm, pointing to the southeast where the island lay, not more than four or five miles away.

"I think that's it, Cap'n," he said hoarsely. "I think . . . by God, it is! It's the island . . . the island! I swear it is!"

Sutton had no idea that the Captain knew what he was talking about.

From the distance, with the haze over the sea, it would be difficult to recognize anything, let alone an island in an area where they all looked about the same. The wind meanwhile had come up, and the shrouds and halyards were whipping like live things. It was difficult to hear, but he could make out Mr. Hendrickson's orders to "take in the mainsail—lively, lads!"

Benson was bellowing profanely at the crew. "Man the main halyards and lower away, you swabs . . . it'll be over the side and you'll be with it! Damn you—" He actually kicked Willie Fisher forward to the main-stays. The crew worked swiftly and efficiently, and within a matter of seconds, it seemed, the mainsail was furled and the boom lashed down.

Sutton wondered how long the schooner could work under foresail and jib until they would have to run for it. The island was almost abeam, and he hoped fervently the wind would stay to the west until they cleared the point. If not they would have to heave to and hope the force of the gale would not drive them stern-first toward the shoals that he was certain lay outside the long layer of yellow rock that was now visible.

Captain Brown, who had been gripping the after rail and had not taken his eyes off the island, now turned and shouted through the din of the wind and the rattle of tackle: "If ye can get her around . . . good anchorage . . . leeward."

Sutton shook his head. He respected the Captain's seamanship, but this was a situation in which he would have to rely on Mr. Hendrickson and Tommy Benson—and himself. The wind by this time had struck with howling fury, and the waves seemed to be all of the same height, stretching away as far as he could see in an expanse of white foam, as the wind drove the spray across the surface. There was a rending sound and a clap of thunder as the foreboom gave way, swinging like a mighty shillelagh over the water, dipping into the frothing sea.

"Cut it away!" Benson screamed; but Mr. Hendrickson had gone forward and by dint of great effort he and two of the sailors hauled the boom back and made it fast. The foresail was brought down and furled, and the *Herman* was now running under bare poles, with only a jib to keep headway. The wind was forcing the schooner around into a lee helm in spite of Peterson's efforts to hold her steady. The seas were now behind the *Herman,* rolling against her quarter and washing away everything not lashed down on the afterdeck.

Benson was working desperately with the crew to keep the jib in some trim; and even Jimmy had come up to lend a hand. Sutton caught a glimpse of a saffron face—looking almost white in the yellow cast of the sky—staring from the after companionway. It was Hasino, the cook, and the odd thought flashed through Sutton's mind that Hasino might have the can of strychnine . . . He muttered to himself, at his own errant thinking, and again wondered if he were losing his mind.

An instant later he was almost sure he had. A wall of water had rushed from nowhere, it seemed, twisting above them like an avenging apparition in the air, and flung itself down the length of the ship. The *Herman* creaked and groaned in every beam and strake; the deck slanted like a cliff, as she heeled over. But she righted herself after the impact, and Sutton could see the bowsprit, shedding water like a shaking terrier, as it rose from the hollow trough into which the schooner had plunged.

The clouds seemed suddenly to have parted, and Sutton, gasping for air in the water-laden stream of whistling wind that raged across the deck, found himself shouting: "It's over—thank God!"

It wasn't, of course. Benson had come aft, alongside Sutton, and was clutching the stanchion rail on the companionway, trying to keep his feet on the heaving deck. Looking over Sutton's shoulder, he pointed and screamed into Sutton's ear: "Looks like hell, sir . . ."

Sutton found himself—also holding desperately to the stanchion—marveling at the unexpected moderation of Benson's expletives. It seemed to him Benson was capable of more forceful profanity, even in a calm sea. . . . He nodded, and shouted back: "Yes—I guess it is hell . . ."

"No—" Benson was shaking his head violently, pointing distractedly over Sutton's shoulder. "Like hell . . . like hell!" he screamed again. "Looks . . . *like* hell . . ."

Benson was shouting into Sutton's ear, and with the seas raging insanely around them and the decks heaving crazily Sutton could hardly keep his feet, but suddenly he looked to the west and understood what Benson was saying. The clouds had parted, leaving a ragged aperture, crimson and frayed at the edges, like a bloody mouth gaping over the edge of the sea. It hardly seemed important to Sutton at the moment, but he turned and nodded his affirmation.

Benson, gripping the rail to keep from being hurled off the deck, sank his chin in his chest to keep the sting of flying water off his face; apparently he was satisfied, now that he had been understood.

Sutton looked around for other members of the crew, hoping no one had been hurt or washed overboard. He could see Mr. Hendrickson's tall form at the foremast, as he held on with one arm and directed the lashing down of the launch, which had been partly torn loose from the gunwale gripes when the foreboom swung out. Sutton supposed the others were holding fast also . . . but at that moment he forgot everything else.

There was a report like a rifle shot forward and he saw the jib snap loose and trail forward in the wind like a streamer. The *Herman* seemed to be riding the crest of an enormous wave, a massive monster of gray-green water; and forward and below the rail at the waist of the ship Sutton saw a giant scarp of water, curving like an immense scoop of combed glass. Looking over the side he could have sworn he saw a tree—the green spray of a coconut palm, flashing across the bottom of the steep incline.

At that moment, however, the *Herman* seemed to lose way—probably due to the snapping of the jib sheet, and the furious tide of boiling froth that rushed past the gunwale appeared to be swallowing the entire ship. Sutton shook his head, which was almost wrenched loose by each successive slap of water whistling through the air. He saw the bow of the schooner rise, throwing off a great cascade of water that poured down from the steeply inclined forward deck. Sutton took in gulps of salty air. He was almost certain he was now losing his mind. There was a grinding noise, almost a crunch, as the *Herman* settled by the stern in the wake of the giant comber, now rushing off to eastward where the darkness was fast building up.

We've hit something . . . a reef! Sutton thought, and turned to stare at Tommy Benson, who was performing acrobatics at the other side of the wheelhouse, striving to hold to the rail. The second mate was also shaking his head—whether to get the water out of his eyes, or restore his sense, Sutton could not know at the moment.

Benson pulled himself across the back of the wheelhouse. Sutton could see Peterson inside, laboring mightily with the wheel. Benson got close enough to scream again in Sutton's ear: "We're over it, sir . . . over it . . ."

"It's over?" Sutton shouted back, unbelievingly. The wind seemed to have abated slightly, and the *Herman* sank back a bit, with its only canvas flying ahead like an advance pennant, but Sutton could see no reason for any unbounded optimism.

"Over the island . . ." Benson's face was a mask of writhing frustration; he seemed unable to convey his meaning about anything. "Over it . . . we passed *over* . . ."

Sutton, looking back, realized abruptly what had happened. He almost lost his grip on the rail, thinking about it.

Within a half hour the storm seemed to have moved on. Two sailors had crawled forward on the bowsprit and recovered the jib sheet, bending the sail back so that it continued to draw the *Herman* along with the wind. The schooner, a dripping and considerably battered piece of flotsam, was left in the wake of the winds, and somehow managed to retain a following course.

Mr. Hendrickson, exhausted from his labors but still able to drive the crew to action, was supervising an effort to raise the foresail. He finally came back to where Sutton was standing, still gripping the rail of the companionway stanchion.

Sutton's face was pale and strained, as if he had seen a ghost.

"Where's the Captain . . . everybody?"

"The Captain's at the foremast, sir. He wanted to help, and we needed every hand . . . I'll check the others . . . all safe . . . I think . . ."

The wind still whipped snatches of his speech away; but Sutton nodded. He turned and looked at Tommy Benson, who was staring at him, also white-faced.

"Did you see it, sir . . . the tree?"

Sutton nodded. The second mate made his way forward along the midship rail, to help rig the foresail and make ready to hoist the main gaff when the wind had been sufficiently expended.

Sutton looked back several times, after the storm had subsided enough to see anything; but there was no sign of anything on the horizon, except for the long swells that followed them, still tossing spray off the caps.

At one point, Sutton turned to look at the set of the foresail as the *Herman* paid off to turn into the wind, now reduced to a heavy blow; and as he looked forward, he saw Captain Brown, a gray ghostly figure, clinging with both hands to the halyard cleats on the mainmast, staring back in the direction from which they had come. Sutton doubted if the Captain even saw him, clutching the wheelhouse rail. He simply stared, his eyes wide open and completely rimmed with white, his mass of tangled hair and whiskers blowing back from his bare head. The old man looked as if he were completely mad, as if he had seen something that snapped his senses like a broken fiddle string. His eyes were filled with horror—and fear.

"He saw it!" Sutton thought. "He saw it, too!"

Makatea: End of the Treasure Trail

[1]

The *Herman* wallowed throughout the night through sluggish seas, with the gusty winds carrying her miles to the east. Just before dawn, with the foresail and jib raised, Sutton ordered her hove to. After examining the decks to find out how much damage had been done by the typhoon, he ordered the vessel put around on a westerly course.

The battered little schooner was soaked to the keelson, with rigging torn loose and the foreboom yoke partly smashed by the errant swing of the heavy spar out over the water; but it appeared as if repairs could be made within a few hours, and Sutton decided to sail back over the course and see if any trace of the mysterious island could be found.

One of the sailors was sent below to check the garboard strakes and see if the blow the keel had taken during that awful moment when the ship seemed ready to plunge down into the trough of the giant wave, had ripped her bottom. There appeared to be no serious damage, however; and further examination would have to await the arrival at Makatea.

Captain Brown came on deck shortly after dawn, and Sutton asked bluntly, "Did you see us pass over that island?"

The old man seemed to shudder. He closed his eyes and shook his head slightly.

"I don't know what I seen," he mumbled, and made his way aft.

It was Sutton's plan to sail close enough to the island to find an anchorage and go ashore, if possible. Captain Brown's shout—"It's the island!"—was not much to go on, but they were coming to the last stages of the search, and Sutton did not want to overlook any possibility. He reckoned the location where the island had been sighted, just before the storm, to be about forty or fifty miles northwest of Makatea.

If there were an anchorage on the lee shore of the island—as Captain Brown had said—he would drop anchor and try to examine the hull from the outside; otherwise they would turn back to Makatea.

The Captain meanwhile remained by himself on the afterdeck, sunk into one of his spells of torpor, staring out across the water and saying nothing. Even when Willie Peterson came by and spoke to him—under the sharp surveillance of Mr. Hendrickson, who had been instructed to keep a lookout on the bosun's actions—the Captain did not appear to respond to anything the bosun said. Peterson walked away, shaking his head; and later Sutton observed him in what seemed to be a furtive conversation with Willie Fisher, the Australian sailor.

The thought passed through Sutton's mind that something was afoot, but when he went forward the two separated, and he did not pursue the matter. Meanwhile he was busy calculating the probable area of the island; but after the *Herman* had tacked back and forth for several hours across a path several miles wide, there was still no sign of an island or anything that resembled land.

By noon it was evident that either they had lost track of the bit of coral rock, or it had been washed away by the typhoon. The latter explanation was becoming apparent to Sutton, and it held ominous possibilities.

He talked with Chetwood about this, telling him of his startling experience during the storm when he and Benson had actually seen the top of a coconut tree as the *Herman* was swept along on the crest of the monstrous wave.

"It might have been just a floating treetop that had been broken off by the wind," he said. "But in that case, it seems to me it would have moved along with the wave—at least rising and falling. This thing simply flashed past under us."

"Benson saw it, too?"

Sutton nodded.

"He was pretty well shaken up by it—as I was. It looked as if the *Herman* had been carried right across some part of the island, large enough to support a tree, which means it wasn't a reef. Then I heard the noise and felt the shock of the keel striking something. The jib had just carried away, or we'd probably have pitched right down on the rock —or whatever it was."

Chetwood puckered up his mouth and shook his head.

"Maybe the Captain saw it, too—he was somewhere amidships at the time. That may be the reason for his present state of mind. If he saw the wave take us over the island, then he can be pretty sure that what he's been scared of all along is true—that is, these islands *do* get washed away in big storms."

Sutton nodded.

"I think he saw it," he said. "It may not have been his island, of course . . . but if it was, then the old man's worst fears have come true."

The *Herman* raised Makatea before nightfall and Sutton ordered the schooner hove to outside the lagoon while they put out in the jolly boat to sound the channel entrance into the lagoon. There was about six fathoms of water just outside the entrance, and Mr. Hendrickson thought it safer to lie at anchor outside, in case another storm should blow up.

"We can move outside and run with it," he explained. "Any of those big waves would carry us right up on the beach if we lay inside the reef. In the meantime, we can repair the damage caused by the storm."

Tommy Benson, who was a powerful swimmer, stripped and went over the side, diving under the schooner to inspect the keel in spite of the risk of sharks. He reported there was some damage to the keel itself, but no indication that the side of the hull had been damaged.

Sutton had already decided to take the Captain ashore on Makatea—by whatever means or ruse might prove necessary; but first he wanted to explore the area himself and try to find Dr. Luce's deserted village.

That night, as they lay at anchor, Sutton went below to the Captain's cabin. Dr. Luce had stayed pretty much in his own cabin since the storm, saying very little to either Sutton or Chetwood, and did not go with him; but Chetwood decided to accompany Sutton on his visit to the Captain.

"Maybe we can pry something out of him—and if it comes to a tussle, it might be that two of us could handle him easier than just one."

Sutton grinned, rather grimly.

"I can handle the old boy—if it comes to that. But beating him down won't give us any answers, John. There's something in the old man's craw and I mean to find out what it is."

The Captain lay on his bed, staring feverishly at the ceiling. He hardly noticed Sutton and Chetwood when they came in, but when they both seated themselves and seemed likely to remain, he turned and glared for a moment at Sutton.

"I'm sick, Cap'n," he said finally. "Ye got to get me ashore . . . in Tahiti! It's your duty, Cap'n. I can see them damn ghosts all around now, jest waitin' for me." He shook his head slightly, as if to rid his vision of occult visitors.

Sutton decided to plunge in.

"Look here, Captain—we've reached the end of this trip right here, unless you give us enough information to locate the island. Tomorrow morning we've got to decide—one way or another. You've got to come ashore and look at the island. Do you understand that, Captain?" Without waiting for an answer, Sutton asked abruptly, "Captain Brown, did you ship any natives on the *Sea Foam*—when you were down here?"

The Captain raised himself on one elbow, and stared at Sutton. His broad chest, matted with white hair, was uncovered, and he was breathing heavily. Sutton wondered if the old man was having "the fevers" again.

"Hell, yes," the Captain rumbled. "We took 'em on when our own sailors died, or got killed . . . Damn good sailors, too! I told you, Cap'n—them Kanakas don't talk an' they don't look around, tryin' to find out how much gold ye got. Not like the riffraff ye got on this ship—always up to some damn tricks! Bunch o' scum—that's what they are! I told ye to get rid of 'em an' hire a black crew."

"Did any of the natives die—on the ship?" Sutton asked, persistently.

"Hell—of course they did! The fevers killed 'em—except those that we lost in the fights. Kanakas can't stand the fevers, Cap'n. . . . They get hot and run for the water, an' that kills 'em."

"What about those ghosts—that you told me about in San Francisco?" Sutton asked. Chetwood, listening to the colloquy, looked at Sutton with astonishment. It was a line of questioning he had not anticipated; but he said nothing.

The Captain waved his free hand in a sweeping gesture that included most of the room. Chetwood involuntarily glanced around, as if he wanted to see whether there were any incorporeal guests in the room.

"Kanakas don't have ghosts, Cap'n. . . . But there's lots of the others here. Lots of 'em . . ." Captain Brown lifted himself almost to a sitting position. "Don't try any of yer damn tricks, Cap'n—or they'll get ye . . . the whole scurvy lot of you!" He sank back, and his pale eyes seemed to be blurred. "Didn't mean that," he mumbled. "Ye've been pretty decent to me, Cap'n Sutton . . . but that damned doctor!"

Sutton wondered whether the old man was in possession of his senses, or had suddenly collapsed mentally into senile dementia. Chetwood looked worried, and shook his head. They arose to leave.

"We'll go ashore tomorrow, Captain," Sutton said, firmly, from the doorway. "That will be your last chance to make good on your promises. . . . After that we will head for home and you will be put in irons if you raise your hand."

The Captain lifted his hand in what might have been a token gesture of defiance.

"The damn ghosts are still there, Cap'n . . . sittin' on them casks of gold like buzzards sittin' on a dead body." His eyes suddenly seemed to acquire an intelligent gleam. He pointed at Sutton. "Look in that lagoon, Cap'n—see if there's oysters there! If the oysters are red—that's the place!"

Sutton remembered that Captain Brown had referred to a "large plant of oysters in the lagoon" when he had talked with him at Auburn; and Dr. Luce had also told of his strange, feverish reference to "blood all over the place" and oysters that were "red in the lagoon."

Afterward, he and Chetwood went to Dr. Luce's cabin; and while the doctor was not overly communicative, he admitted he was getting tired.

"I'm a damn sight older than either of you!" he told Sutton and Chetwood. He tried to recall what the Captain had told him during the time Captain Brown had been sick in San Francisco.

"He did talk of oysters," the doctor said. "I remember that quite distinctly. I assumed it was some kind of fixation—and perhaps it is."

The following morning Sutton arranged with Chetwood to go ashore with him in the landing party to reconnoiter the area back of the beach. Makatea was one of the few volcanic islands in the outer Paumotus that rose to a fair height from the flat coral beach. From the deck of the *Herman* they could see limestone cliffs, perhaps a quarter of a mile back from the beach, ascending sharply to what apparently was the rim of an old volcano, some three hundred feet high.

Sutton waited for Captain Brown to come on deck, and establish himself in his customary deck chair. He intended to outline the plan to the Captain before leaving to reconnoiter, and arrange a second trip later in the day with Captain Brown accompanying them.

As he began to speak to the Captain, he saw Jimmy Akahito coming through the companionway entrance, carrying one of the Lee-Enfield repeaters. The Japanese steward walked across the few feet of deck and handed the rifle to the Captain.

Dr. Luce had been standing at the rail, watching the shore. As the steward handed the rifle to Captain Brown, the doctor shouted and leaped for him. Sutton, who was standing beside the Captain, was so startled at the actions of the Japanese steward and Dr. Luce that he hardly moved.

The doctor grabbed the rifle and began to wrench it from Captain Brown's grasp. There was a sudden spat! of a rifle shot; and Tommy Benson, who had come forward from the transom where he had been looking to the rigging, plunged headlong to the deck with a howl of pain.

Sutton moved in and knocked the rifle away from both the Captain and Dr. Luce. It went spinning across the deck, stopping in front of Jimmy Akahito, who now stood in a kind of frozen surprise, making no effort to pick it up.

Mr. Hendrickson had come running back from where he was directing the lowering of the jolly boat. He snatched up the gun as Dr. Luce wound up his tussle sitting on Captain Brown's lap, his arm around the old man's neck as if he were embracing him—except that he was actually trying to choke him.

Sutton looked over and saw that the first mate had the gun, and was holding Jimmy by the collar. The other sailors came running back, with Willie Fisher and Peterson in the lead, both white-faced and obviously frightened.

Sutton managed to pull Dr. Luce off the Captain. "Better see to Benson—he's hurt," he said. The second mate was squatting on the deck, his eyes wide open with a mixture of wonder and pain.

Sutton walked over and took the rifle from Mr. Hendrickson. He stepped to the lee of the wheelhouse and said to the two sailors: "Stand back! The first man who moves to the quarterdack will be shot down." He looked at Captain Brown. "What is this all about, Captain? You'd better talk straight!"

The Captain shook his head.

"I don't know . . ." He held out his hands, helplessly. Jimmy, the steward, was chattering excitedly, waving his hands, obviously terrified.

"Did you ask for this gun?" Sutton asked the Captain. His face was pale, but his voice was quite firm. "You understand the penalty for using firearms aboard ship, Captain . . . What were you doing?"

"I wanted to shoot birds, Cap'n! I asked the steward to bring me the gun—to shoot birds. That's the damned truth—"

Dr. Luce looked up from Benson's leg, which he had been examining.

"Get my medical kit from below," he called out. "The shot must have gone through the leg. Not very bad from what I can see."

Benson's face was twisted with pain; but he managed to say, "It ain't *your* leg, Doc—or you'd think it was damn bad!"

Sutton turned to the first mate. "Mr. Hendrickson, take the steward below and put him in handcuffs. Station one man—better make it Wilson—to guard him. Check the weapons chest and see if it's unlocked."

Chetwood spoke up. "It's unlocked—I took one of the rifles this morning. I was going to take it ashore to shoot"—he hesitated, and glanced at the Captain—"birds," he said. "I forgot to lock it."

Sutton spent several minutes on deck, questioning Captain Brown. The old man seemed almost stupefied; but whether it was shock at the failure of some scheme to take over the ship, or surprise at what had happened, Sutton could not determine. Chetwood stood beside Sutton, watching the Captain, while Dr. Luce helped Benson into the waist of the ship, where he put the second mate on a deck chair and cleaned and bandaged the wound. It appeared to be only a flesh wound, the bullet having gone through the inside of the calf of his right leg. He took a flask of brandy out of his kit, and handed it to Benson.

"An inch more and you'd have had a broken leg," the doctor told him.

"Yeah—" Benson grimaced with pain, gulping down the brandy as the doctor probed the wound. "An inch the other way, Doc—an' I wouldn't have got hit."

After interrogating Jimmy, the steward, Sutton ordered Mr. Hendrickson to post guard over the Captain. He then asked Chetwood and the doctor to come into his cabin. He held up a can and a small bottle.

"This is the strychnine," he said. "Jimmy turned it over to me."

"Jimmy!" Dr. Luce looked at the others. "I would never have supposed it was Jimmy."

Sutton shrugged.

"He says the Captain asked him to keep it—when they were in Honolulu. He said the Captain was afraid the doctor would feed it to him—and poison him."

"Why, the damned old fool—"

Sutton allowed himself a weak grin, and sighed.

"I know—it is all pretty mixed up. But the trouble is, there is nothing absolutely wrong with Jimmy's story—or the Captain's. The gun—and the strychnine. It sounds fishy, but there's no way of proving anything wrong."

Chetwood stood up and pounded his fist against his hand.

"That's the trouble—with this whole trip! Everything can be either one way, or the other. And nobody can tell which! Was the Captain going to shoot birds—or us? Was he afraid he would be poisoned—or did he expect to poison somebody? Everything is sixes and sevens. If I didn't have a conviction, George, that there aren't any such things as ghosts, by God, I'd believe the ship was haunted by those damn ghosts you and the Captain talked about!"

Dr. Luce spoke up.

"Why do you suppose it happened this morning? Are we getting warm, do you think—in this treasure hunt?" He half smiled. "I suppose that's reversing my position—but look at what's happened! The gun locker had been left opened—and it just happened that Jimmy passed by and picked up a rifle . . . which the Captain just happened to ask for. I'm damned if I know what to make of it—but I don't intend to say here much longer and be a target for anybody."

Sutton said, "We'll have to keep watch ourselves, around the clock. One of us is going to have to be on guard all the time. Mr. Hendrickson is all right—he's an old hand. And I'd vouch for Tommy Benson. Peterson's always been a question mark in my mind. Jack Jensen and Jimmy Wilson are apparently just sailors, and Fisher is a rat. I'm going to give orders to Mr. Hendrickson that they cannot be on the same watch—until we reach Tahiti. Peterson and Fisher, I mean. Whoever is on watch will have to keep an eye on the crew. I'd suggest each of us carry a gun from now on, and we'll check the gun locker after every watch."

He turned to Dr. Luce. "John and I are going ashore to try to locate that old village. If you'd rather come, John or I can stay on the ship—but one of us will have to be aboard at all times."

The doctor shook his head.

"I'm too damn tired to go anywhere. My heart isn't too strong, you know. I'll keep watch—you and John go ashore, and if you dig up any treasure, fire three shots."

Chetwood grinned. "Good—and if you get in trouble, just fire one shot."

[2]

Sutton boarded the jolly boat with Chetwood and two sailors, Jensen and Wilson, after instructing Mr. Hendrickson to keep a close watch on the Captain and the two sailors, Peterson and Fisher, who were more or less under suspicion of plotting with Captain Brown. Jimmy Akahito, who apparently was so terrified he could not have mounted an insurrection against the cook, was locked incommunicado in the small bulkheaded area used as a brig in the forward part of the ship, his hands manacled, until the shore party returned.

Sutton and Chetwood each had a pistol; and Chetwood had taken one of the Lee-Enfield repeating rifles. Dr. Luce sat in a deck chair, with his heavy-duty shotgun across his lap, ready to blast a load of buckshot across the deck; and the rest of the arms were presumably locked up.

As the landing boat headed toward the reef, looking for a break in the rim of coral rock that surrounded the lagoon, Sutton outlined to Chetwood his general summary of the situation.

"Everything seems to point to the possibility that Makatea was the base from which the *Sea Foam* operated," he said. "We'll know more about that after we've looked over the place where the doctor saw the abandoned village . . . When the Captain comes ashore this afternoon, we ought to be able to get some kind of spark. But I doubt very much if this is the place where they buried the treasure."

"Why?" Chetwood asked.

"For one thing, it wouldn't make good sense to bury the treasure here and then remain here any length of time—if that's what they did. It would offer a constant temptation to the members of the crew . . . and it would expose the treasure cache to passing ships. In all probability, they took the stuff to some outlying atoll with probably only a few men knowing exactly where it was buried. You remember, the Captain described the actual place where the treasure was buried in some detail. He told me it was buried in a cliff. He didn't seem worried about that part of it. . . . It was the location of the island itself that he kept such a close secret."

"What's the good of bringing him ashore—if the treasure isn't here?" Chetwood asked.

"Maybe we can jar something loose. He seems to be in a kind of daze, but if we get any indication that Makatea is the place where the *Sea Foam* was based, we've got the problem narrowed down quite a lot." Sutton told Chetwood of the story he had heard from Mapuana Davis in Honolulu, which had been confirmed to some extent by the Captain's remarks about taking on Kanakas from the "low islands" as crew members.

The boat meanwhile had skirted the reef to the point through which the earlier landing was made. The outer reef was broken down, but the break was not very deep, and they had to wait for a large wave to carry the jolly boat over the slope of jagged coral that formed the reef. Sutton looked back at the sharp rocks projecting above the surface of the water behind them. The wave seemed to boil through the break, and then was sucked back with a gurgling sound as the jutting overhang of coral formation was exposed.

"Damn glad we kept the *Herman* outside," Chetwood remarked. "I don't think she'd get through this—and if she did, we'd have a rough time getting out again."

Jimmy Wilson, at the helm, grinned and emitted a low whistle through a gap in his teeth. "It ain't going to be any picnic getting back with this boat, sir. It's a lot easier coming in than going out."

Sutton remembered that there was a deeper break, farther along the lee side of the island. He told Wilson to head toward the beach opposite the deep entrance to the lagoon. This would enable them to get back quickly if there were signs of trouble aboard the schooner.

The jolly boat veered its course, passing along the inner edge of the reef. Chetwood suddenly pointed down into the clear water, perhaps twenty-five feet in depth.

"Oysters," he said.

Sutton looked down. The bottom of the lagoon was covered with gray shells, which seemed to be plastered along the lower level of rocks.

Sutton directed Wilson to take the boat in a circle, rowing as close to the reef as possible. Looking down into the clear water, Sutton saw a considerable scattering of red-shelled scallops, which lay on the sand. These are migratory shellfish that may be plentiful one year and almost disappear the next; nevertheless, in some intangible way they might be related to Captain Brown's reference to "red oysters" in the lagoon, during his spell of "the fevers."

The jolly boat was beached and Sutton and Chetwood, the latter carrying the rifle, went ashore. They followed the coast for a short distance and then veered in toward the volcanic cliffs. Dr. Luce had described the route to the village. At first there seemed to be no possible way of breaching the face of the cliffs, but finally Chetwood found a semblance of a trail that led around the base of the ridge.

On the southern end of the island, about a mile and a half from the lagoon, the volcanic rim broke away. Sutton scrambled to the crest of this incline and Chetwood followed. They could see the glint of water deep in the jungled hollow of the crater.

These four watercolor portraits were drawn by Hasino, the cook, who was an amateur artist. *Upper left:* George Sutton. *Upper right:* Captain Brown. *Lower left:* Dr. Luce. *Lower right:* John Chetwood.

"That's the kind of lake the old man talked about—when we were at Penrhyn," Chetwood told Sutton. The cliff was too steep to descend, and they returned to the foot of the rise.

Below the rim, on the windward side, they found traces of the abandoned village, or settlement, that Dr. Luce had described; but aside from a few slabs of dried or rotten wood, and some pieces of rusted tin that might have been brought by natives establishing a fishing village, there was nothing that would indicate whether natives or white men had lived there. It was obviously years since anyone had been there; and it appeared to Sutton that the place had probably been occupied in successive stages.

"Why do you suppose it's on the windward side?" Chetwood asked. "Most of the native villages seem to be along the leeward lagoons."

"Water, I suppose," Sutton said. "The lake in the center should be fresh water and probably can't be reached from the leeward side. Or they may have wanted to be out of sight of any ship coming up on the leeward side."

At Sutton's suggestion, they separated, Chetwood taking the trail across a narrow peninsula which would lead back to the lagoon on the leeward side of the volcanic rim, where he hoped to get a few shots at birds that appeared to nest in the crevices below the crater rim. Sutton decided to push on past the abandoned village, in the hope of finding some more definite signs of former inhabitants.

However, the heavy brush and apparent lack of any trails blocked his attack on this side of the island, and he turned back after a half hour or so, intending to follow Chetwood's trail back to the lagoon where the jolly boat was beached.

The sun was now high overhead, and the blazing heat poured directly down upon the island. There were a few heavy stands of pandanus and clusters of coconut palms along the beach; and some distance below were trees that Sutton thought must be breadfruit—that widely scattered tropical plant which grows everywhere in the South Sea Islands and forms one of the staples of Polynesian diet. It is almost always found where there has been human habitation.

As Sutton clambered around the shoulder of the volcanic upthrust, looking down on the lagoon where the jolly boat lay on the beach, he heard a terrific blast . . . the sound of a shotgun. He looked off across the lagoon at the *Herman* and started to run down the inclined slope. He could see the vessel turning slowly with the wind and heading out to sea!

Sutton shouted. Below, on the beach, he saw Chetwood, waving frantically at him. The two sailors were at the gunwales of the jolly boat, apparently pushing it into the water.

In a few minutes Sutton, risking his neck literally as he sprinted down the slope, pawing desperately through the underbrush, came puffing up to the beach.

"What's happening?" he called.

"Damned if I know," Chetwood said, with a worried frown. "I heard a shot—"

"It was the doctor's shotgun," Sutton said. "There's no other gun on the boat that can make that kind of noise."

Chetwood had already ordered the jolly boat cleared from the beach, and it was in the water as they waited for Sutton to come up. At that moment there was a sound of a second shot from the *Herman.*

Aboard the *Herman,* after the shore party headed for the lagoon, Dr. Luce had established himself comfortably on the afterdeck, sitting under the main boom topping lift, just forward of the transom. The heavy shotgun lay across his lap, and from this point he was able to cover the sweep of the afterdeck and main deck.

Captain Brown sat in a chair a short distance forward, near the starboard rail, ignoring everyone and for the most part staring at the island or the empty sea. Once Peterson walked past him and stopped to talk.

"Get forward, Peterson!" Mr. Hendrickson called out. "Captain Sutton has ordered that no member of the crew is to remain on the afterdeck."

Peterson looked slantingly at the first mate, and growled "Aye, sir!" Dr. Luce, who had been dozing, straightened up and looked at the bosun over the rim of his glasses. Mr. Hendrickson came aft to speak to the doctor.

"We're going to move the ship about a mile farther to leeward," he explained. "It looks as if some dirty weather may be stirring up to the south and I'd like to be more in the lee of the island." He turned and called out: "Man the foresail halyards, bosun—make ready to take up anchor. We'll move around to the north of the island."

Dr. Luce glanced across the sea and could not detect a single mar in the peaceful serenity of water and sky. A few low clouds were drifting from the southeast but otherwise there was no indication of unsettled weather. He supposed, however, that men who sailed the seas could spot imperfections not noticeable to a landsman; and with this comforting thought, he disposed himself again for a catnap.

Mr. Hendrickson had sent Peterson and Fisher forward to release the peak and throat halyards and the lanyards on the foreboom, preparatory to hoisting sail. The jib was run up, and Peterson came back to the wheelhouse. Within a few minutes the *Herman* was under way, moving slowly to seaward in a wide arc.

"We'll anchor north of the lagoon, sir," Mr. Hendrickson informed Dr. Luce.

The doctor nodded, not paying much attention. The sun was warm on the afterdeck, with a slight offshore breeze coming from the southeast, and after the turbulent events of the morning he wanted to rest comfortably. He was soon half asleep.

Benson sat in a chair in the waist forward of the wheelhouse, his injured leg propped on the rail, observing out of the corner of his eye all that went on within range of his vision. He saw Willie Fisher come up through the after companionway, and wondered what he had been doing below deck in the passengers' quarters, with the ship under way.

The shore party had been away more than two hours when Benson observed Fisher come on deck. He had been forward, setting the halyards in cleats after hoisting the foresail gaff and setting the foreboom. Benson thought he must have gone below through the forward companionway to the forecastle, and come aft through the main cabin. He thought little of it until he noticed Fisher go into the wheelhouse and pass something to Peterson, the bosun, who was at the wheel.

Benson still thought nothing of this, until Peterson came out a few seconds later and walked across the afterdeck to where Captain Brown was sitting. He handed him a black object that Benson thought (as he later told Sutton) "looked like a pistol."

The second mate reared himself up, twisting his injured leg.

"Avast there! What's that you're doing? . . . Doctor!" He shouted the last word and Dr. Luce awakened with a start. Peterson was walking back toward the wheelhouse, quite rapidly, when Benson roared again: "Doctor . . . the old man's got a gun!"

Dr. Luce swung his shotgun around, and Captain Brown suddenly stood up. His torpid state seemed to have vanished. He stood erect, his mane of white hair blowing back from his face. He waved his pistol, without actually pointing it at anyone. The *Herman* rolled slightly in the swell of the sea, but the Captain stood with legs well braced, rolling with the motion of the deck.

"Captain Brown—put that gun down!" Dr. Luce's voice was a bit high-pitched, but quite firm. His big shotgun was pointed in the general direction of the Captain, about twenty feet across the quarterdeck.

"If you raise arms on this ship, you will suffer the consequences, Captain. You'll be put in irons—you understand that, don't you?"

Captain Brown at first said nothing, rolling his shaggy head from side to side, raking the ship with his pale eyes that were now blazing with wild fury. Then he roared out: "Shoot, an' be damned to ye, doctor! Ye've tried to poison me—that's what ye've done! But ye'll never get at my treasure—ye can be damned sure o' that, doctor! Ye'll never find it . . . I've got my arms now, an' be damned to ye!"

Dr. Luce advanced a step or two, and his face suddenly became twisted with pain. He backed up and sat down, still holding the shotgun aimed rather unsteadily in the direction of the Captain.

Willie Peterson and Fisher were together at the wheelhouse, staring at the tableau. Peterson had left the wheel, and the vessel was running free on a light southeasterly wind. Mr. Hendrickson had come aft, and was standing hesitantly behind the wheelhouse. He would be almost in the line of fire between the Captain and the doctor if he stepped to the quarterdeck.

Meanwhile Captain Brown was waving his pistol in half circles, not aiming at anyone; and the doctor had managed to raise himself from the deck chair again, his face white and hurt as he stood in front of the transom.

"Put down the gun . . . and we'll talk, Captain. If you have some grievance—" the doctor was saying, in short, jerky words that were almost gasps. "Nothing will be done . . . if you . . . drop . . . gun . . . understand . . ."

Willie Peterson seemed about to edge forward and approach the Captain—whether to assist him, or take the gun, Dr. Luce did not know. The old man suddenly roared out again: "Stand back, ye swabs! I'll shoot the first man crosses the deck—"

At that moment, Dr. Luce's gun went off with a booming roar. It had been aimed at the port rail, and the load of shot swept across the deck, shattering part of the main rigging and blowing most of the rail into the sea. Whether Dr. Luce intended to fire the gun, or its discharge was accidental, he could never be certain; but the effect was to freeze the Captain into immobility. The doctor slowly turned the gun—which was double-barreled—toward the Captain. His face was now contorted in a spasm of pain.

Mr. Hendrickson, driven by some impulse native to a man of the sea, stepped to the quarterdeck, and walked straight to the Captain. He held out his hand.

"Give me the gun, Captain," he said, in a firm, unyielding tone. "I am in command of this ship—with Captain Sutton ashore. I order you to hand over that gun."

The Captain's blazing anger seemed to have receded miraculously. His old face took on an expression of bewilderment, and he handed the gun to the first mate. Then he turned to look for his chair, and sat down.

Mr. Hendrickson pointed the pistol to seaward, and fired a single shot.

"There is now only one loaded gun," he said. "Dr. Luce has that." He turned to the wheelhouse, where Willie Peterson stood with one hand on the wheel. "Hold a course of 350 degrees, bosun . . . See that you do not leave that wheel again. Fisher, go forward and pay out the jib sheet as we come around. Step lively, now!" He turned back to the Captain, who was slumped in his chair.

"Captain Brown, I will not put you in irons until Captain Sutton returns to make the decision. But you are under charges, sir . . . I respect your position as former master of this ship, but you have raised arms, and that is mutiny, sir!"

[3]

Back in the lagoon, Sutton and Chetwood had heard the second shot—which they recognized as a pistol shot, in contrast to the dull boom of the shotgun blast.

"Move lively!" Sutton called to the sailors, Jensen and Wilson. His face was grim, and slightly pale in spite of the deep tan he had acquired in two months of sailing under the tropical sun. Chetwood climbed into the bow as they pushed the jolly boat away from shore and the two sailors, rowing at a furious pace, drove the boat toward the break in the reef.

Sutton, watching the *Herman,* saw that it was veering around to the west and coming into anchorage again just north of the lagoon. He looked at Chetwood, and the lawyer nodded, his face set in a worried frown. He had seen the schooner coming around, too; but whether this meant that whatever trouble occurred aboard was now under control—or that the Captain had taken over the ship—was something they could not determine until they reached the *Herman.*

"I think they would have pulled out—and left us," Sutton called out to Chetwood. "That is . . . if anything had gone wrong."

Chetwood nodded again.

The reef entrance was passed, with the loss of only one oar, which was broken as Wilson tried desperately to fend the little boat off one of the jagged rocks that seemed to leap against the side of the boat as they rowed against the force of the inbound waves. Fortunately, the tide seemed to be going out and the current through the gap in the reef carried the boat past the ragged edges that showed cruel teeth on either side of the narrow break.

There were two spare oars in the boat, and Wilson and Jensen, both pulling lustily, sent the little craft rapidly toward the *Herman,* which was now turning slowly into the wind, preparatory to dropping anchor, less than a half mile away.

Dr. Luce was still sitting under the main boom holding the shotgun across his lap, when the jolly boat came up to the side of the *Herman,* which was already at anchor. Mr. Hendrickson helped them aboard; and he quickly told Sutton what had happened.

Sutton went over to speak to the Captain; but the old man, sitting with his grizzled face bowed forward, staring at the deck, had almost nothing to say. Sutton glanced at Peterson, who stood rigidly at the wheel.

"How did Peterson get the gun?" Sutton asked, looking first at the Captain and then at Dr. Luce. The doctor shrugged, but Chetwood suddenly spoke up:

"I think he had it, George. . . . You remember the pistol you and Hoffman found in the chart box?" Sutton nodded. "I don't think that was ever taken back in the weapons locker. I always counted the guns that were there—there were seven pistols and the three rifles, and the doctor's shotgun. But I don't think we ever checked on the Captain's other gun. He must have turned it over to Peterson to keep for him."

Sutton nodded slightly; it was quite possible, he thought, that the Captain had kept the gun—probably thinking he needed it to protect himself—ever since they were in Honolulu! By accident, they had neglected to count it with the other arms on the ship.

"How did Peterson get it?" he asked Captain Brown.

"I—I asked Fisher to bring it up to me. It was in my cabin an' I wanted to . . . to shoot birds," the Captain ended, lamely.

"The hell you did, Captain!" Dr. Luce exclaimed harshly. He had recovered from his seizure, and his usually mild expression was now grim with rising anger. "You threatened us, Captain Brown—you know you did!"

The Captain looked up, his blue eyes almost glazed; and he shook his head. "You wanted to poison me . . . that's why I got that damn strychnine away from you."

"What about the arsenic—and rat poison?" Dr. Luce asked.

The Captain nodded. "I threw it overboard. I got it away from your medicine box, too."

"But you kept the strychnine! Why?"

The old man looked up, his eyes suddenly gleaming with an expression of cunning.

"I figured if you'd poison me—I'd poison you! That's why, Doctor!"

Dr. Luce turned angrily away, and Chetwood put his hand on his shoulder.

"Calm down, George . . . You've had one bad shock today, and getting mad again won't help it. Things are under control now. . . . The thing to do is for us to decide what course to take next." He looked at Sutton. "Don't you agree?"

Sutton nodded. He looked down at the old man.

"We've got to make a decision—right now, Captain Brown." His voice again was firm but not unkind. "You think it over. If you cannot tell us now—today—where the island is, we'll turn back to Tahiti or Penrhyn. You'll be turned over to the authorities. . . . You don't leave us any other choice, Captain."

Sutton, Chetwood and the doctor started below, leaving one of the sailors who had gone ashore with them to guard the Captain. As they passed Tommy Benson, still sitting on his chair with his bandaged leg propped on the rail, he motioned to Sutton. Sutton came over to his chair.

"I saw it all, Cap'n," he said. "That old man ain't trying to take over the ship, sir. . . . He's just gone clean batty. I've seen 'em like that before. He's a beaten-down old man, that's what he is. He ought to be in sick bay."

Sutton nodded, and said, "Thanks, Benson." He followed the other two below to his cabin. Chetwood looked at him expectantly, but Dr. Luce merely scowled.

Sutton sighed deeply, and shook his head.

"I guess this is the end of the trail, boys," he said, finally, "Unless the Captain gives us a location we can depend on—and by now I think we can pretty well discount that. We can certainly figure out whether it will be another wild-goose chase or not. It begins to look as if we've got only one choice. To go home!"

Sutton's face seemed to have aged ten years in the past two months. He had recognized more and more, as the voyage continued, that he was the only one who could hold the expedition together. Dr. Luce was ill; his heart attack in Honolulu had actually made him unfit for the voyage, but his ability to balance conflicting temperaments had been so necessary that he had been urged to come along. Sutton realized also that the doctor had done it at some personal sacrifice, since Louis Mooser and some of the others in San Francisco had blamed Dr. Luce for the Hoffman affair.

Chetwood had a kind of ingrained loyalty to Sutton, and would probably continue; but his heart was no longer in it. Sutton, looking at him, realized that the slim lawyer had about come to the end of his physical resources, too.

"I'm pretty well convinced that Captain Brown actually buried that treasure—somewhere in these islands," he went on. "I think we could also prove to our own satisfaction that the ship was at this island—Makatea. He's been looking at it for some time, trying to locate places . . . I've watched him. But"—he shook his head firmly—"I agree with you that this isn't enough. Even if the *Sea Foam* was based here, and all the rest of his yarn is true—we still can't find the location of the treasure without the Captain's help."

He stopped for a moment, and Chetwood asked: "You think it's time to quit, George?"

Sutton shrugged.

"The treasure is supposed to be worth seventy to a hundred million —and that's a lot of money, John. We all put our chips in this pot, and I don't like to throw in our hand when it almost seems as if we're on the edge of winning. But we've had two shooting affairs—or near shootings —today. I've got a hunch if we don't do something to the Captain, he's going to kill somebody. I've tried everything I know—" He lifted his hands helplessly, and Chetwood smiled slightly.

"You have, George . . . I don't think anybody on this ship—or in San Francisco—has any doubt on that score. You've put all the courage and patience and persistence anyone could ask. At first I began to doubt the whole thing, particularly after the way the Captain acted at Penrhyn. But I think I've come around to your way of thinking. I believe the old man's story was true—that the treasure was buried in these islands as he said it was."

Chetwood paused an instant, turning about the cabin like a lawyer summing up a case.

"It comes right down to two things, doesn't it? How much does he really remember? Can he actually point out the location of the treasure —and if he can, will he do it? I'm pretty well convinced by now that not much can be done unless he changes his attitude. And from what happened this morning, it doesn't look as if he will."

Dr. Luce, who had remained silent up to now, coughed a bit. "Your summary is about what all of us have had in mind. Except that none of us, as John said, have had the stamina or patience that you have shown. But what it really boils down to is the old man's attitude. I'm absolutely convinced that nothing can be done with the old fool. He's a childish, arrogant, irresponsible old idiot . . . probably in an advanced stage of paranoia or senile dementia. I damn near died on deck this afternoon, you know—"

"I know, George," Sutton put in. "That more than anything else is why I think we've got to call it off. Your heart won't stand much more of this. And he's going to kill somebody—unless he gets killed first. We can't do anything with him, and we can't do anything without him." He stopped and pulled a chart out of the chart rack over the small table fastened to the wall. "Look here—"

He spread the chart on the table.

"I've worked out almost every mile of sea we've covered—first on our way north, and since we headed back down here from Penrhyn. The only track I'm not sure of is exactly where we were blown by that storm. We took our position that morning—" Sutton pointed to a mark on the chart. "The island was probably over here, but I'm not sure." He indicated another point to the southeast of the first position.

"There's quite a lot of sea around here we haven't covered, and we could probably cruise around for several days and pick up a few of the islands—which aren't shown on this chart, and aren't mentioned in the *Sailing Directions*. But that won't answer our problem, unless the Captain is willing to try to identify the place."

"He did identify the island we saw *before* the typhoon," Chetwood put in.

"Yes—and I think he meant it. That is, he thought it was the island. But we weren't close enough for him to be sure, and of course, it may have been one of his damn tricks, or just imagination. On the other hand, he was pretty shaken up when we passed it—or over it, as I think we did. You remember how he reacted when Tommy Eustace told us about the typhoon of '93?"

Chetwood nodded, with a wry grin. "It scared hell out of him!"

Sutton said, "I think that's what's gotten into him now. He's been thinking about those typhoons ever since I talked with him back in Auburn. He's afraid the island may have been blown away—if the treasure was buried somewhere in the area of Makatea, but not on the island itself. He's an old man, with a single fixed idea—to recover that treasure. He's had that idea now for upwards of twenty years, and I think it's made him cracked."

Dr. Luce, stroking his mustache, said firmly:

"I'm sure of it—and that's why I don't want to trust him any further. None of us is going to spend any of that treasure money if we have to be buried at sea."

The *Herman* sailed for Penrhyn at about four o'clock on July 15, and after four days of fairly good sailing weather, driven by a brisk southeast wind, the schooner put in at Penrhyn late on the nineteenth. That night the problem of Captain Brown was presented to Captain Nagle, the Resident Agent.

The Captain had remained under surveillance for the entire trip from Makatea. At one point he had asked to see Sutton, and the latter came to his cabin—which he had been allowed to retain, with a sailor on guard outside the door.

"Ye've been fair to me, Cap'n," the old man said. "I ain't got any bad feelings against you—or even Mr. Chetwood. It's the doctor that caused all my trouble, an' if it was just you an' me, an' maybe Mr. Chetwood, we could go to that island together. What do ye say to that?"

Sutton looked at the old man, feeling a deeper sense of pity for him than he had at any time before. He shook his head.

"The doctor has treated you for sickness, Captain. He saved your life. He's done everything for you that any human being could do. The fact is, you've lied to him and to all of us repeatedly. Unless you are willing to give us the information now—to tell us the truth, and let us put you ashore at Penrhyn while we make the search—there is no possible way of carrying on any further."

The Captain shook his head wearily, as if this ultimatum was too much for him to comprehend; finally he spread his gnarled hands on his knees, but he said nothing. Sutton turned abruptly and left his cabin. After that no one spoke to the old man. Even Jimmy Akahito, who had been completely demoralized by the day he spent in handcuffs in the brig, avoided the Captain as if he had cholera. The cook brought his food at each mealtime; otherwise the old man remained brooding alone in his cabin.

"We can't hold him here in Penrhyn," Captain Nagle told them. "If you want to prefer charges and deposit the amount of his fare to Auckland, we'll send him out on the first steamer to Rarotonga, but you might find yourselves indebted for any costs entailed."

It was decided to proceed to Papeete with the Captain, and from that point the future disposition of the *Herman*—as well as Captain Brown—would be determined.

Tahiti: Home from the Hunt

[1]

At two o'clock on July 20—just one year to the day since the *Herman* sailed from San Francisco—the little schooner weighed anchor off Penrhyn for Papeete, the principal village of Tahiti, six hundred miles to the southeast. On that day a year ago when the *Herman* broke out sail off the Golden Gate, starting on the long argosy into the South Pacific with the high hopes of those aboard and ashore, it had seemed to Sutton he was setting forth on a great adventure.

Now it was considerably less than that. The departure from Penrhyn two weeks before had been in an atmosphere of moderate hopefulness; but now there seemed no hope.

Captain Nagle and his entire establishment—including his wife and five children—augmented by Tommy Eustace and old MacDonald, who had come over from Tautoa, were at the jetty to wave farewell. Sutton had gone over to say goodbye to Maeva, who stood off at one side, smiling gravely.

She shook hands with him, and said in a low voice, "Please try to come back some day, Captain Sutton. . . . We shall miss you." Her dark eyes lighted up as she smiled. Sutton felt a small tug of sadness. He was again struck by the remarkable maturity of this girl, who was young enough to have been his daughter.

Captain Brown had come ashore that morning to register his final protest, and ask that he be allowed to remain in Penrhyn. He said he was afraid to remain on the ship. When he was told the *Herman* was going to Tahiti, however, rather than San Francisco, he quickly withdrew the protest.

As the *Herman* wore off to the eastward, Sutton looked back across the blue water at the receding outline of the island, stretching for miles in either direction in the great circle of coral and volcanic rock that formed the land around the lagoon. He thought to himself: "This trip has literally taken a full year out of my life." He was not sure how much of a loss or gain it might have been; but he knew he was now heading for home . . . emptyhanded, after a year of virtually wasted effort!

A few *guni* birds soared after them, high in the air; and it occurred to Sutton that he was no more firmly fixed than these "birds of passage" that came to island after island and flew on again, leaving little trace of their coming or going. He thought of Captain Brown's "ghosts" and the remarkably efficient, if somewhat mysterious, means they used to keep interlopers away from the lost "church treasure" buried somewhere in a remote island to the southward—or perhaps scattered over miles of ocean floor by a devastating typhoon!

Squalls and headwinds slowed the *Herman* in its passage from Penrhyn to Papeete; but at four o'clock on Tuesday, July 28, the lookout at the foremast sighted Moorea, a beautiful island to the northwest of Tahiti that lifts craggy spires into the blue sky, its deep gorges massed with wildly colored trees that were visible as the *Herman* passed to windward en route to Papeete harbor.

At six o'clock the following morning the pilot came aboard and took the schooner into the clustered harbor. The town itself lay at the foot of a series of rising hills that extended back to the towering, mist-covered peaks of the Oro-hina. It seemed to Sutton that Tahiti-nui—the larger of the two islands connected with the smaller by a neck of land—was even more beautiful than Oahu; and the city of Papeete, although smaller than Honolulu, seemed to have even more extravagant tropical beauty—with fewer of the intrusive effects of civilization visible along the harbor front.

The *Herman* was towed into a mooring—the last mooring, as it happened, that the little schooner would make under command of Captain Sutton and the small group of voyagers who had set out from San Francisco with such high hopes a year ago!

There was one curious development which Sutton had observed during the passage down from Penrhyn. He mentioned this to both Chetwood and Dr. Luce. It concerned a certain recrudescence of spirit, a revitalization of the ego, which seemed to have come over Captain Brown on this last leg of the voyage of the *Herman*.

"The old boy seems to have revived," he said. "I passed him on the deck this morning and he actually spoke to me. He was looking off toward Tahiti—or maybe it was further south—with that old look of arrogance and importance. Do you suppose he has some new scheme up his sleeve?"

Dr. Luce had also noticed the old man shambling back and forth along the deck, stopping to stare over the forward rail and stroking his whiskers as if he were pondering some new problem or plan. He even greeted the doctor—against whom he seemed to harbor his deepest resentment—with a cheery nod and a wave of his hand.

"He does seem to have taken a new lease on life," the doctor remarked. "When he passed me he was looking as if he expected to see something—maybe an island, or a ship."

Chetwood snorted slightly.

"Or a mermaid," he said. "He may be looking for one with a chest of gold."

"A young one—about seventeen, I suppose," Sutton said, drily.

The old man had stayed on deck a good deal of the time during the week-long voyage from Penrhyn to Papeete, although he said very little to anyone. Willie Peterson now avoided him like a plague. Sutton had decided not to press charges against the bosun. Peterson had insisted, under the sharpest questioning by Sutton and Chetwood, that he was merely accommodating what seemed a normal request when he handed the Captain the gun "to shoot birds," and he had kept sedulously free of the old man's company since then. Sutton had warned him that if there was another incident that was at all suspicious, Peterson would be held in the brig in irons.

The only person who ever spoke to the Captain during this time, except to greet him briefly as he shambled along the deck, was Hasino, and his limited use of the English language usually restricted him to simple replies about what food was to be on the menu for the day. When the Captain would pass the galley, which was amidships, forward of the main cabin, he would poke his head into the doorway and ask, "What's on the table today, Cookie?" Hasino would offer only the most laconic answers: "Got only chop stuff. Sor't po'k. Spuds. No beans." The Captain would usually nod and walk on.

By the time they neared Papeete his rejuvenation of spirits had become not only a puzzle, but a matter of some slight worry to the partners. It was odd that at the point when the venture was to be abandoned as a hopeless failure, Captain Brown should suddenly display an attitude of exhilaration and renewed interest.

This became a topic of conversation and of wonder; and it served, in a small way, to relieve the weariness and disappointment that had settled on the adventurers with the realization that the voyage was coming to its end . . . and a dismal and empty end it would be!

"He may be just as sick of the trip as we are—and glad it's over," Chetwood suggested; but Sutton shook his head.

"That old man doesn't give up that way," he said. "I've gotten to know him. . . . If there is one thing he doesn't do, it's give up. No—there's some other reason."

"If he never intended to reveal his bloody 'secret'—providing he has one—then he has certainly paid the price in full for his deception," Chetwood said.

Dr. Luce, who had resumed some of his old good nature and seemed to have dropped the attitude of angry disenchantment with the whole affair that he had displayed on the earlier voyage down from Penrhyn, was frankly puzzled.

"George is right," he said. "The old fellow has a determination that exceeds anything I've ever known. Why did he start in the first place—if he's ready to stop now? It couldn't have been just to take a voyage into his old stamping ground, could it?"

"Not unless you assume that his story is the truth," Sutton pointed out. "It would only have been his 'stamping ground' if he had actually been in these waters—and that would mean that his story about the *Sea Foam* was true."

Now that all hope of discovering the treasure island seemed to have faded away, they gave themselves over to speculation about what "might have been." And Sutton held to one firm and unyielding conviction: "He wasn't lying. I'm as sure of that as I am of sitting here. The story he told was checked and rechecked in every respect, you remember. The *Sea Foam* actually was off Callao in 1851. The church treasure was reported to have been loaded on the *Black Witch* thirty years before that, and it disappeared. The Captain's story is the only one that explains all the facts—and that's why I've spent a year of my life and a lot of my money following this damned rainbow trail. You don't think I relish going home emptyhanded, do you?"

He shrugged helplessly. All this speculation seemed useless now; yet they could not avoid it. The memories of the trials they had gone through—the angry fights with Hoffman, and then the Captain; the frustrations and the exhausting periods of uncertainty, in which they struggled with only the thinnest of hopes to hold the expedition together, and now the end of all their hopes, giving up the venture . . . all this was too deeply scarred to permit it to be pushed into the background of memory and forgotten.

And now there was Captain Brown—the only one of the voyagers who seemed to be on a rising tide, as it were! Sutton finally put it into words: "He's got some new scheme cooked up—but whether it is one of his damn fool lies, or self-deceptions, or part of his stubborn persistence, we probably won't ever know."

The mystery was solved—and the Captain's rejuvenated spirits correspondingly reduced—soon after they arrived in Papeete. After they had gone ashore, the Captain quickly left the others; and Sutton and Chetwood, after arranging for a mooring, went over to the American Consul's office to present their papers to the consul, the Honorable W. F. Doty, an amiable and helpful man, who seemed to know quite a bit about the *Herman*.

"Your Captain Brown was in a few minutes ago," he said. Sutton was startled; the Captain must have made an unusual effort to reach the consulate ahead of them. "He seemed to be anxious to contact some old friends of yours—from Sydney. A gentleman named Short and his wife. I had to give him some unsatisfactory news. They were here—for several weeks—but they left for Samoa on the steamer last week."

Sutton sat back in his chair and looked at Mr. Doty; then he looked at Chetwood. Mr. Doty looked keenly at the two, and half smiled.

"Information travels quite rapidly in the Islands," he said. "It was learned that Mr. Short and his wife—and their daughter—expected to meet the Captain and the rest of your group here, and would join the expedition. Is that correct?"

Sutton shook his head.

"There is no expedition—at least not any longer," he said. "We were on a combined pleasure cruise and also—as you undoubtedly know from the stories published in the Sydney papers—we were looking for an island where a substantial amount of old treasures taken from South America were supposed to have been buried. Mrs. Short was our landlady in Sydney—that's all!"

"Yes." Mr. Doty nodded. "I know about your expedition . . . and so does the British consul here, and the French government representatives in Papeete. You would have quite a following if you left here looking for the island."

"The British?" Chetwood asked. Mr. Doty nodded.

"They seem interested in some of the treasure that was not supposed to have come from South America. You know, there were a number of specie ships from Australia that disappeared back in the middle of the last century. They think that if Captain Brown was in this area, as he said he was, he might know something about them."

Sutton nodded. It struck him that the departure of Mrs. Short, the red-haired mistress of "The Repose"—and her daughter—must have been a staggering blow to the Captain. As they left, Chetwood muttered in disgust:

"The old fool was getting ready to double-cross us again, wasn't he?"

Sutton nodded. "It seems to be another indication of what I think we all agree on—that the treasure is there, or at least the Captain is so sure of its being there, that he will not balk at any means to find it."

"But why didn't he tell us where it was—when we were down in the Paumotus? There certainly was enough to go around—and the one fourth of the lot that he was to get would be better than nothing."

Sutton thought a moment.

"I think he distrusted everyone—and perhaps he had reason to. Some of our associates rather richly deserved his suspicion, John—if you will recall? They tried to cheat him on the sale of the *Herman*. Someone tried to make money on the insurance. Hoffman tried to get information about the island from him, and could have taken over the ship if he had gotten it. Even if the Captain didn't know this, he must have suspected it. The committee held up funds, so he couldn't pay his bills. All this must have been sinking into his mind—and he's a suspicious old scoundrel by nature! Put it all together, John, and it adds up to the thing that seems to beset all treasure hunts—just plain greed, treachery . . . and a large mixture of suspicion all around." Sutton grinned, without much humor. "The Captain's 'ghosts' that he thinks guard the treasure may be a lot more real than we imagined, John. As he said, there were at least a hundred men died as a result of that treasure. We might be lucky, at that—that we didn't find it!"

Chetwood smiled. "I think I'd take my chances—for a hundred million dollars!"

Sutton looked at Chetwood.

"You don't really believe the Captain's story, do you, John?"

Chetwood thought a moment, as they strolled down toward the wharf, and finally he said, "George, I'm damned if I know what to believe. At one time I did believe there was a good chance—perhaps ten to one. But no amount of rationalizing can explain to me why the Captain failed to point out the location of the island when we must have been within a day's sailing distance of its position—if there ever was a position."

Sutton nodded. "I believe his story," he said. "I believed it when he first told me the full story, and I believe it now. . . . But I agree that the whole venture is pretty well washed up. I think the Captain's problem was fear—and suspicion. He was afraid he couldn't locate the place, possibly because it had been blown away. I'll never forget the look on his face after we passed over that bit of land, or reef—or whatever it was. It was not only a look of horror, but absolute fear—crazy fear! And it wasn't fear of dying. He's too much of a seaman for that."

Chetwood considered this; and then he asked, "What do you suppose revived him—on the way here from Penrhyn? I don't think the prospect of meeting Ruby Short again—and even her daughter—would have quite that effect."

"No—it wouldn't. But he had some time to think about it. Remember, he only saw the island from a distance. It *might* have been his island—and then again, they might have buried the treasure on more than one island. I think the thing that struck fear into him was the actual realization that his island might or *could have blown away!* That realization must have struck him with full force after we were carried over the island by that enormous wave. Don't you think so?"

Chetwood shook his head, with a worried frown. He didn't really know what to think. Sutton, his calm features again set in the determined expression which Chetwood had come to recognize, finally said, "I'm going to have one final talk with the Captain, John—alone this time. I think he trusts me. I can't just drop this whole thing without a final try."

Chetwood grinned wanly, and said, "You can do it alone, George. I haven't got much stomach for the old scoundrel—and I don't think I could hold my temper the way you do. . . ." The lawyer paused a minute, and then added, "Don't get the notion anybody blames you for this failure, George. You did more than anyone to keep it together, and the fact that it failed can't be laid at your doorstep."

Sutton shook his head, without smiling.

"It has failed, John—or at least I think it has. That's the important point. That's all anyone's going to remember—in San Francisco, and back home."

[2]

Captain Brown was allowed to remain aboard the *Herman,* since he had no quarters ashore and no money to pay for a room. Sutton, Chetwood and the doctor had decided, on the advice of the American consul, to take a small cottage facing the beach which could be rented for a few francs. They offered the Captain the use of a room, but he refused.

"I ain't master of this ship any more," he told Sutton. "Just part of the crew, so I'll stay aboard ship."

Chetwood was amused at the Captain's unexpected self-effacement; normally, he would have established himself in a master suite in the best local hotel. Dr. Luce, however, was not particularly amused.

"Either he's acting like an old fool—or he's got something up his sleeve," he said. Sutton ordered Mr. Hendrickson to allow the Captain the freedom of the ship, but to keep a watch on him at all times.

"The guns are all locked securely," he said. "But he's gotten hold of a gun before, when we thought they were locked up. The old pirate might decide to take over the ship and sail off on his own, so don't take any chances."

The next morning Sutton planned to go aboard the *Herman,* which was moored at the far end of the fishing wharf, tall-masted and stately beside the assortment of small fishing boats, luggers and inter-island craft clustered in the lower harbor. He intended to have a final settlement with the Captain.

Before going down to the dock, however, Sutton had one point upon which he wanted to assure himself. He called at Mr. Doty's office in a small, neat house near the governor's palace. Mr. Doty was a cheerful man, with bright blue eyes in which there was an unfailing gleam of curiosity as well as friendliness.

"What can we do for you, Captain Sutton? You are established and comfortable, I hope."

Sutton nodded and thanked him for his friendly offices. "We're all settled," he said. "Our next business is to sell the schooner and then leave for home, I guess."

Mr. Doty inclined his head, politely.

"What do you know—if anything—about Makatea Island?" Sutton asked. "We stopped in there—anchored offshore, that is—on our way north. I wondered if it had been inhabited at any time recently."

The incandescent curiosity in Mr. Doty's eyes brightened visibly.

"Indeed . . . I know little about it. Why don't you ask Monsieur Langomazino—the mayor, you know? He lives very near to your cottage. I'm sure he would know, if anyone does. Makatea? That's off to the west, isn't it?"

Sutton nodded.

"About three hundred miles. We thought we saw some signs of habitation, but there was no evidence of anyone living on the island at present. I merely wondered."

"Yes . . . indeed!" Mr. Doty pursed his lips thoughtfully. "Well, you might ask Maurice. He would know. He will be at home . . . He seldom has much to do, and usually does not leave until midday."

Sutton thanked the consul. He stopped by the mayor's beautiful home—practically a villa—on the way to the wharf. The Honorable Maurice Langomazino was a dark-haired, swarthy man, probably of French origin, but with miscellaneous admixtures common to the South Pacific.

"Of course—Makatea! I know the place . . . I have been on the island a few times. There used to be some quantities of oysters in the lagoons but they have been cleaned out in recent years. It is officially named Aurore—or Aurora, you would call it. Many years ago it was known as Moku-iti."

"Moku-iti? What does that mean?"

"Little Smoke Island, I suppose. There is a volcano there, but it has been inactive as long as anyone remembers. I can't imagine what the 'smoke' refers to . . . unless perhaps there were inhabitants on the island at one time. There once were pirates in that area, but that was long before my time."

Sutton nodded and thanked the mayor.

"Do visit us this evening," the mayor said. "Madame Langomazino and my daughters, as well as myself, would be most happy to have you come. You will be staying in Papeete for several weeks, I understand?"

Sutton said he was not certain how long they would remain; their schedule would depend upon many things. He thanked the mayor again, and promised they would visit his home that evening.

As he walked slowly down the coral road toward the wharves, he pondered upon what he had heard. In a way, it upset him, because it was an additional confirmation of what he feared: that now that they were turning back from their search, because of the intractable attitude of Captain Brown, they were closer than ever to uncovering the "secret," as the Captain called it, of the island's location.

Mapuana Davis had referred to the "Island of Smoke"—and Makatea was once known as "Little Smoke Island." The word *moku* in the Polynesian tongue was of recent origin, having been derived from English; therefore the use of the name Moku-iti must have been within the past century. It strengthened Sutton's growing conviction that Makatea must have been the hideout of the *Sea Foam*. But this, of course, added little to what they knew about the actual location of the treasure, which was almost nothing.

Sutton mused, as he strode down the wharf. It was no use to grasp at straws. There had to be something tangible, and only the Captain could supply this. He felt, as he paced down the wooden dock toward the *Herman*, as if he was walking to his own execution.

The Captain was below, in his cabin. Sutton found him lying on the bed, staring upward at the ceiling. His eyes seemed almost sightless, and for an instant Sutton had the impression that the Captain was dead. But the old man turned his head and glared at Sutton. Then he waved for him to sit on a chair.

"It ain't no use for us to talk any more, Cap'n," he said at last, in a voice so low and husky it seemed to rumble out of his chest. "The spirits won't let us go back—unless you let me take over this ship, Cap'n."

He glanced sideways at Sutton, as if to determine how well this suggestion had registered; but Sutton merely said, "I'm not likely to."

Sutton leaned forward in his chair, as if he were getting physically ready for a final assault on the Captain. In spite of the disgust and frustration which had descended upon the treasure hunters, Sutton could not help feeling sorry for the old man. He might have been a pirate and a murderer, and he was certainly a liar—as well as being treacherous, obstinate, arrogant and insanely suspicious—but he still was an old man fighting for what seemed to be his last chance in life, and the fight was slowly ebbing out of him.

Sutton explained, calmly and carefully, the decision he had reached with Chetwood and Dr. Luce. Neither of the others was willing to talk to the Captain again; but Sutton had agreed to come to him to present the final proposal. After this talk, he intended to return to their cottage, and unless he had precise information that would lead them to the island where the treasure was buried, they would sell the *Herman* and return to San Francisco.

"You know quite well what that will mean to you, Captain Brown," Sutton said, measuring his words carefully. "You will return in disgrace, and perhaps face a prison sentence for your actions on the ship. Your wife will know exactly why this happened—"

The old man turned on his side, and seemed to shrivel slightly at the mere mention of his wife. Sutton remembered that during their first talk, back in Auburn, the Captain had confided in a whisper that his wife knew the "secret" of the island. He wondered what queer relationship existed—with respect to the treasure—between Captain Brown and Mrs. Brown. She seemed to be a quiet, sweet woman; yet the Captain—while he feared no man—seemed to be afraid of his wife's opinion of him. It struck Sutton that this was the crack in the old man's armor, the break in his pride: the tall, calm-faced woman who was his wife was the one living person who could not be thrust aside by the Captain's arrogance and self-importance. He was afraid of what she would think of him because he had no weapons to use against her! He was like a boy facing his mother's anger.

The Captain swung his feet around and drew himself into a sitting position, facing Sutton. His shirt was open and his matted chest gleamed with sweat. He was having "the fevers" again, Sutton supposed. He wondered if he should call Dr. Luce down to the ship, but he doubted if the doctor would come.

"You've got only one chance left," he went on, without taking his eyes from Captain Brown's face. "It isn't much of a chance. If you give me the information now—the position and the description of the island, as well as you remember it—we'll sail back. You will have money deposited with the consul to take you to San Francisco. If we find the island, we'll meet you in San Francisco and you'll have your share. Otherwise—"

"You mean I can't go with you?" The old man's voice was husky.

"No—you can't go back with us. We've gone through that enough times. You haven't helped us—and you got hold of a gun twice. You know that, Captain."

"I—I was aimin' to shoot birds," he said.

Sutton had gone over the entire matter in his mind prior to walking down to where the schooner lay at the wharf. It seemed to him there were three possibilities to consider: first, Captain Brown either had no knowledge of the location of the island, or he had forgotten it, and therefore was unable to direct them to the place; or he still distrusted them so deeply he wanted to be in full command—to control all that happened—when they located the island. The third possibility was that some kind of fear held him back from disclosing his secret.

He was startled to hear the Captain suddenly say, in a voice so hoarse that it was almost unintelligible: "You can't go back—without me, Cap'n! You can't go alone . . . they'd kill you!" He stopped a few seconds, and was breathing heavily. "Ye got to put me in command again, Cap'n! Ye put me back in command an' you an' I will go there—just the two of us, Cap'n. They've killed every man that knew about that treasure—except me!"

"Who killed them? Who is 'they'—?"

"The spirits—that's who they are! The damn ghosts—of a hundred men! I seen 'em, Cap'n . . . when I went back. They're sittin' on that treasure like I told you—like buzzards . . ."

Sutton had a curious impression, as he stared at the old man, torn as he was between anger and frustration, that Captain Brown actually was in the grip of an insane fear. His eyes were almost white, with round dark spots in the center, and he looked at Sutton with a kind of naked terror that seemed to come from some subconscious element of his being. He worked his jaw back and forth, his cavernous mouth opening without uttering a sound.

Could it be possible, Sutton thought, that the old man's terror came from some subliminal source? Could the memory of the murders he had committed, the treachery and betrayal of his "partners" during those times of poisoning and shooting on the *Sea Foam,* have descended upon him like an avenging lash of conscience?

Sutton shook his head and prepared to leave. As he arose, he looked down on the old man. There were little flecks of white along the ragged rim of whiskers that fringed the Captain's mouth. He continued to open and close his jaw without saying anything.

"Is that your final answer, Captain? You aren't going to give us the information?"

"Don't leave me here, Cap'n! . . . Don't leave me alone!" He finally got out the words and then put his hands over his face, the gnarled fingers clutching like claws into his whiskers. It seemed to Sutton the old man was crying again.

The Captain shook his head and muttered, as Sutton turned to leave: "You'll never find it . . . without me . . ."

Sutton went out, thinking as he left the cabin: "The old man has gone completely mad. I'll have to warn Mr. Hendrickson to put a guard on him."

Sutton could hear the creak of the bed as he left, Captain Brown apparently having flung himself back lengthwise, probably to stare once more at the ceiling. He could mentally see the old, bitter eyes, looking sightlessly upward, possibly into a mélange of discarnate forms of dead and dying men that clogged his vision. . . .

These thoughts were not usual to Sutton, and a bit staggering. But the experiences of the past months had produced many strange impressions which he had never known before. He found himself unable to disentangle that which was real from things that were unreal . . . The voyage of the *Herman* itself, and his own position on it—the Chairman of the Board of Sewer Commissioners of New Rochelle, now pacing along a jetty in the harbor of Tahiti, trying to make up his mind whether to continue as master of a treasure-hunting ship, on a senseless search for a hundred million dollars—or to go home! Sutton shook his head, in wonderment. This welter of inexplicable happenings seemed beyond the pale of human reason, and he felt utterly unequal to the task of sorting things out as to what was reasonable and what was not.

The result of his interview with the Captain was reported to Chetwood and Dr. Luce; and by common agreement they decided to sell the *Herman* and go home. It was sold—for $8250—on August 28, a month after they arrived in Papeete. A few days later the small band of adventurers, taking Captain Brown with them, a sullen and unwilling companion, left Papeete on the *S.S. Mariposa* bound for San Francisco and the dismal end of fourteen months of futile wandering across the Pacific. They arrived there on September 13, 1903.

This is the last photograph of the *Herman* in Papeete harbor. It was taken after the schooner was sold. She is under the French flag.

Epilogue

It was February, in the year 1922. Almost twenty years had passed since the *Herman* sailed away from San Francisco on that foggy summer day in 1902 on what might now be regarded in retrospect as a fantastic and futile voyage. Sutton's brown, curly hair, still parted in the middle, was becoming gray; and his mustache, still neatly trimmed, was also gray. Sitting in the glass-enclosed porch on the second story of his New Rochelle home overlooking the cold waters of Long Island Sound, watching flurries of drifting snow outside, he was able to contemplate with some equanimity—if not with satisfaction—the curious aftermath of that strange voyage into the hot and stormy waters of the South Pacific.

Time, Sutton reflected, might be the healer of most of man's troubles, but in the matter of treasure hunting, the process seemed to reverse the normal order of things. The trail to buried treasures, instead of growing colder with the passage of time, seemed to grow warmer.

He had just clipped from the New York *Herald* a dispatch from Iowa City, Iowa, dated February 25, 1922, giving an account of a proposed anthropological expedition into the islands of the South Seas to be led by Professor Homer R. Dill of the University of Iowa, for the purpose of collecting artifacts for museums.

The dispatch contained information which was of considerable interest to Sutton:

> Since it was announced some time ago that Prof. Homer R. Dill of the University of Iowa is to cruise in the South Seas next year in search of museum material, he has received a letter from Frederick Mason of

> Augusta, Me., offering to obtain for him the maps and charts of a certain island where treasure worth $60,000,000 is buried.
>
> The treasure, according to Mr. Mason, is part of the plunder from the insurrection in Peru in the early part of the eighteenth [sic] century.

A dispatch from Augusta, Maine, appended to the story, carried the following information:

> Maps and charts of an isolated island in the South Seas on which treasure worth $60,000,000 is said to have been buried in 1820, are in the possession of Mrs. James Brown, widow of an aged retired sea captain who died here three years ago. These are the papers which Frederick Mason, a newspaper correspondent of this city, has offered to obtain for Prof. Homer R. Dill of the University of Iowa, who is to cruise the South Seas next year in search of museum material.

The dispatch then recited in some detail the story of Captain Brown, which was already quite familiar to Sutton. It added one significant bit of information:

> Several companies have been formed in the last five years in different parts of the world to recover the gold, silver, jewels, diamonds and other precious stones. One or two expeditions are said to have found the island, but to have had no success in the search for treasure. . . . The Brown Exploring Company about two years ago, with the yacht Gennessee, made an investigation on Cocos Island, also on Zubia [evidently "Tubuai"], a reef ring in the Society group, but did not locate the plunder.

Sutton was familiar with the affairs of the "Brown Exploring Company" and the expedition of the *Gennessee.* It was organized by Captain James T. Houghton of New York, late in 1919. The schooner had sailed first to Cocos Island and then to the Low Archipelago. A story in the New York *Sun* of June 17, 1920—which Sutton also had clipped and pasted in his scrapbook—gave the following account:

> The expedition to the South Seas for recovery of $80,000,000 [sic] in gold reported buried there, has failed, according to a member of the expedition who has returned after taking part in the futile undertaking in which he and thirty-five others sailed on the schooner Gennessee . . . After three weeks of digging, all the treasure-hunters uncovered were the skeletons of a dozen men.
>
> The great mass of gold was reported to have been buried there decades ago, and the story acted upon came from a sailor named Brown.

N. Y. Herald Feb 26/1924

THE N

CHARTS OFFERED TO SEARCH FOR $60,000,000 TREASURE

Augusta Man Willing to Obtain Maps if Prof. Dill of Iowa Will Seek Buried Plunder From Peru Revolt While on Cruise in South Seas.

IOWA CITY, Iowa, Feb. 25.—Since it was announced a short time ago that Prof. Homer R. Dill of the University of Iowa is to cruise the South Seas next year in search of museum material, he has received a letter from Frederick Mason of Augusta, Me., offering to obtain for him the maps and charts of a certain island where treasure worth $60,000,000 is buried.

The treasure, according to Mr. Mason, is part of the plunder from the insurrection in Peru in the early part of the eighteenth century.

AUGUSTA, Me., Feb. 25.—Maps and charts of an isolated ilsand in the South Seas on which treasure worth $60,000,000 is said to have been buried in 1820, are in the possession of Mrs. James Brown, widow of an aged retired sea captain who died here three years ago. These are the papers which Frederick Mason, a newspaper correspondent of this city, has offered to obtain for Prof. Homer R. Dill of the University of Iowa, who is to cruise the South Seas next year in search of museum material.

Capt. Brown said he was the only man in the world who held the key to the location of the treasure. He said he helped transfer it in 1850 from the island on which it originally was hidden to another island where it was again buried. Cocos Island, about 550 miles southwest of Panama, is said to have been the original location of the hoard.

Several companies have been formed in the last five years in different parts of the world to recover the gold, silver, jewels, diamonds and other precious stones. One or two expeditions are said to have found the island, but to have had no success in the search for treasure.

Capt. Brown was mate of the schooner Seafoam, in which Capt. Henry Smith of Salem, Mass., set out from Kingston, Jamaica, in 1850, to recover the fortune. Capt. Smith told his mate it was loot obtained during the Peruvian insurrection in 1820, and that his father, master of the schooner Black Witch of Salem, had buried it on Cocos Island.

The expedition, Capt. Brown told his friends, found the treasure and moved it to another island. There all the crew died except the captain, steward and himself. They started in the ship's long boat for Australia, taking about $1,000,000, but on the passage the other two died. He arrived at Cochin Bay, West Australia, and was sure he was the only person who knew where the treasure was buried.

The Brown Exploring Company about two years ago, with the yacht Gennessee, made an investigation on Cocos Island, also on Zubia, a reef ring in the Society group, but did not locate the plunder.

Mr. Mason said to-night he never had seen the maps and charts.

This story appeared in the *New York Herald* twenty years after the search ended.

The member of the expedition who had returned—and was being quoted by the *Sun*—had given a more detailed report of the actual search:

> On February 27 [1920] we sailed out of Tahiti for an island in the Tubuai group. We left our craft outside the harbor of a beautiful island and went ashore. Excitement ran high as news of the search spread among the crew. Captain Crowley [Arthur L. Crowley, of Boston] was armed with maps and charts. The point we sought was inland, and we found a mound where the treasure should have been. We began digging and continued to dig for three weeks, uncovering a huge area. But we found only the bones and we finally gave up the task.

Sutton had been poring over these memorabilia of Captain Brown's "treasure island" for some time—in fact for year after year, as he gradually accumulated bits of information, adding each new item to the vast collection of notes, letters, excerpts from his own diary and entries in the log of the *Herman*. The material had mounted steadily until it filled a large scrapbook. In this case, he had written to Captain Houghton and later met him at the Harvard Club in New York, where he learned that the "sailor named Brown" was indeed Captain James Brown, who then lived in Augusta, Maine. At the time of the *Gennessee* expedition the old Captain would have been eighty-nine; he had died, however, a few months before the schooner sailed on what was probably the old man's final effort to recover the treasure—*in absentia* as it were.

The pieces of the puzzle were gradually beginning to take shape in Sutton's mind. For instance, only a couple of years ago Sutton had received a letter from Donzel Stoney, dated February 11, 1920:

> Perhaps you have not entirely forgotten the existence of Captain James Brown, with whom we were more or less associated in the early days of this century. If not, the following information may be of interest to you.
>
> You will remember about three years ago some young men from the East brought him out here for the purpose of making a trip to the treasure island to recover the loot of the Peruvian churches. . . . A few days ago one of the men who was with him called to tell me he knew I would be interested in some corroboration of the Captain's story which he had acquired since he was here before.

The "corroboration" consisted of a story told by a man then living in Los Angeles, "a very sick old man who had spent his life in the South Sea Islands." Stoney's informant described this old man's story in some detail: the "sick old man" had at one time helped nurse a derelict sailor whom he had somehow met in Australia, and the old sailor, "sick and dying" at the time, had finally died after several weeks of failing health. Before he expired, however, he told the following story—as reported in Stoney's letter:

> Many years before a number of Peruvian churches had been looted of gold and silver treasures, which had been buried near the coast. This old sailor and some others apparently had a hand in finding this loot. They took a boat from Balboa and sailed for the treasure, loaded it aboard and sailed in a due westerly course.

Among the sailors on the ship was a man named Brown.

The rambling account of the dying sailor, which reached Stoney third-hand, recited a story with familiar details. The ship "in due course sighted an island, where they deposited and buried the treasure." There was one added bit of information, however, that interested Sutton:

> No one on the ship knew the name of the island. They sailed off again and, sighting another island, went ashore and got in contact with some natives. They learned from these natives the name of the island. Later, sailing to Australia, their boat was wrecked on a reef, and this man survived.

According to the information given Stoney, the "sick old man" in Los Angeles had been given the name of this island by the dying sailor; and he subsequently organized a group of sailing men and sailed to the island, where he said he found the treasure. However, a French warship came into sight, and they hastily covered over the treasure and reported nothing to the Frenchmen who landed on the island.

Stoney's letter continued:

> The man went to the French Government to take up the basis on which he would get a share of the treasure if he recovered it. He was informed that he would get one third and the French Government would get the balance. He asked for an official statement to this effect in writing, but it has not been forthcoming, so he has kept the knowledge to himself.

Stoney concluded:

> You may remember that Captain Brown said he had the loot from several treasure ships in addition to the Peruvian relics, and these were taken at different times and hidden in different places. Now, if the Captain's story is corroborated with regard to the Peruvian church relics, perhaps it is true as to the other parts of his story, also.

While Sutton recognized that almost every account of buried treasures must have gaps and inconsistencies, being of dubious origin for the most part, and usually passing through a number of intermediate handlings before anything is set down in writing, he was nevertheless beginning to formulate a theory about the old Captain's "treasure island."

For example, among the assorted bits of information gleaned from letters, newspaper stories and other sources, he was able to list certain thematic consistencies, a sort of underlying set of similar characteristics:

First, there was the identification of the treasure itself. Many treasures were known to have been buried in the days of piracy in the Pacific, particularly on Cocos Island; but in all cases involving lost treasures of the South Pacific, they were referred to as "church treasures" of Peru. No others were mentioned, except for the Australian specie ships, about which the old Captain himself had displayed a marked reticence.

Second, there was the location of the island. In every account, it was somewhere in the western outposts of the Low Archipelago, or the Tubuai group. And in most cases, its position conformed generally with the location of Makatea.

Third—and perhaps most significant—there was the unrelenting interest of the British Government in Captain Brown's activities.

Much of this impression of thematic consistency was gained from the letters that John Chetwood wrote to Sutton during the years following the voyage of the *Herman*. There had been a brief period of bitterness and recrimination when the voyagers returned to San Francisco on the *Mariposa;* but through it all, Chetwood had remained firm in his support of Sutton, and they had weathered the legal storms together.

In one letter, dated November 26, 1915, Chetwood had written:

> About a year ago a friend called on me who had a rich eastern friend who was then dickering with Captain Brown. On my suggestion, Brown's record was looked up. My friend now advises me that British agents have been shadowing Brown for years (I saw a copy of a report) and watching all his moves. The plan seems to be to let Brown find the goods, and then catch him with them . . .
>
> Perhaps we might have had some explaining to do, even if we had been successful. At all events, the British seem to believe the Australian piracy part of it, whatever they may think of the Cocos end of the story.

Some time later, in a letter dated August 15, 1918, Chetwood again wrote Sutton, further confirming the British Government's curious interest in Captain Brown's activities:

> A couple of years ago I stopped an eastern friend from embarking with Brown by having his attention drawn to "our search." Through inquiries made in the east and elsewhere, this man found that the British Government for many years has watched Brown's expeditions after the treasure very closely. This tallies with what we noticed all thru the trip. The reason is [that] said government believes the tale, that is, the Australian piracy part of it. . . .

This strange brew of old memories and new reports was not without its mixture of bitterness for Sutton. He had come home not only in deep disappointment, but in some measure a man marked by failure. It was one thing to set forth as a bold adventurer, seeking buried treasure in the romantic context of pirates' gold; but it was a horse of a different color when he arrived back in New Rochelle as the publicly proclaimed victim of a hoax—a man who had gone on a fool's errand!

As the years passed, bits of information drifted in, confirming in Sutton's own mind his belief in that "solid grain of truth" in the old Captain's story; and it became impossible not to swallow the accompanying dose of medicine: the bitter realization that, if the treasure *did* exist somewhere on a lonely island in the Low Archipelago, there had to be also the galling thought that they might have been on the very threshold of finding it when an evil blow of fate struck them down—at the very moment when untold riches lay almost within their grasp!

The final chain of circumstances which gave life to this viewpoint was provided by Captain Brown himself.

During the years following the voyage of the *Herman,* the old Captain had made three more efforts to organize a search for the island. In 1909 he persuaded a syndicate in Boston to finance an expedition, and sailed on February 9 from San Francisco for Australia on the *Mariposa* —the same vessel that brought the members of the *Herman* expedition back to San Francisco. Brown had intended to charter a small steamer in Sydney, where he arrived with a suitcase full of maps and sailing directions; but instead he obtained a sailing vessel which left Sydney on March 3 for the mysterious "treasure island."

Chetwood later wrote Sutton about this expedition, in which Captain Brown got as far as the Tonga Islands and "said he sighted his bloody island, but just then a storm broke and drove him back on the New Caledonia reefs—as reported in the press."

In July of that year Captain Brown secured the backing of another group in Boston and New York, and the steamer *Ethelwold,* a British fruit ship, was chartered in New York. After some mysterious events

blame you at all, but put it all on
the doctor & Chetwood, they were the two ringleaders
& I blame them for spoiling the work in Sydney
when the trouble came at the courthouse.
If you are in good health dont you
think you can raise money enough
& you & I go by ourselves after this treasure
as it is a pitty to let all that money
lay there to be wasted, you always believed
me that I [illegible] regarding that treasure
& I have always been sorry that that trouble
started in Sydney, it started in Honolulu
& then again in Sydney, but I think if you
& I could start now, I think we could
get it, as I have stated before the Island
& treasure is there, as I have seen the Island
three times & have been pretty close to it, —
without anyone knowing it, so be sure &
answer, with kindest regards to yourself
& family in which Mrs Brown joins me

Yours truly

Capt James Brown

Segment of Captain Brown's last pleading letter to George Sutton wherein he stated, "I have seen the Island three times & have been pretty close to it,— without anyone knowing it . . ."

aboard ship, it was seized by Internal Revenue agents, who hinted that it carried contraband cargo, and the expedition never got beyond the Narrows of New York Harbor.

The old man's final attempt was in the year 1919. This was the *Gennessee* expedition, backed by several wealthy yachtsmen; and the Captain—then verging on ninety—did not live to see the fruits of his efforts, having died in his home in Augusta, Maine, before the *Gennessee* left for the South Seas.

Sutton had been in irregular correspondence with the Captain since 1912, when he unexpectedly received a letter from the aging ex-pirate. The letter, dated March 19, 1912, began: "Dear George." It read:

> It is now 10 years ago since yourself & some others & myself started after the Cocos Island treasure, it failed & I do not kno wether it was my fault or whoes, but we lost.
>
> Three years ago I went to Sydney, Aust., & fitted out an expedition & left the 3 of March for the Island, but on the 6th of March a typhoon struck me & drove me on the New Caledonia Island. We got ashore at a place called "Nouma" & a French man of war picked us up & the Consul sent us home . . .

The letter went on to explain the old man's reason for writing: he had been contacted by a "party" that was interested in outfitting an expedition "but they want to go by themselves, & that I do not care about very much." He then concluded with the surprising suggestion: "Will you go in my place—as my representative as I think I can trust you. . . ."

A few days later the Captain wrote again, and this time he added a startling postscript: "You have seen this island once." And to add to Sutton's frustration, he enclosed a map which he said was "a sketch of the island & the Lat. and Long. I have in my head just as clear as it ever was."

It was five years before Sutton received the next—and last—communication from the Captain. He had replied briefly to the old man's letter, declining the offer to "represent" him; and the Captain, apparently in failing health, had moved meanwhile to Augusta. He was now, according to Sutton's reckoning, eighty-seven years old. He wrote:

> Dear Sutton:—
>
> I thought I would write to you as I expect you are getting along in age as well as myself, & I should like to know how you are getting on, before anything happens, as both you & I were pretty good friends when we were on the trip for the treasure. I did not blame you at all,

> but put it all on the doctor & Chetwood. They were the two ringleaders & I blame them for spoiling the work in Sydney when the trouble came at the courthouse.

The letter then included what Sutton felt must be the most astounding suggestion he had ever received:

> If you are in good health don't you think you can raise money enough & you & I go by ourselves after this treasure as it is a pitty to let all that money lay there to be wasted, you always believed me that I know regarding that treasure & I have always been sorry that that trouble started in Sydney, it started in Honolulu & then again in Sydney, but I think if you & I could start now, I think we could get it, as I have stated before the Island & treasure is there, as I have seen the Island three times & I have been pretty close to it, without anyone knowing it, so be sure & answer, with kind regards to yourself & family in which Mrs. Brown joins me.
>
> Yours truly,
> Capt. James Brown

Sutton had read and reread that letter many times. It was like a last will and testament. . . . Even now, looking out into the white flurries of snow that swept past the window of his house, Sutton could close his eyes and see once again the old man as he stood on the afterdeck of the *Herman,* his legs braced as solidly as the trunks of trees against the roll of the deck, his leathery face fringed with a circle of white hair, blown by the wind, pale eyes fixed upon the horizon . . . looking out day after day for a sun-dried slab of coral rock, somewhere in that blazing blue ocean . . . the rim of surf beating on sharp rocks of a coral reef, the calm sweep of the green lagoon, the clusters of coconut palms on the beach bending toward the trade winds . . . and behind the beach a cliff rising among the pandanus and matted shrubs, a cliff that hid from human eyes an immense store of gold and silver and jewels—a treasure worth a hundred million dollars!

Sutton sighed and laid his clippings down. There was a crude map, drawn on a piece of scratch paper, which the Captain had enclosed with his last letter. Whether it meant anything, Sutton did not know. It was roughly drawn, probably from his memory "just as clear as it ever was" —and hardly legible. It failed to give either the position or a description of the island.

It was the Captain's last message, and Sutton could never decide in his own mind whether it was a sincere effort to help him find the treasure, or a last bitter gesture of farewell to the old man's dream.

Appendix: The Legends of Cocos Island

Cocos Island—or *Isla del Coco,* to give the place its Spanish name—is undoubtedly the most mysterious depository of buried treasures on earth. It was the prototype for Robert Louis Stevenson's "Treasure Island" and many of the scenes of Daniel Defoe's story of *Robinson Crusoe* were taken from actual reports of forays in the waters around Cocos—although the Crusoe locale was at Juan Fernández Island, farther south along the West Coast of South America.

Cocos Island has two claims to distinction. It is known to have been the burial ground of more authentic pirates' treasures than any other similar place in the world; and almost none of these buried treasures have been found—at least not officially. It is this paradox of piratology that still continues to lure treasure hunters to Cocos year after year.

The fact that *none* of the treasures are reliably known to have been dug up—although some may have been taken off surreptitiously by persons who for reasons best known to themselves did not want to advertise their efforts—has not been due to lack of diligence on the part of treasure seekers. Nor has failure to find the treasures dampened their ardor.

Since the last decade of the nineteenth century, Cocos Island has been an almost continual camping ground for expeditions equipped with maps, charts, directions for finding the treasures, cases of dynamite, digging implements and diving gear and even electric divining rods. Its mist-shrouded gorges and rocky beaches have been crisscrossed with trenches, excavated, blasted and tunneled until the accessible areas look more like a battlefield in Flanders than a lush tropical island. The lure of Cocos gold has attracted some of the most dedicated men in the adventuring business, including Count Felix von Luckner, the old German "sea devil" of World War I; Sir Malcolm Campbell, the British race-car driver; Errol Flynn, the actor, and many less notable adventurers, such as Admiral Palliser of the British Royal Navy, an Earl Fitzwilliam and a robust lady from Boston named Mrs. Roswell D. Hitchcock, who once acquired fame by getting lost on a scientific gold-hunting expedition in Alaska.

Companies have been formed and concessions obtained from the government of Costa Rica, which claims ownership of the island; pitched battles have been fought over the sun-dried trenches between rival parties in pursuit of the pirates' loot. One man, August Gissler, who claimed to be "Governor" of Cocos (see Chapter II, 2), spent half his life searching for the lost treasures, a good part of the time on Cocos itself. But all to no avail. The island has never disgorged its major secrets—officially—with the sole exception of the "church treasure" of Peru, which has been the subject of this book. And except for a very few people, little was known of this.

The fascination of Cocos seems to have increased rather than diminished with every new failure. Each party, sallying forth to wrest the secret from the island's jungled gorges, appears to have been convinced that its predecessors missed finding the treasure through some sort of carelessness. All arrived with maps of varying authenticity, and voluminous reports of previous expeditions; and there was usually enough bric-a-brac of piracy scattered around to whet the appetite for digging. But they all left emptyhanded.

By some incredible oversight, possibly a characteristic of treasure-hunting psychology, they all seem to have missed a salient bit of logic that should have been plain to the point of obviousness. If these treasures were known to have been buried on Cocos (at least three were officially confirmed by the governments of Peru and Great Britain) and none could be found, there would seem to be only one logical reason for this phenomenon: they had already been dug up!

This explanation of at least one of the "lost treasures" of Cocos is the basis for the voyage of the *Herman;* but in order to place this case in historical perspective with other similar treasures and treasure hunts, a general review of the legends of Cocos Island treasures seems to be needed, if only to satisfy the unasked questions which some of the more avid *aficionados* of the treasure-hunting sport may have in mind.

First, it should be noted for the record that this particular Cocos Island is only one of three places in the world which have that name:

there is a Cocos Island in the Keeling group, southwest of Java in the Indian Ocean; and a Cocos Island off the southern tip of Guam. The Cocos Island of treasure-hunting fame, however, lies off the West Coast of South America at Lat. 5°35′ N., and Long. 87°2′ W. As noted earlier, it presents a hostile and uninviting view to mariners, with few landing approaches and a narrow, rocky coastline. The interior is a mass of towering ridges, some rising to twenty-five hundred feet, so that from a distance it seems to have fallen sideways into the ocean, like an upended slab of rock. It is shaped like a kidney, less than six miles long and about three miles wide. Parts of the interior have never been explored because of the almost impenetrable jungle. The island has fresh water from streams flowing down the matted cliffs, and it also provides wood, all of which made it an excellent hideout for pirates.

The ridges are slashed with deep gorges which wind down to the narrow, rocky coastline. Two bays on the northern coast form the only approaches. Wafer Bay, on the western slope, has from fourteen to twenty-five fathoms of water and Chatham Bay, guarded by two rocky islands, offers good anchorage inside the cove. The island is well outside the trading routes of ships that tracked down from California to Cape Horn; and as a matter of fact, ships seldom sighted the island due to light winds and calms that lie stagnant in the swirling backwaters of the eastern Pacific.

Cocos Island achieved its unique reputation as a repository for pirates' loot as a result of a change in the sailing routes of Spanish gold ships in the late seventeenth and early eighteenth centuries. For nearly two hundred years of Spanish conquests in the Americas, the route across the Caribbean from Cartagena, known as the Spanish Main, had been the principal playground for pirates and privateers. As the demand for wealth of the New World to support the tottering empires of the Old World increased, with the disintegration of Bourbon power, it became necessary to have more of this wealth arrive at its destination and less find its way into the haches of English and American merchantmen. It seemed safer and more convenient to ship these immense stores of gold and silver down the West Coast and around the Horn, rather than risk a Caribbean crossing.

The buccaneers of the Spanish Main quickly adjusted to this situation. Within a short time the West Coast became a profitable trading ground for British and American privateers, for whom the fine line of distinction between patriotic efforts to reduce enemy shipping and the profits of plain piracy on the high seas was not too carefully drawn. As the buccaneer business increased, Cocos Island became a natural burial place for the loot. A large amount of these riches undoubtedly were dug up later by the men who buried the treasures, but millions of dollars' worth lay for centuries in the hidden caves, small plateaus and winding gorges of Cocos—thus giving nourishment to the many legends that grew up in the latter nineteenth and early twentieth centuries.

At this point, for the sake of establishing some historical sequence, it is advisable to list the persons and ships involved with the major treasures which come under the heading of at least semiauthentic history:

1684—Captain Edward Davis, British buccaneer, in the *Batchelor's Delight,* originally under command of Captain John Cooke.

1818—Captain Benito Bonita, a Spanish pirate known as "Bloody Bonita," in the *Relampago,* originally the English slave ship *Lightning* captured in the West Indies in 1817.

1821—Mutineers of the British warship *H.M.S. Devonshire,* later recaptured by British gunboats and its crew executed or sent to penal colonies.

1821—Captain Henry Smith, of the American schooner *Black Witch,* out of Salem, Massachusetts, which escaped from Callao, Peru, with the fabulous "ecclesiastical treasure of Lima."

1835—Captain Jack Thompson, of the Nova Scotia bark *Mary Deer,* out of Bristol, England, which took aboard the official government treasury of Peru and escaped to Cocos Island. The bark was later recaptured by Peruvian gunboats, but the treasury, estimated at about eighteen million dollars, was never recovered.

The exploits of Captain Edward Davis (later Sir Edward Davis) were dealt with briefly in the introductory remarks, chiefly for the purpose of placing in historical perspective the curious coincidence of the inventory of the treasures, as described in references to the exploits of Captain Davis, being the same as that applied by latter-day historians (and even the archives of Costa Rica) to the "church treasure" of Peru, which disappeared some 140 years later.

Captain Davis was originally quartermaster on the *Batchelor's Delight,* a notorious British privateer of the West Indies, when it was commanded by Captain John Cooke. In 1683 Cooke left the West Indies for more profitable commerce on the West Coast, but died after he had rounded Cape Horn and sailed past Juan Fernández Island. Two highly literary men—William Dampier and Lionel Wafer—were aboard the *Batchelor's Delight* during parts of this voyage. It was Juan Fernández Island, where Dampier participated in the rescue of Alex-

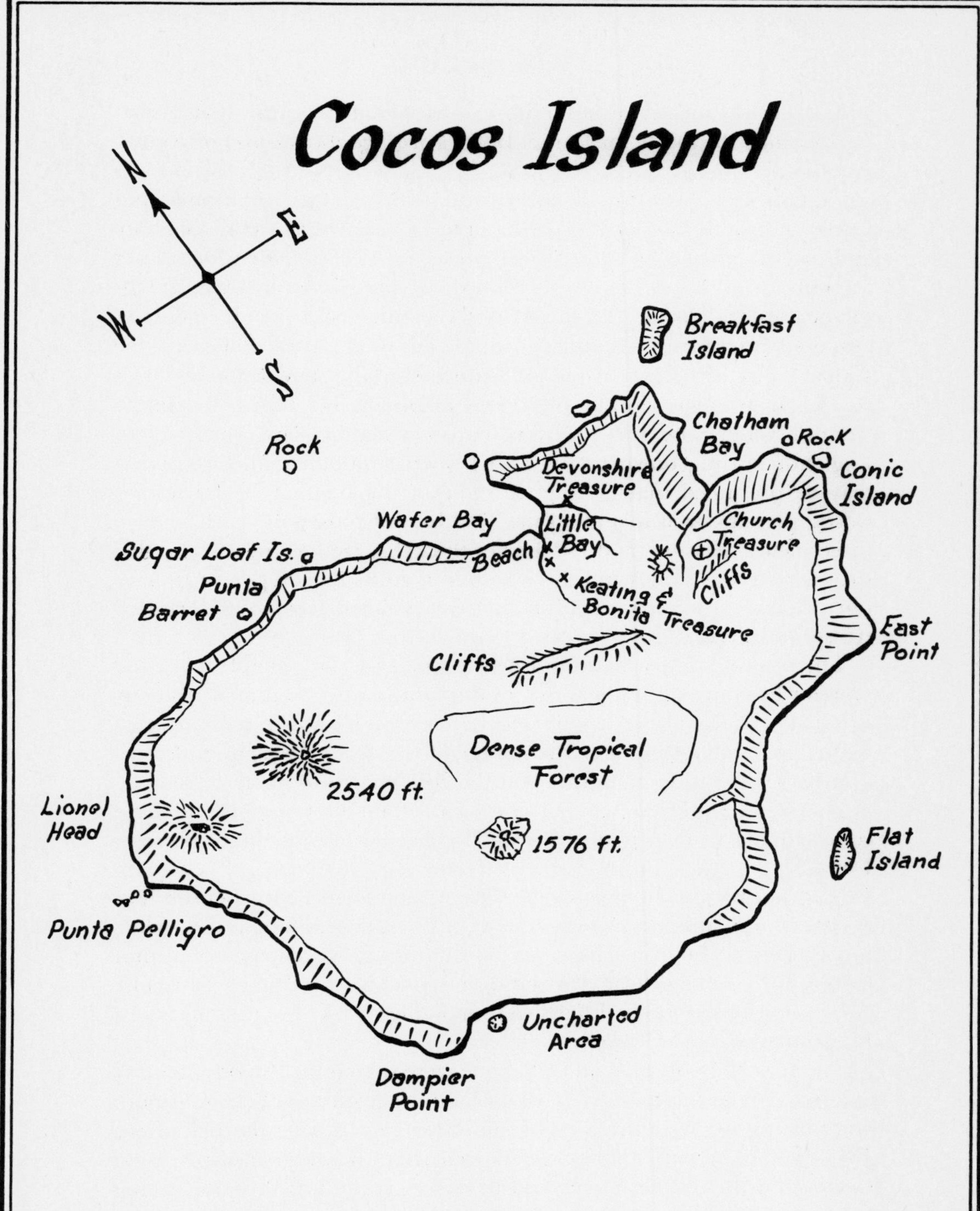

Cocos Island
N
E
W
S
Breakfast Island
Rock
Chatham Bay
Rock
Conic Island
Devonshire Treasure
Water Bay
Little Bay
Church Treasure
Sugar Loaf Is.
Beach
Punta Barret
Keating & Bonita Treasure
Cliffs
East Point
Cliffs
Dense Tropical Forest
2540 ft.
Lionel Head
1576 ft.
Flat Island
Punta Pelligro
Uncharted Area
Dampier Point

ander Selkirk, a Scottish sailor who was marooned on the island, that later formed the locale for Daniel Defoe's *Strange Adventures of Robinson Crusoe.*

Captain Davis continued northward to the Galápagos Islands and finally set up his base on Cocos. Dampier, a scientist as well as a pirate and author, left the *Batchelor's Delight* to join the famed *Cygnet* under Captain Swan. Later he was marooned on one of the Nicobar Islands in the western Pacific. Lionel Wafer remained with Davis and later rendered interesting accounts of his piratical activities. For years the slippery English frigate harassed Spanish shipping and Captain Davis and his men made a profitable career of piracy. He returned later to Atlantic waters and was forgiven his trespasses by King James II of England, settling down finally as a landed gentleman in Virginia. It may be presumed that he dug up some of the treasure he buried on Cocos, perhaps even including the "733 bars of pure gold, each four by three inches measure, and two inches thick," as well as the "bejewelled swords, precious stones and three kettles of gold" he is reported to have buried, which were ascribed by latter-day historians to the church treasure of Peru.

The second fairly well established legend of Cocos Island, involving more or less pure piracy, was that of Captain Benito Bonita, or "Bloody Bonita." His history is interesting because of its possible connection with Jack Thompson, later the master of the *Mary Deer;* and also because of the relation of Bonita and the *Relampago* to many of the ambiguous and confused reports which historians of Cocos Island have collected and made a part of the apocryphal legends of the treasure of Lima.

Bonita, whose real name seems to have been Dom Pedro Benitez, was master of a Spanish privateer, operating in West Indian waters, when he captured an English slave ship, the *Lightning.* He disposed of all but two of her crew and headed around the Horn for the West Coast. The two exceptions were an English sailor named Jack Thompson, and a Frenchman named Chapelle.

The reason Thompson and Chapelle were spared by "Bloody Bonita" was not very clear; but there is considerable reason to believe that both served as pirates with the crew of the *Relampago* during the years from 1818 to 1820, when Bonita and his men were the scourge of the West Coast, raiding Spanish towns and churches, as well as shipping, along the coast of Peru, New Granada (Ecuador) and even as far north as Mexico.

These raids became legendary in the annals of piracy on the West Coast. They are of particular concern in the history of Cocos Island because there seems no doubt that Bonita and his men worked out of that island, which they found quite by accident after capturing a Spanish ship and sinking her with dead and dying aboard. The account of this particular exploit furnished the starting point for August Gissler's years of fruitless effort to find the treasures of Cocos, although he apparently was hopelessly mixed up between various legends, maps and reports.

The *Relampago* was reported to have been wrecked somewhere on the West Coast; but other equally vague stories seemed to indicate that Bonita had returned to the West Indies where his ship was captured by an English warship and its entire crew put to death. However, Thompson and Chapelle, who seem to have had charmed lives, escaped from the ship, and Thompson is reported to have furnished the English with information about the activities of Bonita in return for amnesty. Chapelle was reported to have died some years later in Apia, Samoa. Thompson returned to England, and several years later showed up in Callao as master of the *Mary Deer,* in a sequence of events which may be regarded as the most authentic of all the Cocos Island legends.

Meanwhile, returning to the chronological listing of Cocos Island treasures, there were two other fairly "authentic" treasures of considerable interest, the "Devonshire treasure," named for the English warship *Devonshire,* and the most fabulous of all Cocos Island treasures, the famed treasure of Lima, or "church treasure" of Peru. Both were buried on Cocos in 1821.

The *Devonshire* treasure is less confused than most of the other legends, and its principal importance lies in the fact that the treasures may still lie somewhere in the rocky defiles along Wafer Bay, and that the British Government has continued to feel a proprietary interest in the treasure, said to be worth about seventeen million dollars.

In 1821 the British warship *Devonshire* was dispatched on a "cruise" along the West Coast of South America—a euphemistic naval expression for observing sea traffic along the Spanish gold route and picking up a few boatloads of gold and silver from Spanish ships. The story of what happened is contained in a letter of a descendant of one of the ship's officers, Mr. Hartford of Victoria, B.C., to George Kirkendale, a member of the Blakely Expedition to Cocos Island in 1902:

> In 1821 my grandfather shipped as surgeon on a British warship, the *Devonshire,* for a cruise to the West Coast of South and Central

> America. The vessel captured such a vast amount of treasure from the Spaniards that the crew, overcome with cupidity, mutinied and seized the ship, afterwards continuing to cruise as pirates. They made Cocos Island their headquarters and built a small settlement there, the remains of which may still be seen on Wafer Bay. The British Government sent several ships in pursuit of the pirates, and fearing capture, they finally melted down their treasure into gold and silver bricks and stored these in a cave in a bank near the settlement.
>
> To hide the spot they placed a keg of gunpowder at the entrance to the cave and exploded it, blowing down the face of the cliff. The *Devonshire* afterwards was captured by the British and a number of the crew executed, while the remainder were transported to a penal colony in Australia.
>
> Some of the convicts returned afterwards to Cocos, seeking the treasure, but as far as is known it was never taken away.

The last two authentic stories of Cocos Island—the disappearance of the ecclesiastical treasure of Lima and the *Mary Deer* affair—form the most intriguing chapter in the history of the island, mainly because—as was noted earlier—they have been so confused and intermixed as to detail and sources of information due to the similarity of the two events.

The disappearance of the treasure of Lima, after this huge store of gold and silver relics and ornaments had been loaded aboard the *Black Witch,* in the summer of 1821 was described in some detail in the introductory paragraphs of this book. The second disappearance of a Peruvian treasure—this time the official treasure of the revolutionary government of Peru—occurred fourteen years later when it was loaded aboard the *Mary Deer* for protection under the British flag.

This has not only been the source of most of the maps and directions for locating the treasure, but it has also been the source of most of the confusion surrounding Cocos Island's "lost treasures."

The authority for the *Mary Deer* affair comes not only from the Peruvian Government, but also from the British. The master of the *Mary Deer,* Captain Jack Thompson—who was the same young English sailor who was spared death when "Bloody Bonita" captured the English slaver *Lightning*—is the principal source of information as to what happened to the Peruvian treasury. His account, given as he lay dying in Nova Scotia in 1842, seven years later, follows:

> In 1835 I shipped in Bristol, with a crew of twelve, on the barque *Mary Deer,* bound for Valparaiso with a cargo of coal. On the way out the captain died, leaving eleven souls all told aboard. As mate, I took command. We discharged our coal and went up the coast seeking cargo.

> At this time war was in progress between Peru and Chile, and while we were in Callao Harbor the city was attacked. The crown jewels and other treasures of Peru had been brought from Lima to Callao and placed in the fort for safety, but the Peruvians, being afraid of it being captured, placed it aboard our ship for safekeeping under the protection of the British flag.
>
> We were tempted by the millions and in the night we cut our cables and put to sea. When the Peruvians found we had actually run away with the treasure, they gave chase, but our barque was a swift sailer and we soon left them behind. We anchored in the bay on Cocos Island where a small stream ran out. Stretching back from the beach is a level piece of ground. We selected a spot and buried our treasure. I do not know of its value but there must have been millions, as there were ten boatloads of it.
>
> After leaving the island we were pursued and captured by a Peruvian vessel and taken to Callao, where we were tried and sentenced to be shot. The sentence was carried out on eight men, but myself and two sailors were pardoned on agreeing to take them to the spot where the treasure was buried. Thinking there might be some chance of escape, we said the treasure was on Galápagos.
>
> Before reaching the islands, however, for some reason we put in at the Bay of Dulce [on the coast of Costa Rica] where nearly all of the crew and one of my companions died of the fever. Anchored near us was a whaler, and one night as she put to sea and was passing us, the two of us jumped overboard and swam to her and were taken on board. The captain was glad to have us as he had lost some of his crew from fever. We were on the whaler for several years, saying no word about the treasure, and then went back to Nova Scotia.

Captain Thompson, apparently quite ill from the effect of tropical fevers, lived at the home of a Captain John Keating, where he died. It is from Captain Keating and the rather remarkable sequence of events that proceeded from his story that the so-called "Keating treasure" derives its name.

Captain Keating received maps and directions from Thompson before he died; and with these, he made a trip to the West Coast and to Cocos Island. He returned to Cape Breton probably in 1845, and exhibited some old coins. He interested several people in a venture, including a Captain Bogue (or Boag), and an expedition to Cocos Island was planned.

At this point, research into the legends of Cocos Island and its lost treasures is transferred from the field of buried treasures to that of treasure hunting. The records of treasure seekers are more apocryphal, if possible, than those of treasure burials; yet they form the fascinating end of the business. They also give rise to the many varied stories, reports, maps, letters and other such paraphernalia of the treasure-hunting profession.

Captain Keating seems to have been one of the most prolific sources of such material. According to the basic story, he and Bogue fitted out a ship and after a rough voyage around the Horn, beset by threats of mutiny, they put into Cocos Island late in the year 1846. At this point, the stories begin to diverge.

One summary of what happened is contained in the "Curzon-Howe papers," disclosed in the year 1895. According to this account, which furnished the stimulus for an expensive expedition in 1926 organized and led by Sir Malcolm Campbell, Keating and Bogue went ashore, found the location of the treasure, and became so frightened at threats of mutiny they abandoned the ship. The members of the crew beat the bushes hunting them for a few days and then sailed away. Subsequently, Keating was rescued by a passing whaler and reported that Bogue had died on the island.

In 1894 Lord Curzon-Howe of the British Admiralty received a letter from a man giving the name of Nicholas Fitzgerald, whom he had saved from drowning in Newfoundland some twenty years before. Fitzgerald told of meeting a "Captain John Keating" in the year 1867, when Keating was dying; and that Keating, in gratitude for Fitzgerald's efforts to nurse him back to health, had told him the story of his expedition to Cocos Island and given him maps showing the location of the *Mary Deer* treasure. He also gave the names of officers on the ship Keating and Bogue had fitted out for the trip, and sufficient information to indicate that the ship had been lost at sea.

"I believe the treasure is still buried on Cocos Island, and I believe I am the only person who knows the secret of where it lies," the letter said.

Meanwhile there were other strange offshoots of the Keating story. In the year 1897 the British warship *Imperieuse* was lying off Callao, under command of Admiral Palliser, when the Admiral received a mysterious letter from a man calling himself "Patrick Fitzgerald." The letter said:

"Because you are an Irishman, and sympathetic with those in distress, I appeal to you. I am held incommunicado in a vile prison in this city. I have found a way to communicate with you through the prison keeper. . . ."

The letter then recited in a meandering way a tale which greatly interested the Admiral, and ultimately became a matter of interest to the British Navy.

"Several years ago," Fitzgerald wrote, "when I was captain of a fishing boat, I was wrecked on the shore of Newfoundland. I was able to land my crew and ship's stores near a small village, which I found to be in distress, having been icebound for several months. I was glad to be able to share my ship's stores with these villagers, one of whom I found to be exceedingly ill and near to death's door. This man's name was Keating."

Fitzgerald described this "Keating" as a "man of considerable travel and money, which, however, was useless to him." He said Keating had told "an interesting story" during the last days of his life, apparently in gratitude for the medical help and other kindnesses provided by Fitzgerald. Keating said he had received information "from a pirate named Thompson of the secret of a great store of gold and silver buried by one Captain Morgan in the year 1820 on Cocos Island, five hundred miles from here."

The reference to Morgan was anachronistic, the British buccaneer having died in 1686, but it may have referred to the time when Thompson was a member of the pirate crew of "Bloody Bonita" on the *Relampago*. At any rate, Fitzgerald's letter was sufficiently consistent with some of the known history of the "Keating treasure" to interest Admiral Palliser.

According to Fitzgerald, he spent several days with Keating, during which "he went on to show me evidence he possessed, that he knew where the treasure was buried, and in return for favors I had done him and his wife, he wished to make me owner of the secret." The letter then referred to "details of the knowledge of the traditional history of the gold and silver which belonged to the Governor of Peru and was sent from this city for safety from the revolutionists."

This conflict in "traditional history" is the shoal upon which most of the legends of Cocos Island have foundered. The so-called "Keating treasure" was not removed from Callao to safeguard it from the revolutionists, since they had been in control of the government of Peru for some fourteen years.

In any case, Admiral Palliser—who presumably had some knowledge of the Curzon-Howe papers—was so interested in Fitzgerald's letter that he managed to secure the man's release from prison, and shortly afterward the *Imperieuse* headed for Cocos Island. The Admiral found evidence of prior diggings on the island, including a large stone with the letter "K" carved on it—possibly by Keating during his visit in 1844 or 1846—and a scattering of Spanish coins, all dated prior to 1800. But he was unable to locate any tangible treasure.

He did locate a resident of Cocos Island, however—a Mrs. August Gissler, the wife of the red-bearded German who was probably the most devoted treasure hunter in the long history of the search for the treasures of Cocos Island. Gissler, who had been appointed "Governor" of Cocos Island the same year that Admiral Palliser made his first trip there, was away on another kind of expedition, seeking backing for explorations which he had been conducting for almost a decade.

Gissler's account of his experiences, which he gave in later years to various newspapers and magazine writers, forms one of the most prolific sources of legends of Cocos treasures, and has probably contributed more to the exacerbation of the accumulated confusion surrounding the various stories of "lost treasures" on Cocos than any other treasure-hunter who has hunted on Cocos. He had obtained maps and other memorabilia from an amazing variety of sources, including the descendants of "Bloody Bonita's" pirate crew; but after a dozen years of active searching between 1889 and 1905, all he could turn up was an assortment of old coins raked up from the excavations, all of them dated prior to 1800!

While there is no particular value in recounting all of the treasure-hunting expeditions to Cocos Island, it is worth noting that the year that Admiral Palliser made his first trip to Cocos (he made two more and was invited to join a third) a lady had appeared in Victoria, B.C., with maps and other items purporting to have originated with a Captain John Keating. Her name was Mrs. Trevan, the widow of a Captain Trevan; and as a result of her story an expedition was formed and the schooner *Aurora* outfitted for a voyage to Cocos.

Five years later—at approximately the time the *Herman* was being outfitted in San Francisco for its voyage to the South Sea island—another expedition, stimulated by some maps and other material provided by a Captain Thomas Hackett, reportedly a neighbor of Captain John Keating in St. John's, Newfoundland, was organized and the brigantine *Blakely* outfitted for the voyage to Cocos.

There were perhaps a dozen notable expeditions to Cocos Island, during the first half of the twentieth century—the Earl Fitzwilliam on the *Veronique* in 1905 (with Admiral Palliser as a guest); the expedition of Harold Gray, a wealthy Englishman, on the *Rose Marine,* also in 1905, in which the two groups of treasure hunters were reported to have come to grips over the trenches; the expedition of Major W. A. Desborough of Los Angeles in 1909; Sir Malcolm Campbell's invasion of the island in 1926, and possibly the most elaborate of all, the campaign of "Treasury Recovery, Ltd.," in 1934, which raised almost a half million dollars to carry out a "scientific search" of the island.

Perhaps the only visitor to Cocos who came out of sheer curiosity, with no expectation of finding a treasure hoard, was President Franklin D. Roosevelt, who arrived off Chatham Bay in October, 1935, in the cruiser *Houston,* went ashore for a picnic and later caught a 110-pound fish!

Following is a list of the major expeditions that have searched for buried treasures on Cocos Island:

1844: Captain John Keating, of St. John's Newfoundland, visited Cocos with maps obtained from Captain Thompson of the *Mary Deer,* showing the location of the official treasury of Peru, stolen from Callao Harbor in 1835 and buried near Wafer Bay, Cocos Island. Two years later Keating and a Captain Bogue returned to Cocos and apparently removed much of this treasure, but it was lost in a wreck in which Bogue reportedly died.

1851: Captain Henry Schmid, in the brig *Sea Foam,* with James Brown, was reported by Brown to have visited Cocos and removed the so-called "ecclesiastical treasure of Lima" buried by his father, master of the *Black Witch,* in 1821.

1870: A. D. Carpenter, of San Francisco, with a party including L. B. Mizner, former minister to Costa Rica, and several others, including a "James W. Brown," sailed on August 3 for treasure supposedly buried in 1825 by the crew of the schooner *Rosa;* no results reported.

1889: August Gissler, with a man named Bartels, son-in-law of an old sailor known only as "Old Mack," who may have been a member of the pirate crew of "Bloody Bonita" and the *Relampago;* arrived on Cocos in February on the brig *Wilhelmina,* and intermittently searched the island until 1905. Died in New York on August 8, 1935.

1897: Admiral Palliser of the British warship *Imperieuse* with information furnished by a "Patrick Fitzgerald" looking for the "Keating treasure"; found some old coins and evidence of earlier digging, but no treasure.

1897: The "Aurora expedition" in the schooner *Aurora,* out of Victoria, B.C., arrived in Cocos with maps furnished by Mrs. Trevan, widow of a Captain Trevan, a friend of Captain John Keating; found no treasure, but did uncover a man named Carlos Herford who had been marooned on Cocos and claimed he had located some of the treasures and reburied them. Herford later provided Admiral Palliser of the British Navy with information which caused him to make two additional trips to Cocos.

1902: The "Blakely expedition" on the brig *Blakely,* also out of Victoria, B.C., led by Captain Fred M. Hackett, brother of a Captain Thomas Hackett who had known Captain Keating in Nova Scotia and obtained maps from him. This party used a newly developed "divining rod," which failed to locate the treasure, however. Arrived off Chatham Bay on April 17, 1902, and left May 11; stayed in a house built by August Gissler, who was then away from the island seeking backing for an extensive search.

1904: Major Maude of the British Army, on the schooner *Cavalier;* left Valparaiso, Chile, in March and returned two months later with no reported results.

1905: The Earl Fitzwilliam, on the yacht *Veronique,* with Admiral Palliser aboard, visited Cocos on January 10; reported in the New York *Herald* of January 14 to have encountered another party of treasure hunters led by Harold W. S. Gray, a wealthy Englishman, and fought a pitched battle in which Gray's forces were victors. There was also a report of an "explosion" which injured some of the Earl's party, but details of these events were never fully disclosed.

1905: Harold W. S. Gray, in the yacht *Ros Marin* out of London, arrived in Cocos in January, 1905, reportedly encountered the treasure-hunting party of the Earl Fitzwilliam. Accounts of Gray's expedition indicate he was searching for the Sir Edward Davis treasures, although the New York *Herald* referred to it in rather confusing terms as "a treasure buried by the notorious Dampier on the *Relampago.*" Dampier was at one time on Davis' ship, the *Batchelor's Delight* but never visited Cocos; he died in 1715 and the *Relampago* did not appear in these waters until 1817.

1906: Mrs. Roswell D. Hitchcock, of New York and Boston, who said she possessed "Captain Jack Thompson's confession"—evidently his dying statement to the British Admiralty. The New York *Herald* of April 8, 1906, reported her plans for a voyage to Cocos, backed by "a wealthy group from Boston," but there is no record of what happened.

1909: Major W. A. Desborough of Los Angeles, in the yacht *Ramona,* which sailed for Cocos in February, 1909, on an expedition backed by "an eastern syndicate" but did not report any results. Desborough claimed to have visited Cocos in 1897, found at least one cache of treasure, and covered it over to hide it because he feared his companions would kill him.

1926: Sir Malcolm Campbell, in the yacht *Adventuress,* with Lee Guiness, another noted race-car driver, arrived in Cocos in February, 1926, with the Curzon-Howe papers supposedly obtained from a man named "Nicholas Fitzgerald" who had once befriended Captain John Keating (a story bearing a startling resemblance to the account "Patrick Fitzgerald" gave Admiral Palliser). Campbell suffered from the perennial confusion between the "church treasure" of Lima and the official treasury of Peru. He found a large rock under which he was sure the treasures were buried, but actually dug up nothing except some old pieces of sheet iron.

1932: The Canadian expedition (Metaltone Co., Ltd., of Canada) arrived at Cocos with an official grant from the government of Costa Rica and a new electric "divining rod" on the schooner *Silver Wave,* but reported no results.

1932: Stratford Jolly, an Englishman, in the trawler *Vigilante,* arrived off Cocos in August, 1932, and found no treasure.

1932: The "Southern Pearl Expedition" on the ketch *Southern Pearl;* went to Cocos but had to abandon search because of lack of funds.

1934: Treasury Recovery, Ltd., headed by Captain Charles A. Arthur, with capital of $400,000 from an English syndicate, arrived at Wafer Bay on the *Queen of Scots* on September 26, 1934. The expedition ran into official problems with the Costa Rican government, which sent a gunboat to chase them off the island. Two men formerly with Sir Ernest Shackleton's polar expedition, Commanders Worsley and Stenhouse, were with this expedition, and a year later Treasury Recovery, Ltd., made another try with Worsley and Stenhouse, based on a story told by a Dutch sailor, Petrus Bergmans, who had been a sailor on the ship *Westward,* which was wrecked on Cocos in 1929. Only Bergmans and the captain of the ship were able to get ashore on Cocos. They found a cache of treasure, according to Bergmans, put to sea in a damaged boat which they managed to patch up, and were picked up at sea by the German steamer *Nachwezeld.* The captain, a man named H. Peterson, was supposed to have died later in Portland, Oregon, and Bergmans, after wandering around for a couple of years, wound up in a Dutch jail, where agents of Treasury Recovery, Ltd., found him. After almost two years of searching, Treasury Recovery, Ltd., turned up only a few old coins.

There have been numerous other searches on Cocos Island, some planned and others accidental; and while the results of many of these probably were not reported—for obvious reasons—there have been no tangible returns from the larger expeditions for more than a hundred years. The last expedition of note was in 1963, on the *Bluenose II,* a Gloucester fishing boat out of Halifax, led by Ian MacBean with a party of ten adventurers. Nothing was found.

The most recent and least rewarding effort to find the treasures of Cocos may be found, oddly enough, in Truman Capote's book, *In Cold Blood.* Perry Smith, one of the leading characters of this grisly tale, mentions that he has "a map . . . and the whole history" of a treasure buried on Cocos Island. "No fooling," he says. "This is authentic. It was buried there back in 1821—Peruvian bullion, jewelry. Sixty million dollars—that's what they say it's worth."

One of the most interesting—and possibly informative—incidents in the long record of the search for the "lost treasures" of Cocos Island was a section of a palm tree trunk which August Gissler said he found on Cocos, on the surface of which was carved "The Bird is Gone." This piratical artifact, for whatever it is worth, is now in the archives of Costa Rica in San José; and it probably expresses more accurately than anything else the answer to the mystery of Cocos Island and its treasures.

The Voyage of the Herman *was set on the Linotype in Baskerville, a modern reproduction of the types cut in 1760 by John Baskerville, of Birmingham, England, reflecting the style of stone inscriptions. The type was set by the Harry Sweetman Typesetting Corp., New York City. The books were printed by the Halliday Lithograph Corporation, West Hanover, Massachusetts, and bound by the Vail-Ballou Press, Binghamton, New York.*

A HAWTHORN BOOK